CHALLENGE
A PROGRAM FOR THE MATHEMATICALLY TALENTED

GRADES 3-6

Teacher's Edition

Vincent Haag, Franklin and Marshall College
Burt Kaufman, Broward County Public Schools
Edward Martin, Broward County Public Schools
Gerald Rising, State University of New York at Buffalo

Addison-Wesley Publishing Company

Menlo Park, California • Reading, Massachusetts
Don Mills, Ontario • Wokingham, England • Amsterdam
Sydney • Singapore • Tokyo • Madrid • Bogotá
Santiago • San Juan

Acknowledgments and Dedication

The lineage of the central ideas of this series may be traced to the *Elementary Mathematics* texts developed by the Comprehensive School Mathematics Program (CSMP), a project with which this author team was associated. While we and many others contributed to CSMP, all who know that project would agree that its central ideas about elementary school mathematics curriculum as well as the development of those ideas into creative classroom activities are directly attributable to Frédérique and Georges Papy.

To Georges and Frédérique, respected colleagues who led the way, we therefore dedicate these books.

This book is published by the Addison-Wesley Innovative Division.

Design: Signature Design Associates

Addison-Wesley Publishing Company
Menlo Park, California • Reading, Massachusetts
Don Mills, Ontario • Wokingham, England • Amsterdam
Sydney • Singapore • Tokyo • Madrid • Bogotá
Santiago • San Juan

ISBN-0-201-20154-2
3 4 5 6 7 8 9-WR-95 94 93 92

CONTENTS

To the Teacher

Welcome to the continuation of an exciting intellectual and pedagogical experience. Based on our own classroom use of the activities in this series, we believe that with their help you can broaden the mathematical horizons of bright children and in the process extend your own view of what such students (and you) can do.

In this program you play the central role. Our aim, as minority partners in your enterprise, is to continue providing you with the strongest possible support. The experiences we describe in this series are quite different from, yet highly supportive of, those your students are encountering in their regular mathematics program. As you have found, they include novel situations, games, detective stories, and puzzles involving calculators, all of which are designed to induce logical thinking, strategic reasoning, estimation, mental arithmetic, and—we believe most importantly—genuine problem solving. No matter how careful our descriptions, however, you are ultimately the one who must interpret these materials intelligently, with compassion for and dedication to your students. Only you can know them as individuals.

We remind you that the activities we provide in this series are aimed at students in the upper 5 to 10 percent in ability in their age group who are highly motivated. Some of you are working with a more select group of students, perhaps a very few chosen from a large school district in a community that places high value on educational achievement. In such a case you may have found that you can move somewhat more rapidly through this program once you and your students have become acquainted with the style and intentions of the activities. Equally, others of you could well be working with a group of students some of whom fall below your expectations. With such a class you are more likely to have found constraints than freedom, and you probably adapted carefully to the needs of unusually bright students while easing your pace somewhat for the benefit of your weaker students.

If this is your first experience with the series, please turn to page 224 for notes on preparation.

Selection of the Students

If you are involved in the selection process, we urge you to gather all available information about the pool of students from which classes are to be drawn. Look at students' scores on ability and achievement tests, but also be alert to the recommendations of teachers and counselors who have previously worked with the students. Screening by testing may be necessary in some communities in order to provide an objective basis for decisions about participation. If this is the case, you should recognize the arbitrariness of such a selection process and seek to make it as accurate as possible. We urge you to carry out any such testing in the spring, when students have settled down to their academic endeavors; testing during the first week of school can lead to serious selection errors.

Recognizing these selection problems, what is desired? Most importantly, you want students who have demonstrated their ability to learn and to use mathematical ideas. This usually includes but is not the same as the ability to compute with skill and accuracy. Suitable students will probably have achieved well in the regular school mathematics program. Beyond this you want students who show interest in mathematics and general ability to respond to school programs. Having said that, we recognize that good teachers should sometimes take risks. You or your colleagues may, for example, identify a child who shows some evidence of talent even though test scores may not bear this out. Such a student may be bored or "turned off" by regular school instruction and testing. You may wish to take a chance by including such a child. Particularly in communities where some children come from intellectually impoverished homes, a willingness to take such risks is often richly rewarded.

Once students have been selected for a special class (and especially after this selection has been communicated to parents), you may find it difficult to guide them out of your program even if it later becomes apparent that the program is not suited to them. For this reason we recommend that you make it clear at the time of selection what will be expected of students in the program. We have found the key expectation to be that students do the assigned work with reasonable care and accuracy. If you and your school administrators communicate such a requirement clearly at the outset, you will find it much easier to handle those few cases in which it becomes clear that a student is out of place in the program.

Organization of the Program

Volumes 1 and 2 of this series are designed for use with gifted third-grade students in a supplementary instructional program. However, gifted students who miss the opportunity offered by this program while they are in the third grade can nevertheless derive considerable benefit from starting work on these same materials in the fourth or fifth grade.

Our preference is for the activities to be taught in two one-hour sessions per week. In such a format you would normally use two activities per session. A second option is to teach four half-hour sessions per week, using one activity per session. Other options include altering the rate at which the activities are taught. For example, you might teach only two activities per week, in which case you would complete one rather than two volumes per year.

The contents of this series have been arranged in a spiral fashion, so that by teaching the activities in the order in which they appear in the guides, you will repeatedly be reviewing and extending ideas that have been encountered earlier in the program. One consequence of this system is that you need feel no compulsion to rush through the last few activities of a volume in order to complete it by the end of the school year. We suggest that you simply pick up in September where you left off in June.

Because of the greater ability of its intended audience, we have found that this content may be taught in a "pull-out" format in which the students study with their regular mathematics class for three days each week and participate separately in this program during the other two. Students with whom we have worked have had no difficulty keeping abreast of their less able classmates when following this schedule. Alternatively, the program may be taught as a supplement to the full regular course. It is important to note, however, that under no circumstances should these materials be considered a substitute for the regular school program.

Use in the Classroom

You will find the detailed descriptions of the activities to be particularly useful when you teach this content for the first time. They tell you what materials are needed and what worksheets are appropriate. In many cases, examples of possible teacher-student dialogs based on our classroom tests are also provided. Of course, we urge you to modify and extend these conversations as you become increasingly comfortable with the ideas of the program yourself; in the meantime, the detailed descriptions will provide you with a good basis for your teaching.

The activities in this series are designed for full-group participation, usually followed by independent or small-group work on the worksheets. The L-worksheets are associated directly with specific activities and should be used in this way. The A-worksheets may be used with students whose competence and speed of working on the L-worksheets indicate they need an additional challenge.

The H-worksheets (together with any A- and L-worksheets not covered in class) are designed for homework. We find that gifted children and their parents expect this kind of out-of-class work. You are urged to correct and return all completed worksheets. Some of you may want to involve your students in this process. We have found that this participation can lead to a greater sense of responsibility on the part of the graders and to a better standard of work on the part of the students. Some of them are even more concerned about impressing their peers than they are about impressing you! Keys to the worksheets are provided in a separate section at the end of this guide.

Unlike the A- and L-worksheets, which are associated with specific activities, the H-worksheets provide continuity by ranging over the content of the program, thereby keeping earlier concepts alive. We recommend that a normal homework assignment consist of one or two worksheets per activity.

Some Teaching Suggestions

You will be pleased with the way your students respond to these challenging materials. Try to include all the students in your group activities. One of the many ways to do this is to ask follow-up questions such as, "Is that right, Susan?" or "What do you think, Donny?" Use such questions after both correct and incorrect answers.

One very important outcome of the use of worksheets should be that the students learn to follow directions. When you assign the first few you may wish to ask students to read the simple directions out loud and then check for understanding. The need for reading aloud should diminish as the students become accustomed to the format.

You will probably wish to encourage neatness as well as accuracy and completeness. Use your judgment here, because you want students to correct false starts, which may mean crossing out part of their work. On the other hand, where sloppy work prevents students from solving problems, you will wish to be more severe.

Able students such as these often have a history of being rewarded for any response they give, be it right or wrong. (Wrong answers are often considered cute or funny.) Such unhelpful reinforcement can create serious problems for such students and for you in teaching them. Early in your work with these materials you may find some students who are content with giving you any answer just for the glory of being the first to respond. We urge you to deal with such answers directly but sympathetically. One way to do this is to ask, "Why do you think that?" Very often, thinking about the problem will lead directly to the correct answer. Now you can say, "Remember, everyone, that we're after the correct answer, not the fastest answer. Think before you say anything." Some students will need similar guidance about thoughtlessly dashing off their answers to the worksheets.

Methods Used by the Program

In our view, the strength of these materials lies in the teaching devices they use: strings, arrows, the Papy Minicomputer, detective stories, and so on. These devices may best be described as pedagogical languages in that they break down communication barriers. In so doing, they make additional creative and stimulating problems accessible to your students, thus improving their chances of realizing their full potential. To prove this to yourself, pick one of the worksheets at random and try to communicate the same problems unambiguously without using such pedagogical languages. You will invariably find that the same kinds of questions become at best wordy and cumbersome.

There is an important principle here. When we teach, we should ask ourselves not only, "Are the students able to perform?" but also, "Do the students understand the task?" When tasks are well defined in language the students understand, good performance is much more likely.

ACTIVITY 1

Less Than, Greater Than

Materials Needed
Teacher: Minicomputer kit
Students: None

Place a regular and a negative checker on the Minicomputer as follows:

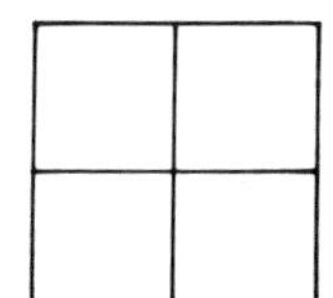 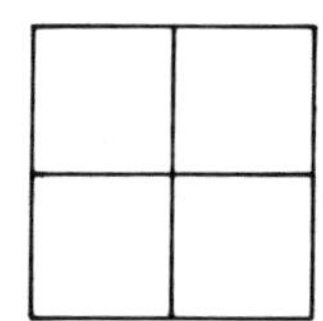 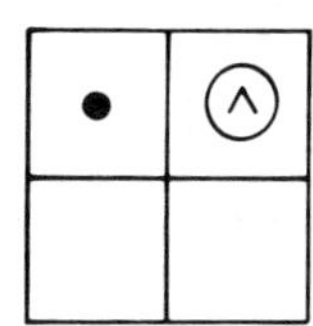

T: What number is on the Minicomputer? (4)
How do you know that? ($8 + \widehat{4} = 4$)

Move the negative checker from the 4-square to the 2-square.

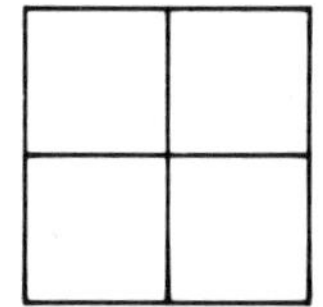 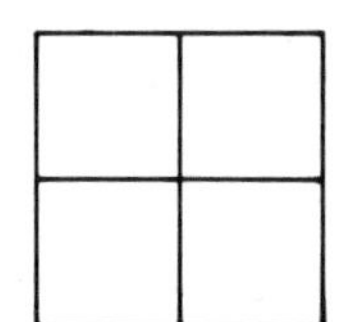 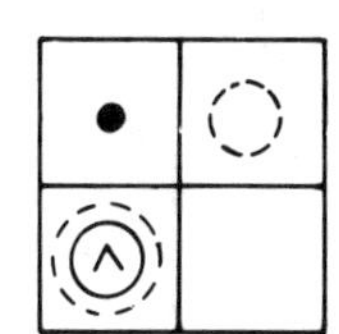

T: What number is on the Minicomputer now? (6) Is it greater or less than before? (two greater) Yes; it's two greater, because $\widehat{2}$ is two greater than $\widehat{4}$.

Return the negative checker to the 4-square and remind the class that the Minicomputer now shows 4 again. Move the negative checker from the 4-square to the 10-square.

T: What number is this? ($\widehat{2}$) Is it greater or less than before? (six less)

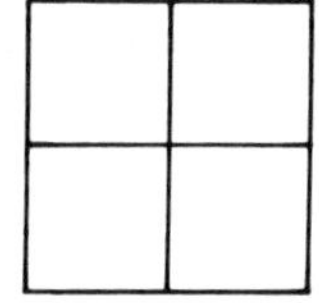 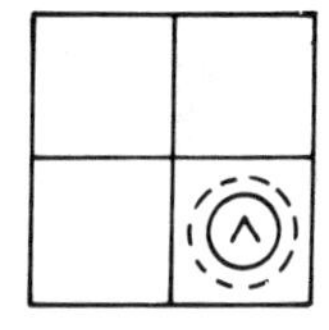 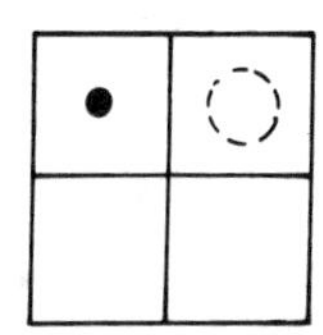

T: Yes; it's six less, because $\widehat{10}$ is six less than $\widehat{4}$.

If necessary, recall the elevator model of negative numbers and relate the above assertions to that model: $\widehat{2}$ is two floors above $\widehat{4}$; $\widehat{10}$ is six floors below $\widehat{4}$.

Remove the checkers from the Minicomputer.

T: I am going to put another number on the Minicomputer. As I place

1

the checkers, try to decide what the number is.

Slowly place the checkers one by one until you have this configuration:

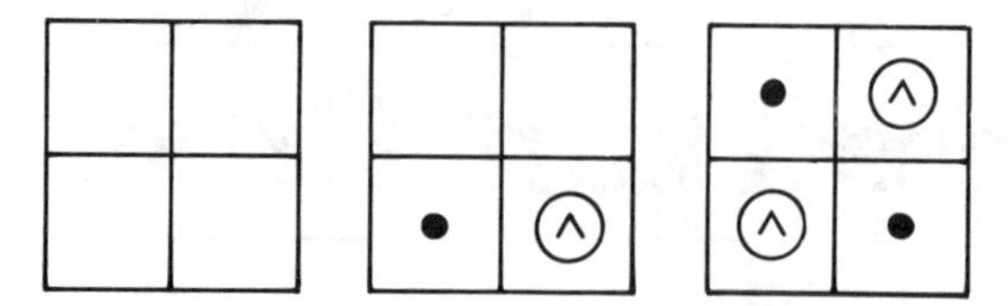

T: What number is it? (13)

After the students have checked this response, write **13** to the right of the Minicomputer.

T: I'm now going to move a checker. Tell me whether the new number is greater or less than the number we started with, and by how much. Also tell me what the new number is.

Move the negative checker from the 2-square to the 10-square.

S: *Eight less. The number is now 5.*

Erase the **13** and write **5**.

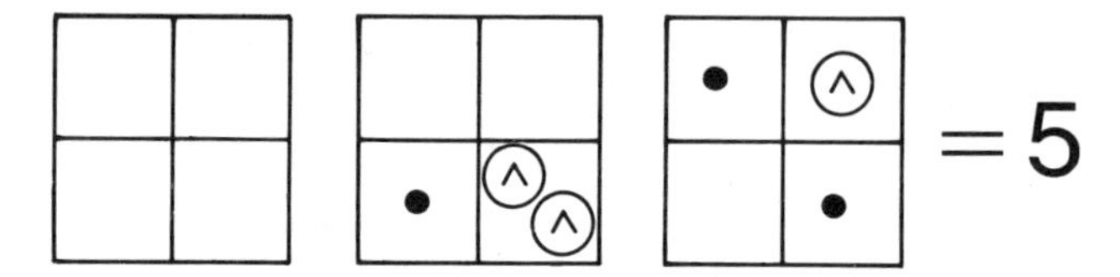

Continue with the following moves, each time asking for the new number before erasing the previous number and writing the new one to the right of the Minicomputer. Each parenthetical phrase explains the reasoning that led to the corresponding new number.

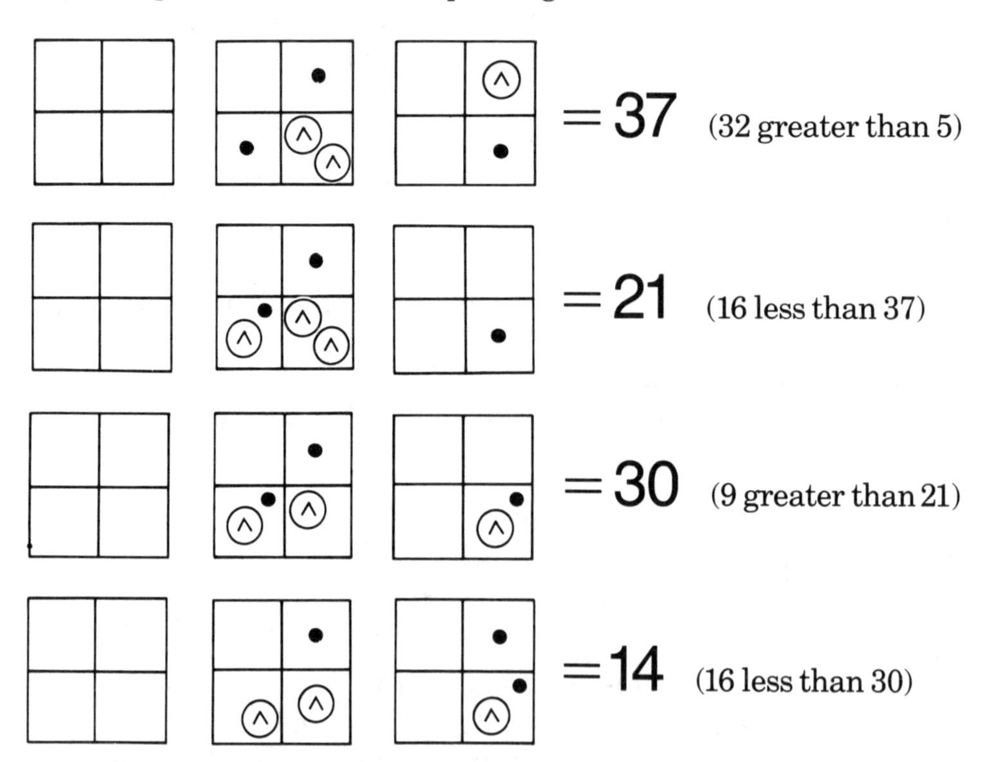

T: Who can move one checker to get a new number that is seven greater than this number?

S: *Move the regular checker from the 1-square to the 8-square.*

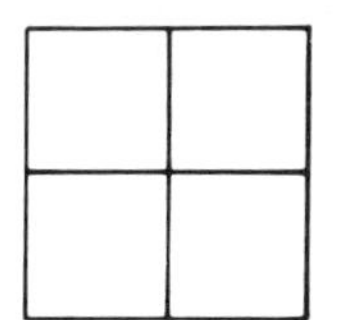 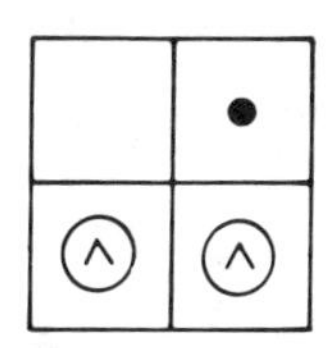 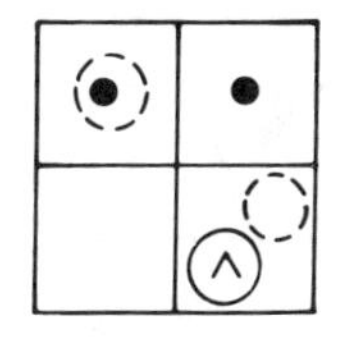 
= 21 (7 greater than 14)

T: Can someone move one checker so that the new number will be two greater than this number?

S: *Move the negative checker from the 10-square to the 8-square.*

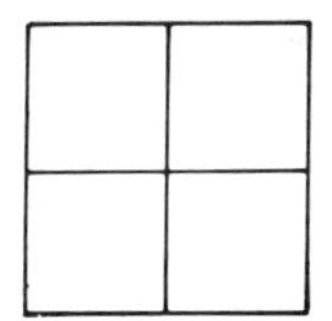 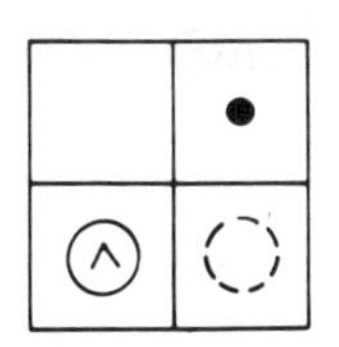 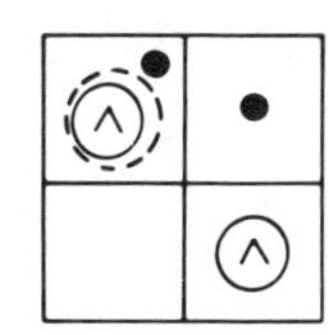 = 23 (2 greater than 21)

S: *I know another way. You could instead have moved the regular checker from the 8-square to the 10-square.*

Continue this activity as follows:

T: Move one checker to make the number six less.

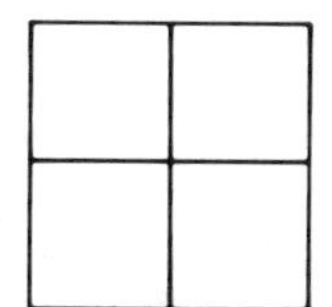 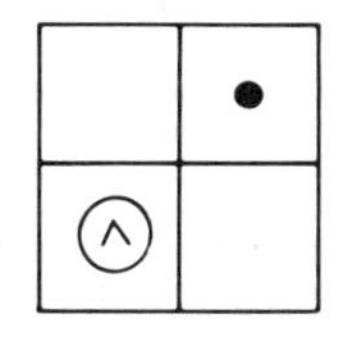 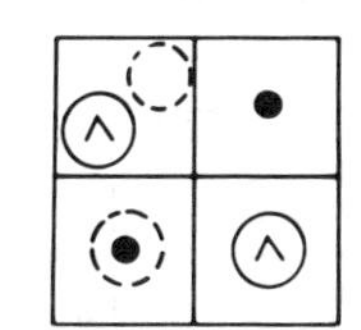 = 17 (6 less than 23)

T: Make the number three less.

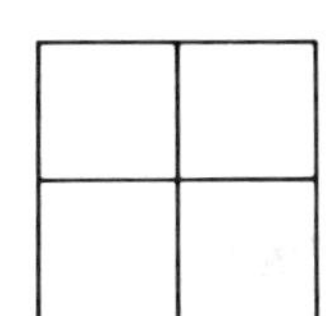 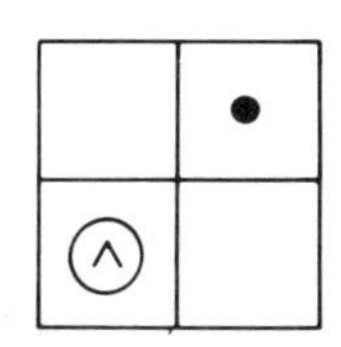 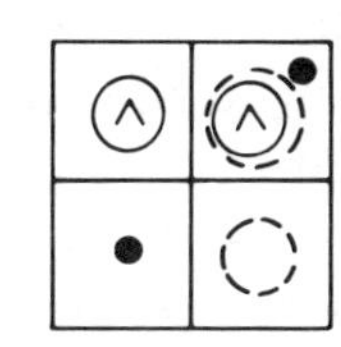 = 14 (3 less than 17)

T: Move one checker so that the new number is 24.

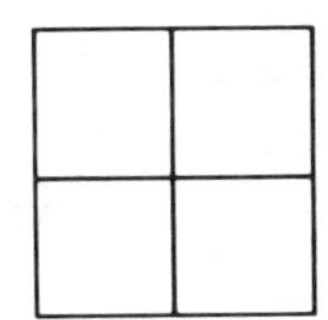 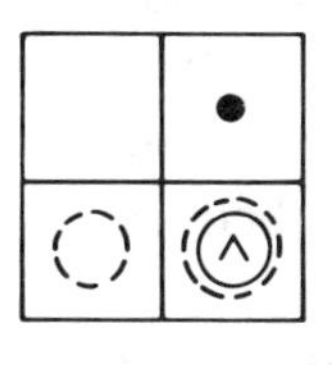 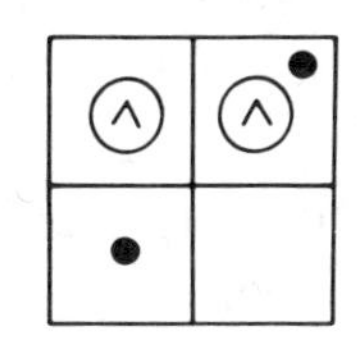 = 24 (10 greater than 14)

For the remainder of the time available, let students assume your role of giving the instructions. (For example, "Move one checker to make the number eight greater" could be obeyed in either of two ways by the rest of the class, whereas "Make the number five less" could not be obeyed in any single move.)

Resources Available

For out-of-class use: Any H-worksheet up through H3

ACTIVITY 2
Minicomputer Golf 1

Materials Needed
Teacher: Minicomputer kit
Students: None

T: Today we're going to play the game Minicomputer Golf again. But this time our starting number is shown on the Minicomputer with both regular and negative checkers.

Slowly put the following configuration of checkers on the Minicomputer:

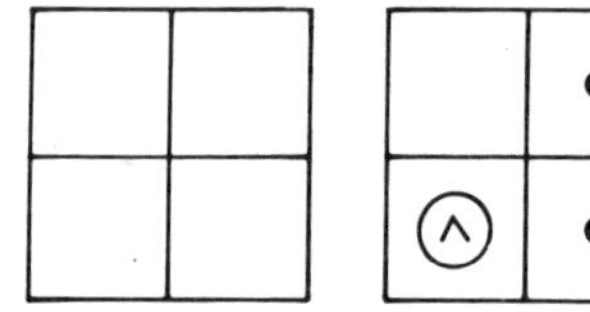

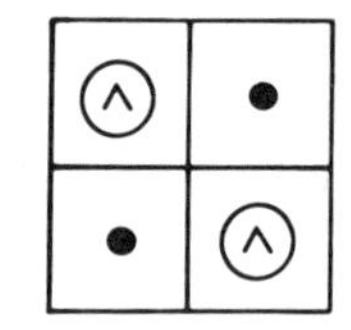

T: What number is this?

After a student has told you that the number is 27, write **= 27** to the right of the Minicomputer.

T: The starting number is 27, and our goal is going to be 200.

Draw and label dots for 27 and 200 some distance apart on the board.

Review the rules of the game:

- Each player must increase the number by moving exactly one checker. Then that player must say by how much the number has been increased and give the new number. If either of these statements includes an error, return the moved checker to its original position and ask for another volunteer.
- The first player to reach the goal is the winner.
- If someone overshoots the goal, the next player must decrease the number until the goal is reached or overshot again, and so on.

Let volunteers make moves, no one having a second turn before everyone has had his or her first. Record the progress of the game by means of an arrow diagram.

A typical game with this starting configuration and goal might proceed as follows:

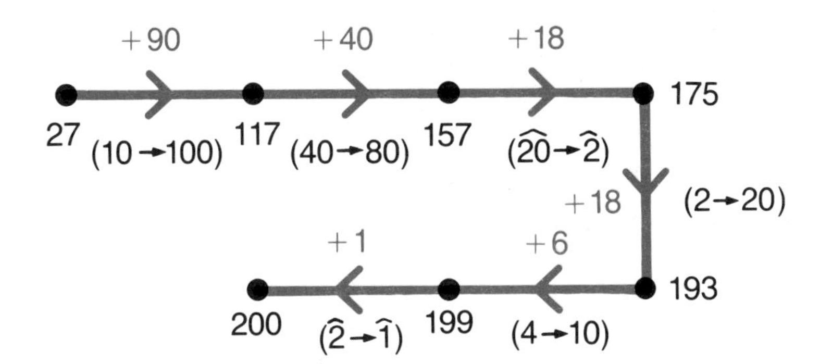

Let the students check their work by verifying that the number now on the Minicomputer really is 200, either by mental calculation or by making robot moves.

Play the game a second time, choosing a different starting configuration involving seven or eight checkers, some regular and some negative, and a different goal. For example:

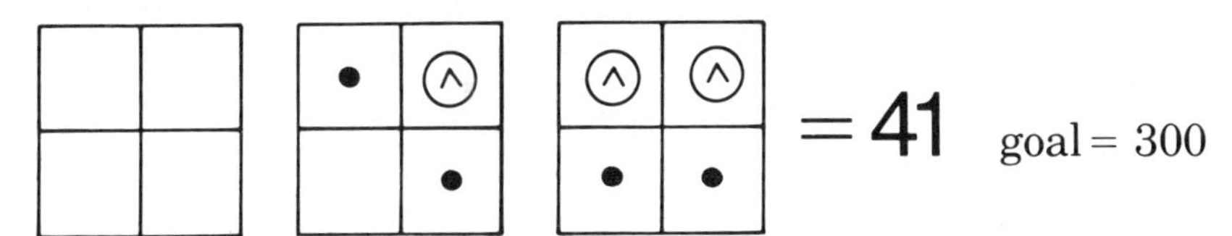

The game can be made competitive by separating the class into a Red team and a Blue team. Play then proceeds with the teams alternating and team members taking turns to move the checkers and announce the changes. The first player to reach the goal wins the game for his or her team. In the arrow picture you draw to record the progress of the game you might indicate which team made which move by using red and blue arrows, as appropriate.

Resources Available

For out-of-class use: Any H-worksheet up through H6

ACTIVITY 3
Divisors 1

Materials Needed
Teacher: Colored chalk
Students: Paper and pencils

Tell your students that during this lesson you will be dealing exclusively with the *positive* numbers such as 1, 2, 3, 4, 5, and so on. No negative numbers will be involved, and neither will 0.

Draw the following on the board:

(Do not write the letters on the board. They are included here so that in the description of the lesson we can refer to particular dots.)

Point to dots A and B and ask the class:

T: What numbers could these dots be for?

Accept any correct answers, such as:

S: *Twelve and 3, because 12 is a multiple of 3; or 4 and 2, because 4 is a multiple of 2; or 0 and 6, because 0 is a multiple of 6.*

(A student who offers a solution such as this last one should be praised for remembering that 0 is a multiple of every number, but he or she should be reminded that during this lesson we have agreed not to use 0.)

Let the students explain why, for example, "3 is a multiple of 12" is *not* a correct response, and why there are red loops at each dot.

Label dot A **12**; point to dot B and ask:

T: What number could this dot be for? (1, 2, 3, 4, or 6)

T: Yes. Remember that 12 is also a multiple of 12, and that is why there is a red loop at the dot for 12.

Begin drawing the blue arrow, loops, and explanatory code shown here:

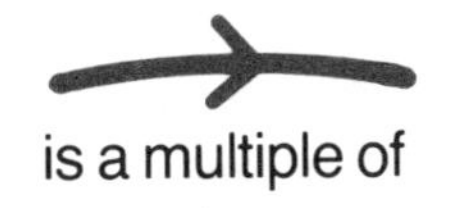

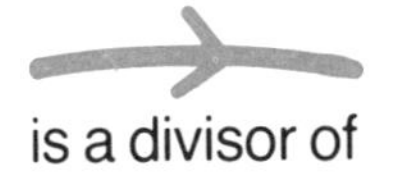

As you do this, say:

T: Here is a new word: *divisor*. By looking at this picture, figure out what it means.

After the students have commented on the new arrows, point to dot B and say:

T: This is a positive divisor of 12. What are some positive divisors of 12? (1, 2, 3, 4, 6, 12) Why do you think these numbers are called divisors of 12?

Accept any response that suggests the idea that a divisor of 12 is a (whole) number that divides into 12 with no remainder; do not press for such an explanation, however. Some students might be specific and say that 4 is a divisor of 12 because 12 is a multiple of 4, as suggested by the diagram.

Replace **12** in the diagram with **15**. Then ask:

T: What are the positive divisors of 15? Write them on your paper. (1, 3, 5, 15)

Replace **15** with **32** and proceed similarly. (1, 2, 4, 8, 16, 32)

Erase what is drawn on the board, and draw the following string picture:

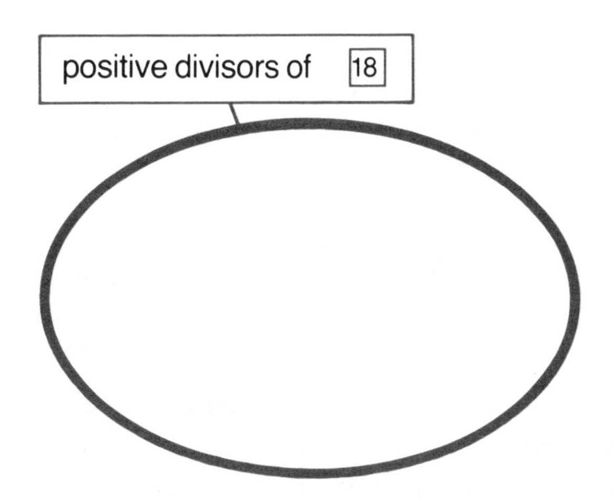

T: How many dots do we need inside the red string to show all the positive divisors of 18? (6) What are the positive divisors of 18? (1, 2, 3, 6, 9, 18)

As each divisor is named by a student, draw and label a dot for it inside the string.

Erase the dots inside the string and replace **18** in the small box with **8**. (4 dots: 1, 2, 4, 8)

3

Erase the dots and replace **8** with **7**. (2 dots: 1, 7)

Erase the dots and replace **7** with **9**. (3 dots: 1, 3, 9)

If the students enjoy this activity, you might continue with some larger numbers such as 21, 36, and 45.

Erase the number in the box and draw three dots inside the string. Then hatch the string as you say,

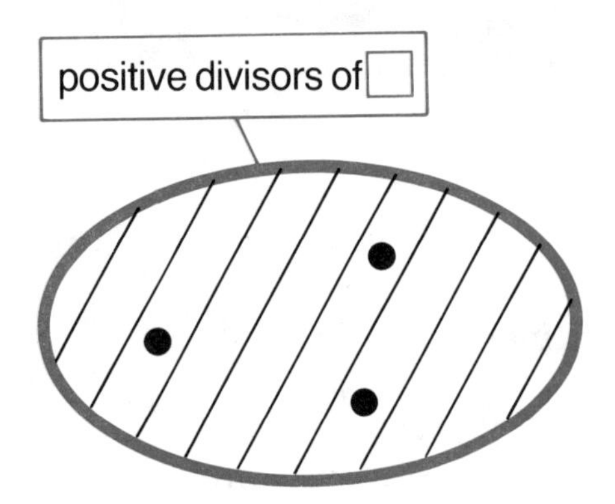

T: I'm hatching this string to tell you that there are no more dots that could be drawn. That is, there are *exactly* three dots inside the red string—no more, no less. This means that whatever the mystery number in the box is, it has *exactly* three positive divisors. What could the mystery number be? There are many possible answers; write some of them on your paper.

The four smallest ones are 4, 9, 25, and 49. Some students might think they see a pattern after 4 and 9 and claim unthinkingly that 16 is a possibility. Point out that 16 has five positive divisors: 1, 2, 4, 8, 16.

Change the string picture on the board until it looks like this:

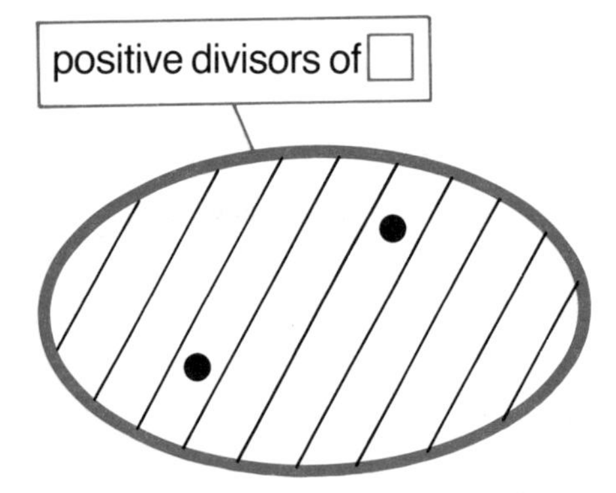

T: This time the number in the box has *exactly* two positive divisors. What number could it be? Write some of the possible answers on your paper.

The eight smallest possibilities are 2, 3, 5, 7, 11, 13, 17, and 19.

T: Numbers that have exactly two positive divisors are very special. They are called *prime numbers*. Write some more prime numbers on your paper. (...23, 29, 31, 37, 41, 43, ...)

Resources Available

For out-of-class use: Any H-worksheet up through H6

ACTIVITY 4
Divisors 2

Materials Needed
Teacher: Colored chalk
Students: Paper and colored pencils

Draw this diagram on the board:

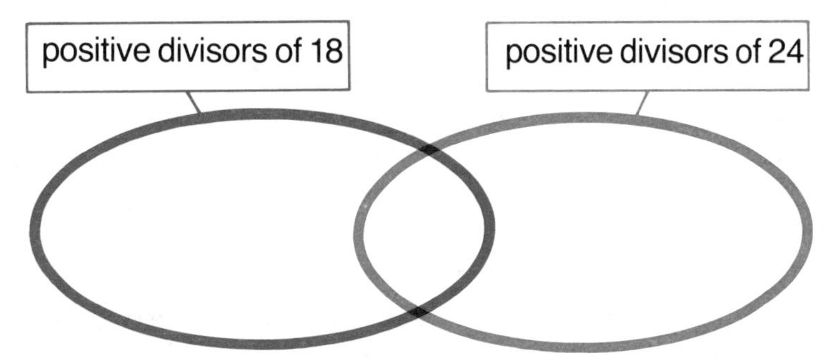

T: Copy this diagram onto your papers. Then draw and label dots for 3, 4, 9, and 10.

Write these numbers on the board as a reminder. After some time, invite students to come to the board one by one and draw dots for these numbers in the string picture.

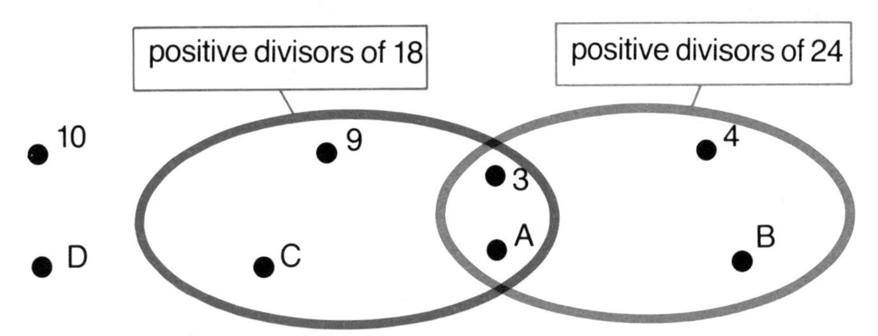

Then draw new dots one at a time, one in each region of the figure, and ask which number(s) each dot could be for. (A could be for 1 or 2 or 6; B could be for 8 or 12 or 24; C could only be for 18; D could be for 5, 7, 10, 11, 13, 14, 15, 16, 17, 19, 20, 21, 22, 23, or any whole number from 25 onward.)

Resources Available
For class use: Worksheets L1 and L2
For out-of-class use: Any H-worksheet up through H6

ACTIVITIES 5 and 6

Taxigeometry 1

Materials Needed

Teacher: Grid board (or a copy of Poster 1 in the Volume 2 kit envelope), colored chalk (or crayons or felt tip pens)

Students: Colored pencils

Notes to the Teacher

1. Taxigeometry differs from ordinary geometry in the way distance is measured. This difference brings many important geometrical concepts well within the scope of elementary-school students. For example, in the taxigeometry activities that are included in volumes 2 to 4, such topics as perpendicular bisectors, circles, ellipses, and the triangle inequality are addressed. Of course, none of this technical language is used. The entire sequence of activities is put in a story context using natural language.
2. In order to give the necessary demonstrations during these taxigeometry activities you will need a grid board. The lines on this board should not be less than 6 cm apart, and the board should not be smaller than 12 squares by 12 squares. Such boards are available commercially. However, if you do not have access to one you can use the grid board poster (Poster 1) in the Volume 2 kit envelope. Tape it to the chalkboard and use crayons or felt tip pens.

Display a grid board on which you have marked the points B and M positioned as shown here. (That is, such that BM is one diagonal of a 7-by-3 rectangle in the middle of the board.)

56

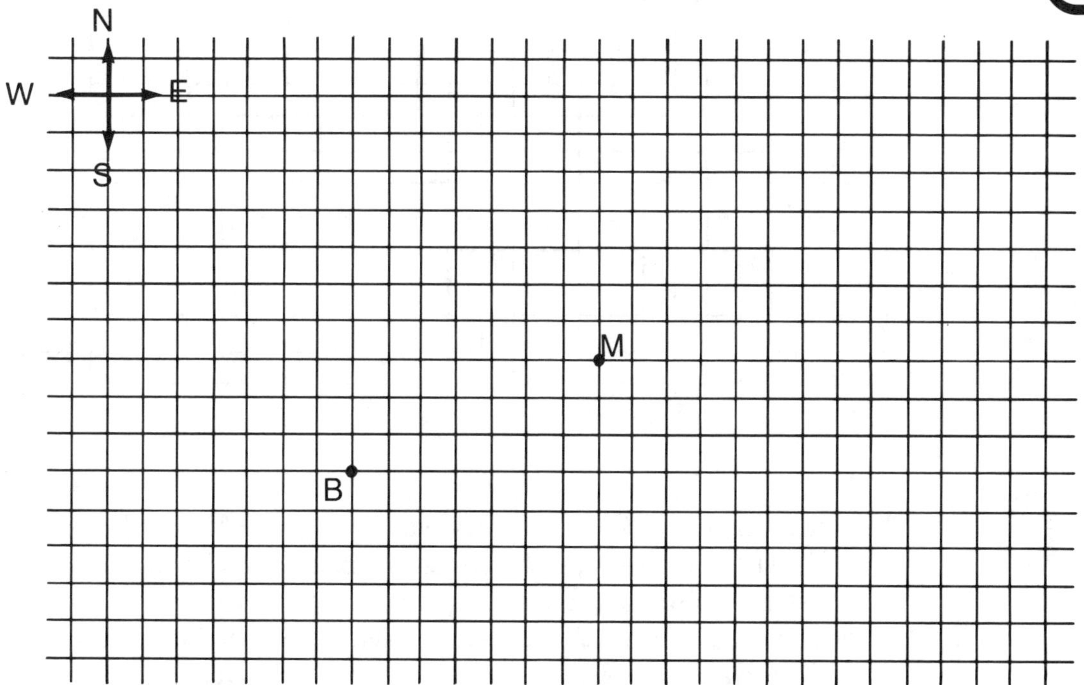

T: This is the map of a large city. These lines are the streets. Notice that all the streets run north–south or east–west. That means that at each intersection, the only directions you can go are north, south, east, or west.

Point to the symbol in the upper left-hand corner of the board.

T: Today I'm going to tell you a story about two friends, Bill and Mike. I've marked where they live on the map. Which do you think is which?

S: *Bill lives at the place marked **B** and Mike lives at the place marked **M**.*

T: Very good. When Bill goes to visit Mike he likes to walk. Obviously, he has to stay on the sidewalks, so any route he takes will have to follow the same directions as the streets. On nice, sunny days he doesn't always take as short a route as he could; he likes to take detours and look in store windows. Who would like to show me some sunny-day routes from Bill's house to Mike's house?

As students come to the board, ask them to trace along their proposed route with their fingers or with a pointer. You should follow along behind, drawing in the suggestions using different colors of chalk. Here are two possibilities:

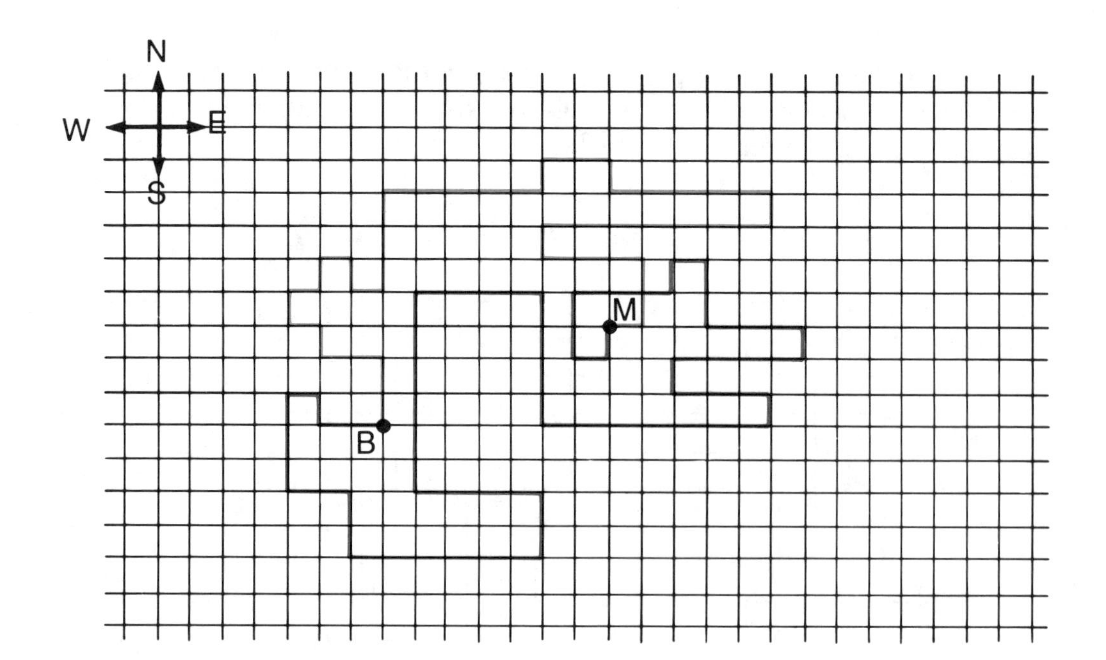

T: On rainy days Bill obviously wants to get to Mike's house as quickly as possible, so he chooses a route that is as short as possible. Who can show me some rainy day routes?

There are 120 "shortest" routes, all having the same length, so accept any of these or routes that are close to being "shortest" routes. (For your information only, all the "shortest" routes are contained within the rectangle of which *BM* is one diagonal.) Once again, the students should trace along their suggested routes while you draw those you accept, each in a different color. Suppose that the various suggestions include the following:

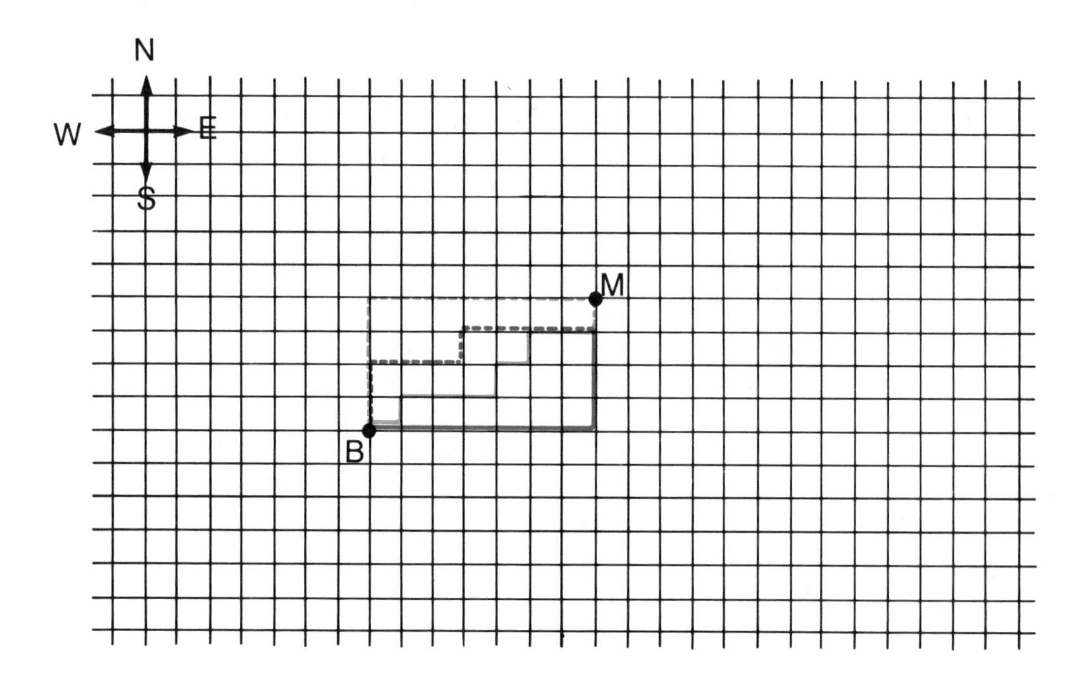

Of these, the red, the blue, and the dotted red routes are all as short as possible, and the dotted blue one is not.

T: How are we going to decide which of these routes is the shortest?
S: *Measure them.*
T: What should we measure them with?
S: *With a ruler.*
S: *You don't need to bother with that. You just have to count the squares.*
T: How far does Bill walk when he goes along the side of one of these squares on our map?
S: *One block.*
T: Right. Let's find out how many blocks long each of these routes is.

Record the unit of measurement in the upper right-hand corner of the board, as follows:

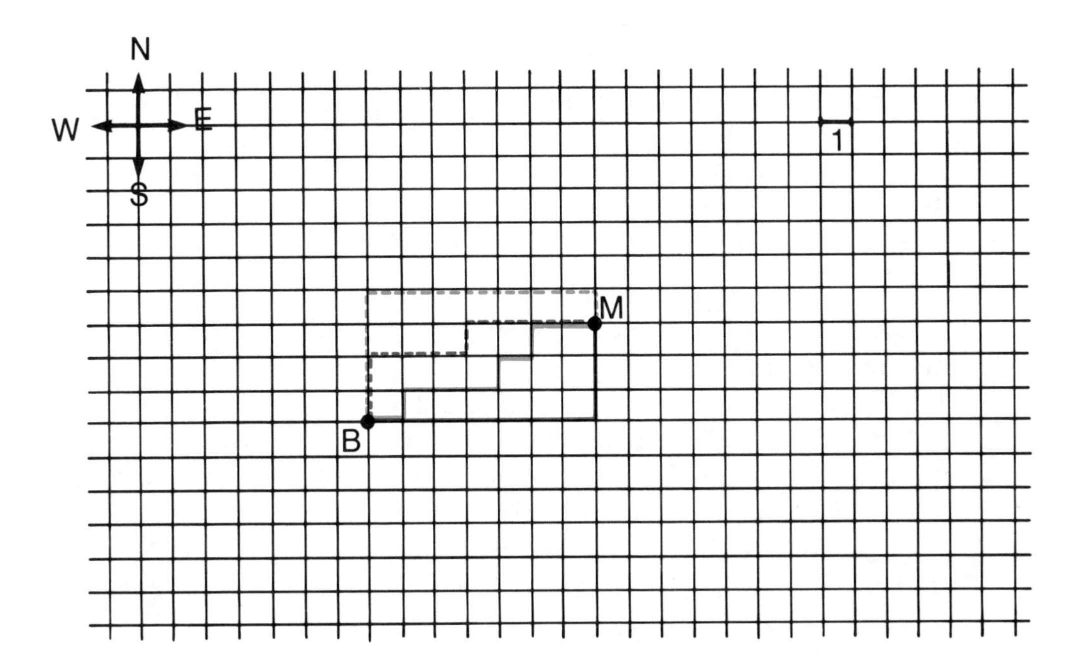

To insure that the lengths of the routes are correctly measured, suggest that the number of blocks in a route is most easily counted by following along the route using the thumb and index finger, as shown below:

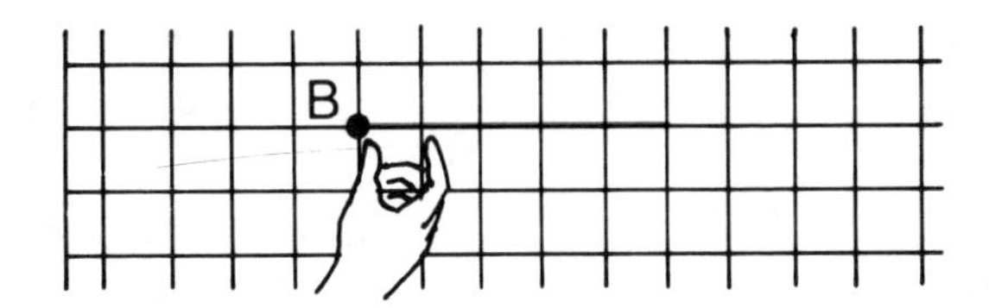

Write the length of each route next to it and in the same color as the route itself.

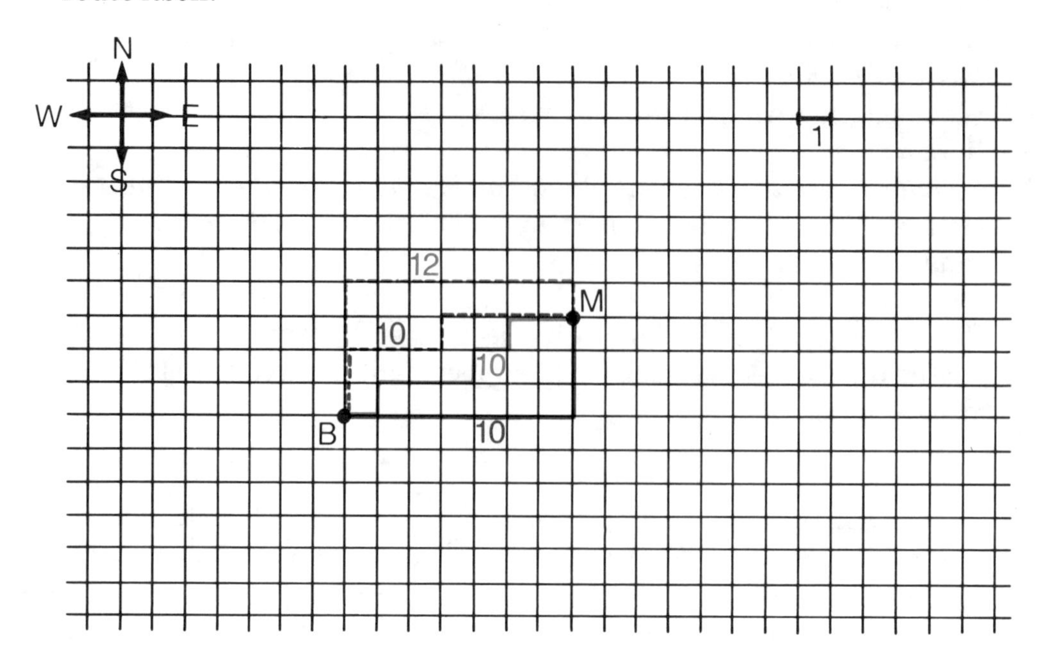

Erase or cross out any routes (such as the dotted blue one above) that are not shortest routes.

T: Well, so far we've managed to find these routes that are all 10 blocks long. Do you think there are any routes shorter than that?

S: *No. Whatever Bill does, he's got to go seven blocks east and three blocks north, and that makes ten blocks already.*

T: Can't he ever go south when he's going to Mike's house?

S: *No. He's eventually got to go three blocks north. So if he goes one block south, he'll have to go one extra block north to make up for taking a wrong turn. Every block he goes south makes his journey two blocks longer.*

S: *The same thing's true about going west.*

T: That's right. Because Mike's house is to the north and east of Bill's, any time Bill goes south or west he's going in the wrong direction and making the journey longer than it needs to be. So we know that these routes we have found are the shortest ones possible. Let's look at each one and see where Bill goes his seven blocks east and where he goes three blocks north.

With the class, check through each of the routes on the board and identify the seven easterly blocks and the three northerly blocks in each one.

T: Because all these shortest routes are made up of seven blocks to the north and three blocks to the east, and because $7 + 3 = 10$, we say that the *taxidistance* from Bill's house to Mike's is 10 blocks.

Write on the board:

Taxidistance from B to M = 10 blocks.

T: Why do you think it's called the taxidistance?

S: *Because it's the distance from* B *to* M *the way a taxi would have to go: along the streets.*

Resources Available

For class use: Worksheets L3 and L4
For out-of-class use: Any H-worksheet up through H10

ACTIVITY 7
Divisors 3

Materials Needed
Teacher: Colored chalk
Students: Paper and colored pencils

Review the idea of a divisor of a number as follows. Draw this string picture on the board:

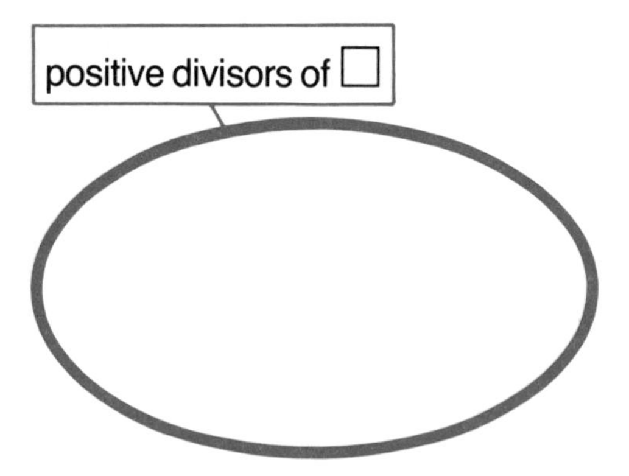

T: What are the positive divisors of 26?
Write **26** in the box. As students mention divisors of 26 (they are 1, 2, 13, and 26), draw a dot for each one and label it.

Repeat the activity, finding the positive divisors of 11, 33, 42, and so on. Erase the string picture and draw this arrow picture:

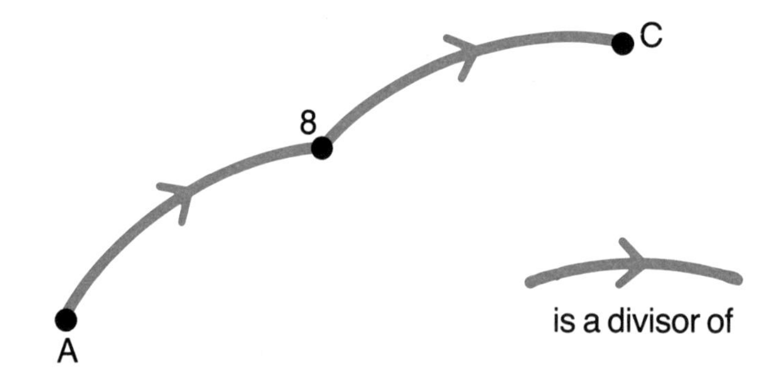

(Do not write the letters *A* and *C*. They are included here to give us a means of referring to specific dots in the description of this activity.)

Point to dot A.

T: What could this dot be for? (1, 2, 4)

T: Why couldn't it be for 8? Eight is a divisor of 8, isn't it?

S: *Yes, but you already have a dot for 8.*

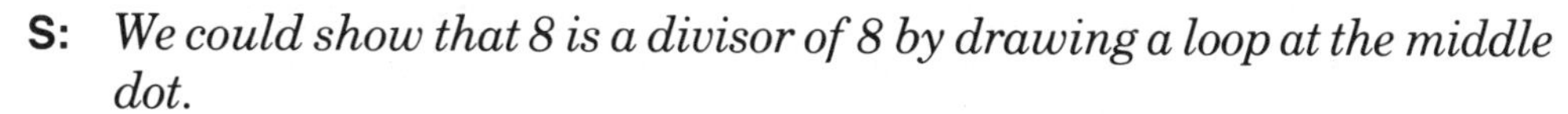

S: *We could show that 8 is a divisor of 8 by drawing a loop at the middle dot.*

Agree, and draw the loop in question. Point to dot C.

T: What number could this other dot be for? (16, 24, 32, ...)

T: What kind of numbers are they?

S: *Multiples of 8.*

Choose one possibility for each of dots A and C (say, 2, and 24), and label the dots accordingly.

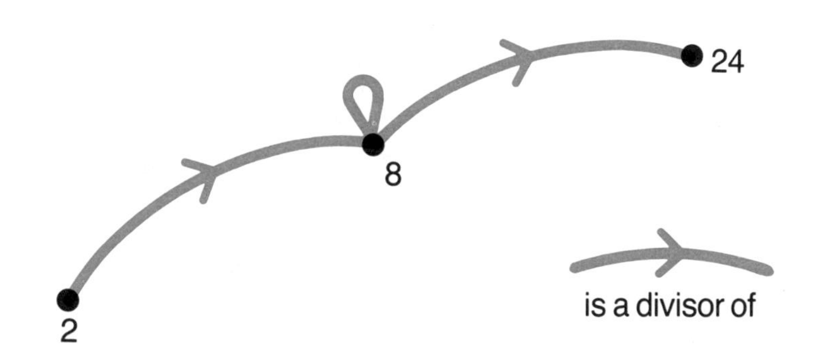

T: Are there any other blue arrows or loops we could draw?

Let three students draw the missing arrow and the two missing loops. Draw the return arrows in red:

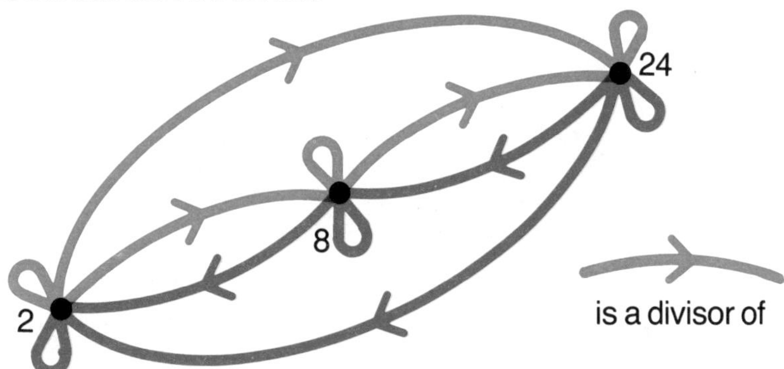

T: What could the red arrows be for?

S: *"Is a multiple of."*

Erase the arrow picture, and replace it with the following one:

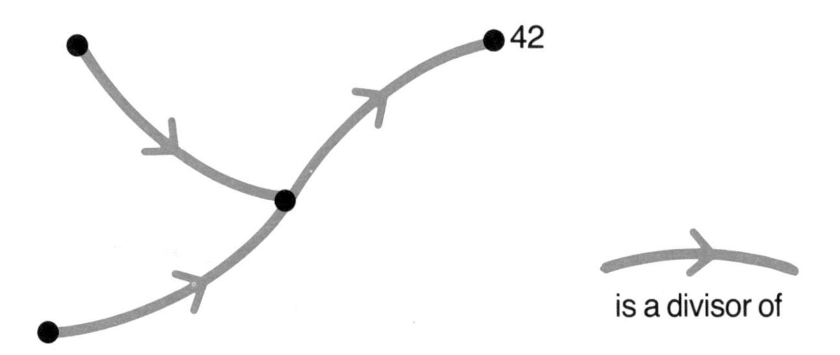

T: Copy this arrow picture onto your papers. Then label the dots and draw any blue arrows and loops that are missing. Try to find more than one solution. There are lots of possibilities.

Here are two possible solutions:

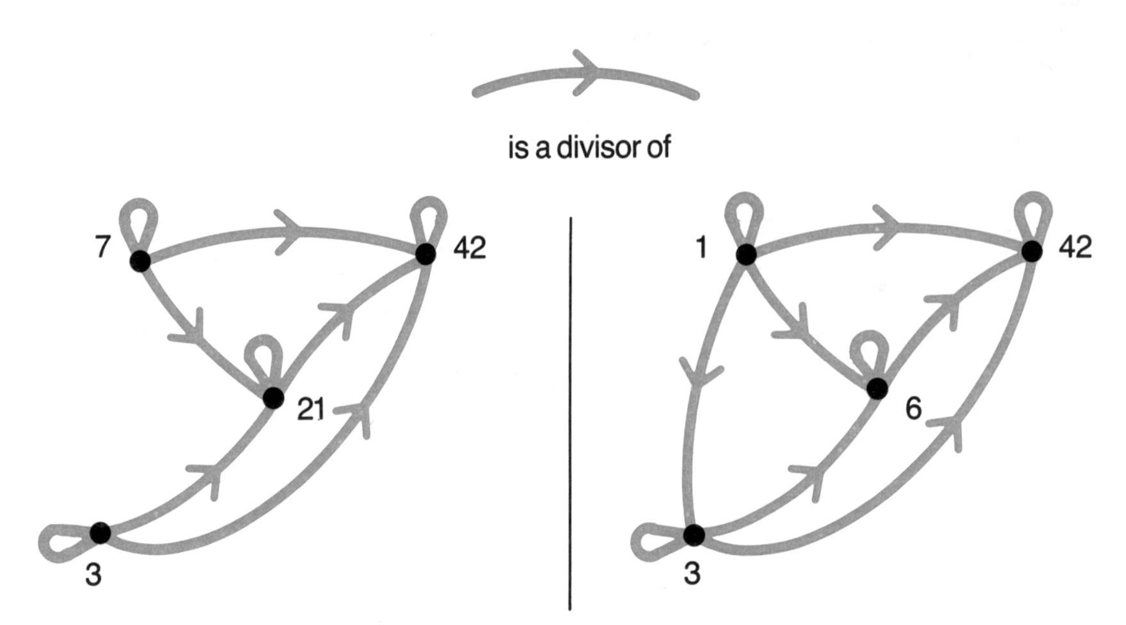

Resources Available

For out-of-class use: Any H-worksheet up through H15

ACTIVITY 8
Divisors 4

Materials Needed
Teacher: Colored chalk
Students: Paper and colored pencils

Draw this string picture on the board:

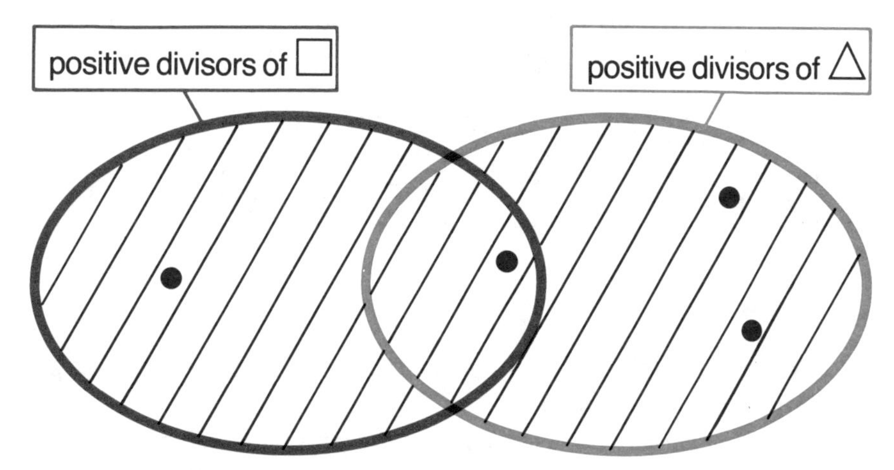

T: How many numbers are there in the red string?
S: *Two.*
T: How do you know?
S: *There are two dots there and the string's hatched. So there are no more.*
T: What kind of numbers have exactly two positive divisors?
S: *Prime numbers.*
T: So the number written in the little square must be a prime number. How many positive divisors does the number written in the little triangle have?
S: *Three.*
T: Copy the string picture onto your papers. Then try to label the dots and find numbers to write in the little square and triangle.

Circulate among the students, giving individual assistance when necessary. For those who find it hard to get started, ask what whole number is a divisor of all whole numbers. Once it has been decided that the dot in the intersection must be for the number 1, the other dot in the red string may be for whichever prime number is chosen for the small square. Then the students are faced with the easier task of finding a number with exactly three positive divisors.

8

After a number of students have found a solution, let one of them transfer it to the board. Here is one possibility:

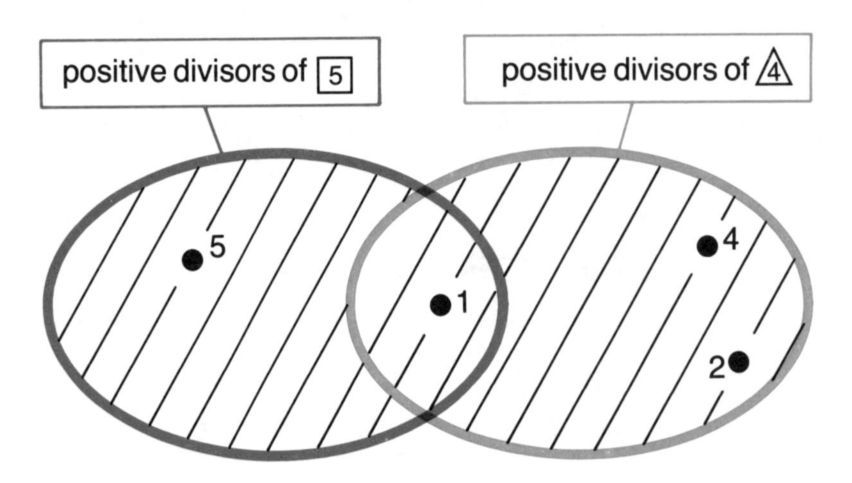

Draw a chart on the board, as as each solution is announced, record it in the chart. Eventually this will contain many solutions. Here are some:

□	5	2	5	7	3	11	13
△	4	9	9	4	25	49	121

After a while, let the class discuss the chart. Comments you might hear include the following:

S: *The numbers in the square are prime numbers.*

S: *The numbers in the triangle are numbers multiplied by themselves:* 2×2, 3×3, 5×5, *and so on.*

T: Let's call them square numbers.

S: *Not every square number:* 4×4 *is a square number but it has five positive divisors.*

S: *They are squares of prime numbers, but not the prime number in the little square.*

Resources Available

For class use: Worksheets L5 and L6

For out-of-class use: Any H-worksheet up through H18

ACTIVITIES 9 and 10

Taxigeometry 2

Materials Needed

Teacher: Grid board and colored chalk (or a copy of Volume 2 Poster 1 and crayons or felt tip pens)

Students: Colored pencils

Begin by reviewing the work of Activities 5 and 6 at a brisk pace. Your review should cover the following points:

- The grid board is the map of a large city whose streets are represented by the lines on the board; at each intersection the only directions you can go are north, south, east, and west.
- Because of the buildings, movement in the city takes place only along the streets.
- There are a large number of possible routes from one place to another in the city (such as from Bill's house to Mike's house), some long and some short.
- All the shortest routes have the same length, because any journey from one point to the other requires at least a certain fixed number of blocks in one direction and a certain number in a second direction. In the case of shortest journeys from Bill's house to Mike's house, seven blocks east and three blocks north are required. Write on the board:

  7 blocks east

  3 blocks north

  (Remind the students that a good way to count the number of blocks in a route is to follow along the route with the thumb and the index finger held the length of a block apart.)
- The length of any of these shortest journeys is called the *taxidistance* from one point to the other. Write on the board:

  Taxidistance from B to M = 10 blocks.

After this review, erase anything drawn on the board, with the exception of the indication of the unit of measurement (one city block). If you are using the poster, replace it with a clean copy. Mark two dots S and P on the grid, as shown below.

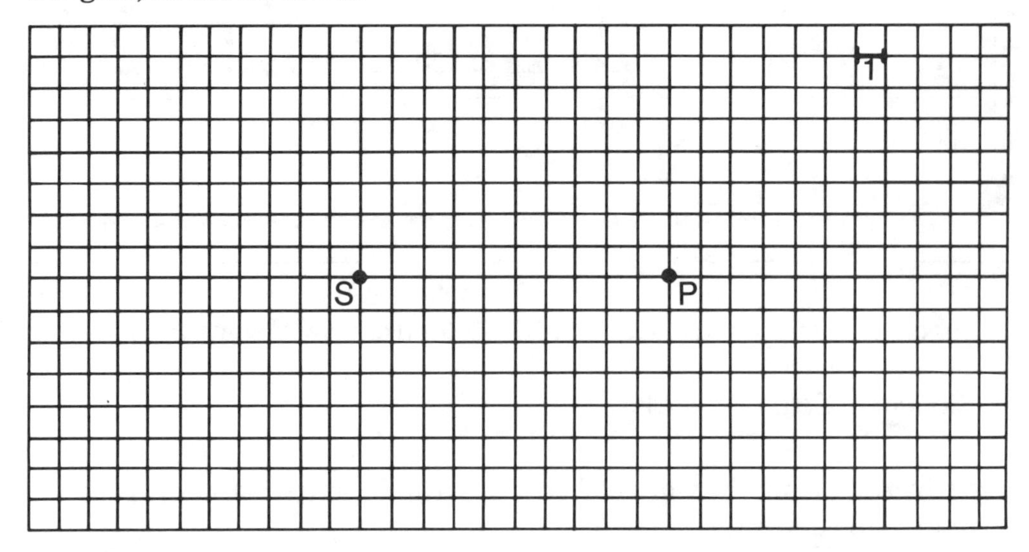

T: Mike and Bill can't decide whether to go to the baseball game or just go swimming. So they agree to meet somewhere that is exactly the same distance away from the swimming pool (S) as it is from the ballpark (P). That way, whatever they decide to do they'll have the same distance to go. It's a nice day, so they're not particularly concerned about meeting as close as possible to S and P.

Who would like to show us some of the places where Mike and Bill might meet?

Check each proposed meeting place by measuring the taxidistances from it to S and to P. Make sure that it is the length of a shortest journey that is being measured in each case. As possible meeting places are discovered, mark them on the grid board in red. After a while, your drawing should look like the following figure:

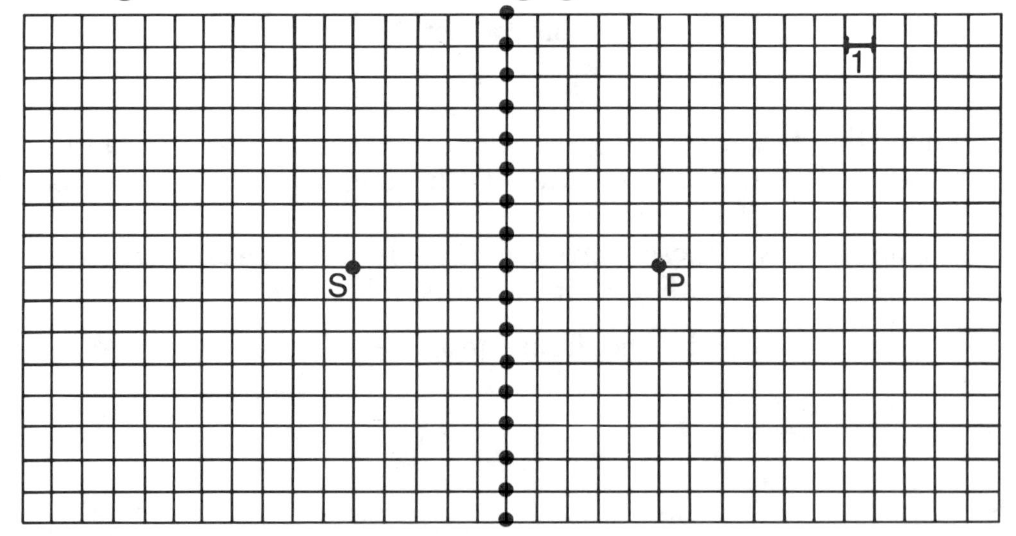

Choose a point not on the line and ask:

T: Would they be happy to meet here?

S: *No. It's closer to one place than the other.*

Check this claim by measuring the two taxidistances.

9
10

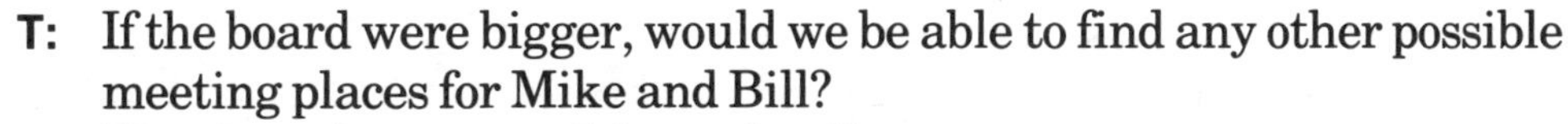

T: If the board were bigger, would we be able to find any other possible meeting places for Mike and Bill?

S: *Yes. Anywhere up and down that line.*

T: That's correct. Well, they finally decide to go swimming. At the pool they meet their friend Nora. She invites them to a party she is holding that evening. A little later they meet Janet, who is also holding a party that evening.

Erase what you have written on the board (or replace the poster with a clean copy) and mark it with the following:

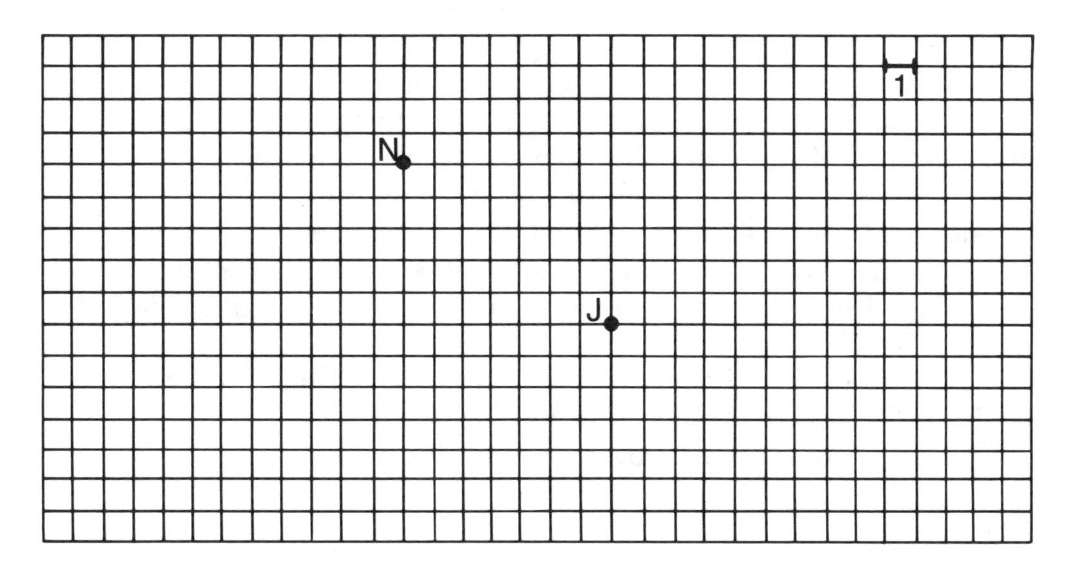

T: Nora lives at N and Janet lives at J. Once again, Mike and Bill can't decide where they want to go, so they agree to meet at a place exactly the same distance away from Nora's as it is from Janet's.
Who can show us a place where they might meet?

After one possibility has been discovered and recorded on the board, distribute copies of Worksheet L7 and let the class continue the search for possible meeting places individually. Circulate among the students, giving individual help as necessary. Every now and then send a student with a correct point to transfer it onto the grid board. The completed picture should look like this:

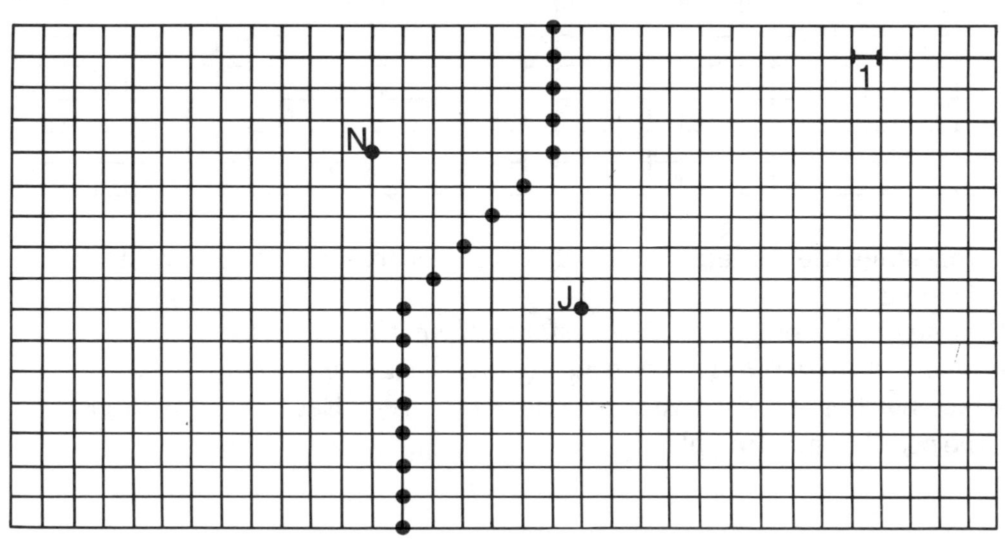

With the students, choose a couple of these points and check that they are equally distant from N and from J. Also choose a couple of points off the red "zigzag" and check that they are closer to one point than the other.

T: If the board were bigger, would we be able to find any other possible meeting places for Mike and Bill?

S: *Yes. Straight upward in this direction (indicating the upward extension of the right-hand red line) and straight downward on this line (the downward extension of the left-hand red line).*

For the remainder of the time allotted to these activities, work in a similar fashion on finding possible meeting places in the situations shown on Worksheets L8 to L10.

If you find that time is pressing, omit Worksheets L8 and L10. With the example covered in the lesson and the remaining worksheet, the students will still encounter all possible outcomes of this exercise.

If you notice that a number of students are having difficulty with Worksheet L9, draw in the square on BN as diagonal on the erased grid board or a clean copy of Poster 1. Mark the other two corners of the square in red (obviously, each of these points is equally distant from B and from N). Then say:

T: Let's concentrate first on the section of the city inside this square. Try to find all the possible meeting places there.

The students should then discover the following points:

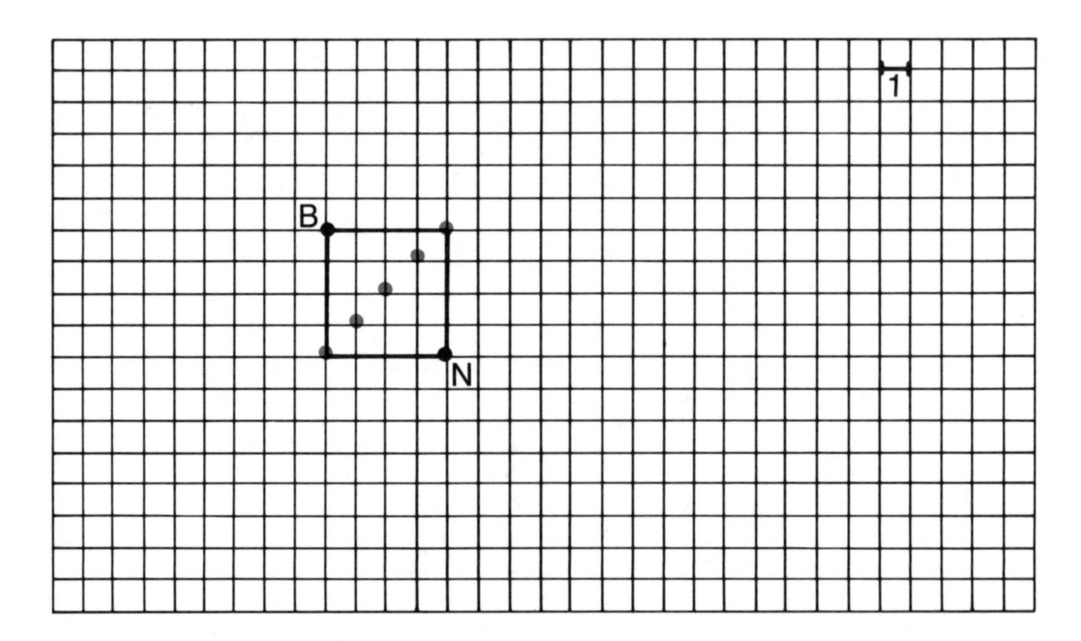

At this stage the students are likely to conjecture one of two possible extensions:

S: *They're all going to be on this sloping line.*

S: *No, I think it's going to be a zigzag like the last one we did.*

In fact, neither of these two suggestions is correct: Each one omits most of the possible meeting places.

T: Let's try Mindy's suggestion.

Choose a point on the continuation of the red diagonal, check its taxidistances from B and from N, and discover that it is a possible meeting place. Let the class check that all the remaining points of the continuation of the red diagonal are also possible meeting places.

T: Now let's check José's suggestion. Which way do you think the zigzag will go, José?

Choose a point on the suggested zigzag, check its taxidistances from B and from N, and (if José's zigzag is one of the two obvious ones having their outside-the-square portions lying along extensions of the sides of the square) discover that it also is a possible meeting place. Let the class check that all the remaining points of the suggested zigzag are possible meeting places.

T: Well, that's a surprise! Mindy and José were both right. I wonder if there are any other possibilities.

Let the students search for them individually. The completed picture (within the limits of the grid) is as follows:

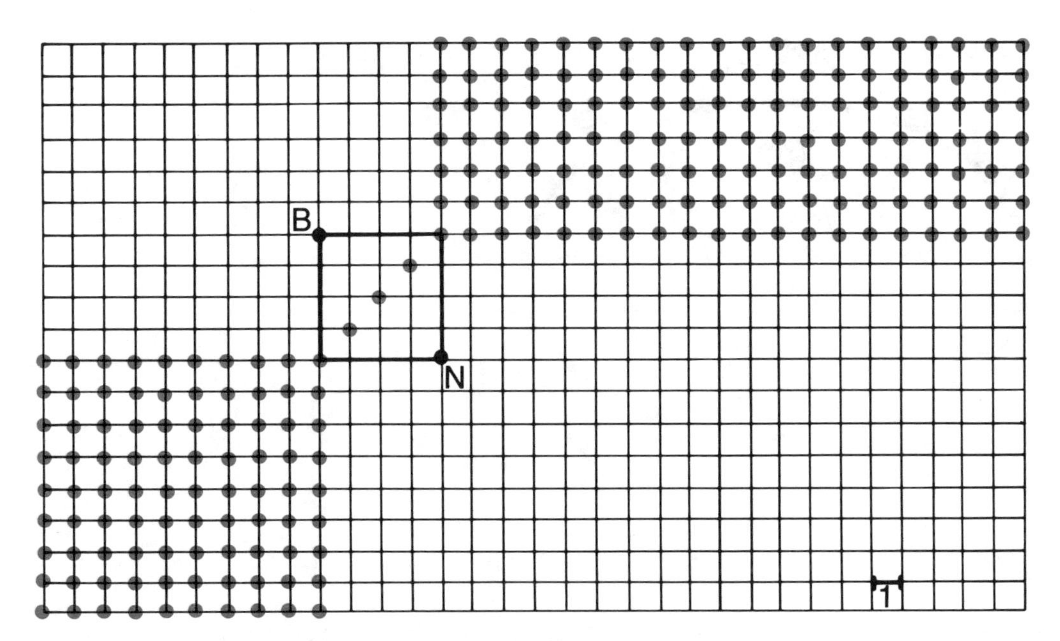

T: If the board were bigger, would we be able to find any other possible meeting places?

S: *Yes; all of these two corners would be filled in.*

T: Right. If I extend the sides of the square in the direction of the red dots we've found already, every intersection between the two lines at each corner will be a possible meeting place.

Resources Available

For class use: Worksheets L7–L10
For out-of-class use: Any H-worksheet up through H20

ACTIVITY 11

The Divisor Game 1

Materials Needed
Teacher: Colored chalk
Students: None

Draw this diagram on the board:

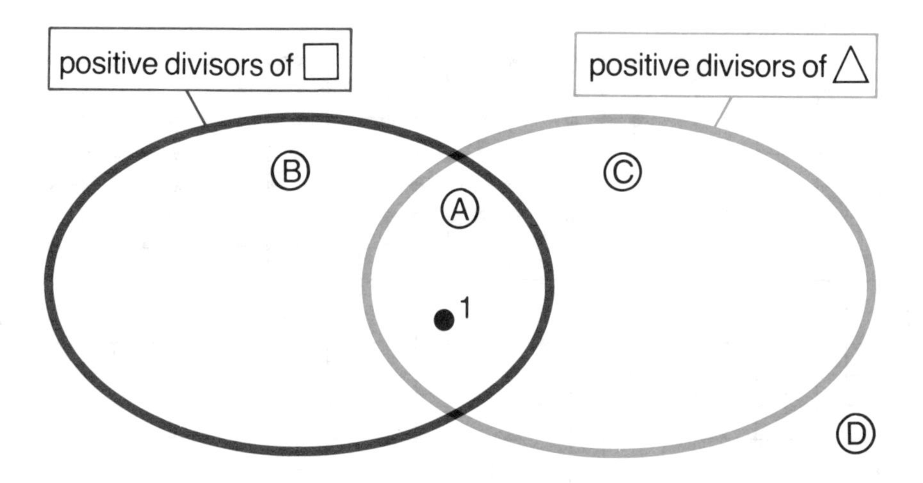

(Don't write the circled letters on the board; we include them here just to make the lesson easier to follow.)

As a warm-up, write **30** in the square and **42** in the triangle.

T: Who can tell me where the number 2 should go in this string picture?

Let a student come to the board and point to the appropriate region. As soon as the correct region (A) is indicated, draw and label a dot for 2 in that region. Proceed similarly for the numbers 3, 4, and 5 (3 belongs in region A, 4 in D, and 5 in B).

Point to region C.

T: Can you think of a number that could go here?

S: *7.*

(The only other possibilities are 14, 21, and 42.)

Draw and label a dot for the suggested number. Point to region B.

T: Which number could go here?

S: *15.*

(The only other possibilities are 10 and 30.)

Draw and label a dot for the suggested number. At this point your string picture might look like this:

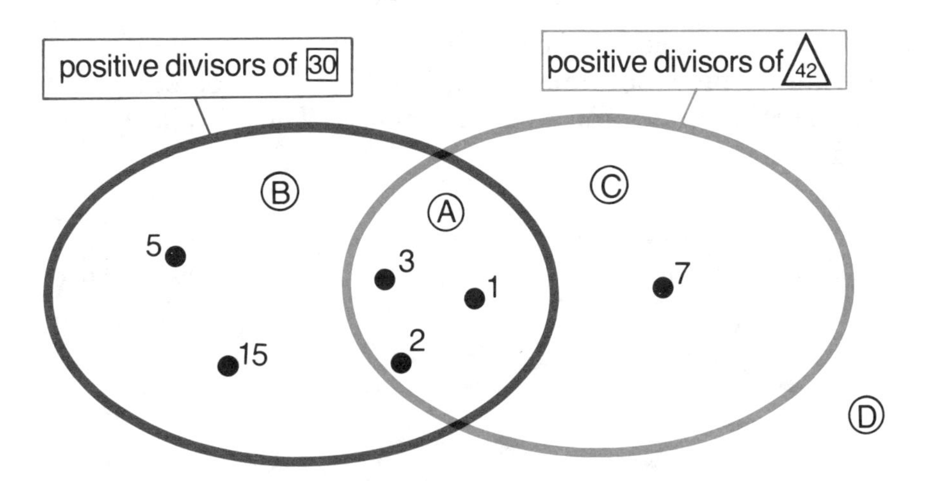

T: Now tell me some other numbers and show me which part of the string picture they belong in. Don't use any numbers greater than 50.

Let students respond one by one, naming a number and indicating where it belongs in the string picture. For each correct suggestion, draw and label a dot.

Continue until the class is satisfied that all the numbers belonging in regions A, B, and C have been identified (1, 2, 3, 6 in A; 5, 10, 15, 30 in B; 7, 14, 21, 42 in C), and that every other number belongs in region D.

Erase all the numbers except **1** in the string picture, including the numbers in the square and the triangle.

T: Now we're going to play the Divisor Game. It's something like the String Game. I have certain numbers in mind that can go in the square and the triangle. You have to find out what those numbers are by taking turns to place numbers in the string picture. In this game we use only the whole numbers from 2 through 50. When it's your turn you can either mention a number from 2 through 50 and I'll put a dot for it on the board, or you can tell me what number you think is in the square or the triangle.

For the first game, your secret numbers should be 12 in the square and 18 in the triangle. As students name numbers from 2 through 50, draw and label dots in the correct regions. If a student elects to guess a string label rather than name a number, either announce that the guess is incorrect (if it is) or record the correct number in the square or triangle.

Here is a crib sheet for this game:

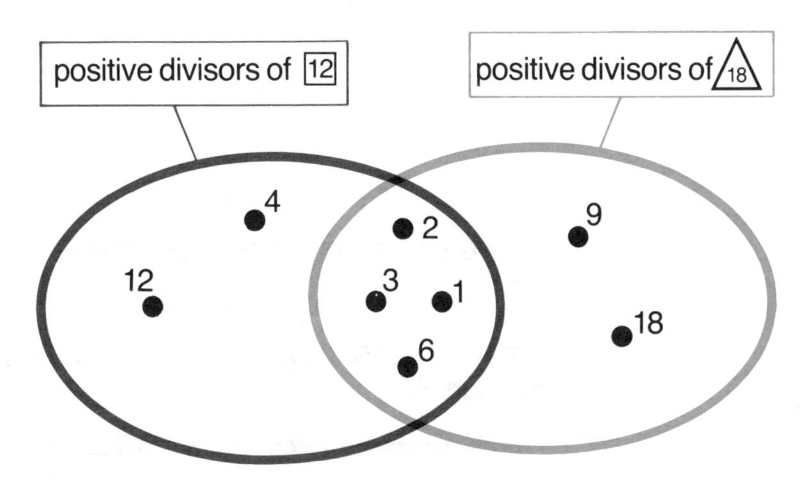

(All other numbers belong to region D.)

If time allows, play the game again. This time your secret numbers could be 36 in the square and 48 in the triangle. The crib sheet for this game is as follows:

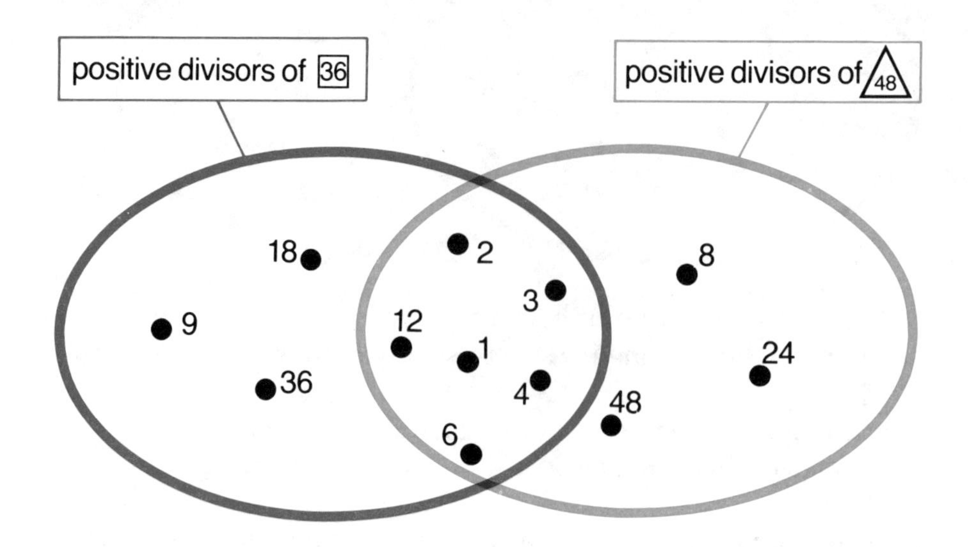

(All other numbers belong to region D.)

Resources Available

For out-of-class use: Any H-worksheet up through H22

ACTIVITY 12

The Divisor Game 2

Materials Needed
Teacher: Colored chalk
Students: None

This activity introduces a competitive version of the game that was played in Activity 11.

Separate the class into two teams, team A and team B. Explain the following rules to the class:

T: The teams take turns to play, and the players on the teams take turns too. When it's your turn you can name a number from 2 through 50, and I'll draw and label a dot for it in the right place in this string picture.

Draw the following diagram on the board:

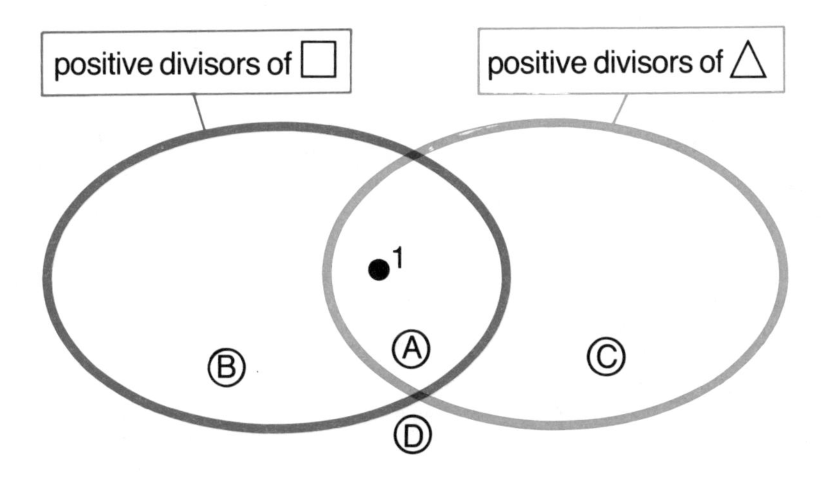

(Omit the circled letters.)

T: Or, if you think you know what number should be in the square or the triangle, you can use your turn to tell me what you think. If you're right, I'll write the number in the label. But if you're wrong, I'll do nothing except tell you so.

To make the game more interesting I'll award points for each turn.

Explain the following scoring rules, pointing to the various regions at the appropriate times rather than referring to them by letter:

- Two points gained if the suggested number belongs in region A.
- One point gained if the suggested number belongs in region B or C.
- No points gained if the number belongs in region D.
- Four points gained if a string is correctly identified.
- One point lost if a string is incorrectly identified.

T: The game is over as soon as both strings' labels have been found. Let me remind you that the only numbers we use in this game are the whole numbers from 2 through 50, and that includes the numbers in the square and the triangle.

The following dialog gives one possible development of the game when the red string is for the positive divisors of 30 and the blue string is for the positive divisors of 40.

S: *2.*

T:

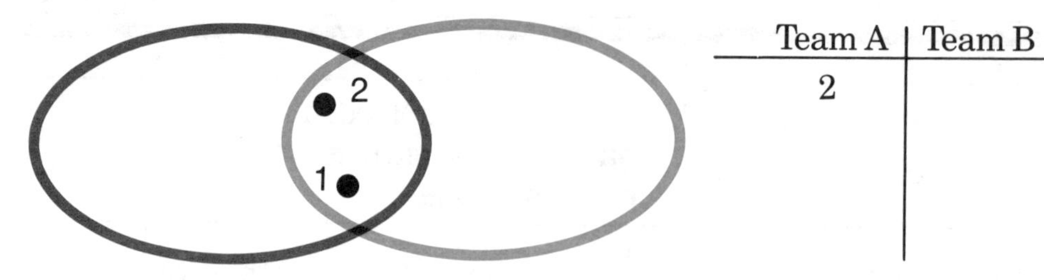

Team A	Team B
2	

S: *3.*

T:

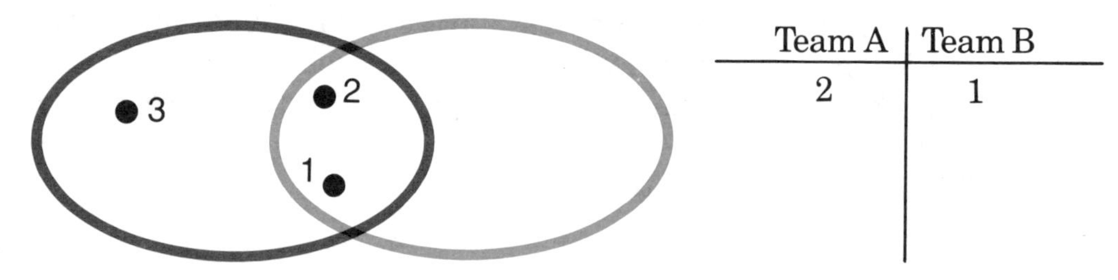

Team A	Team B
2	1

The next four numbers selected are 4, 6, 12, and 10 (in that order).

S: *The red string is for the positive divisors of 30.*

T: Correct!

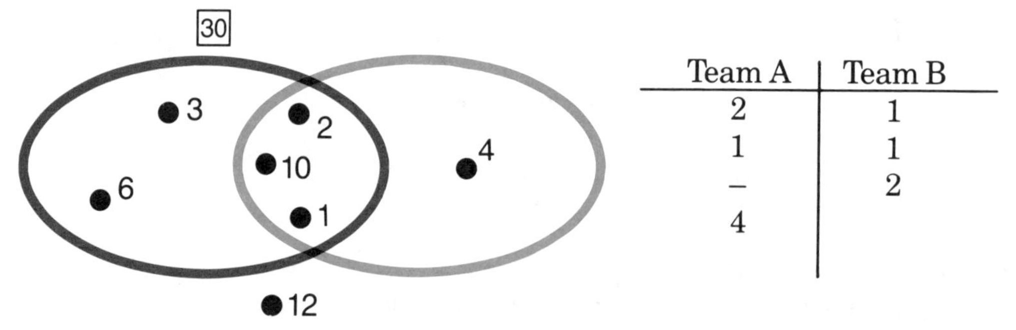

Team A	Team B
2	1
1	1
–	2
4	

The next three numbers selected are 15, 8, and 5 (in that order).

S: *The blue string is for the positive divisors of 20.*

T: No; team A loses a point.

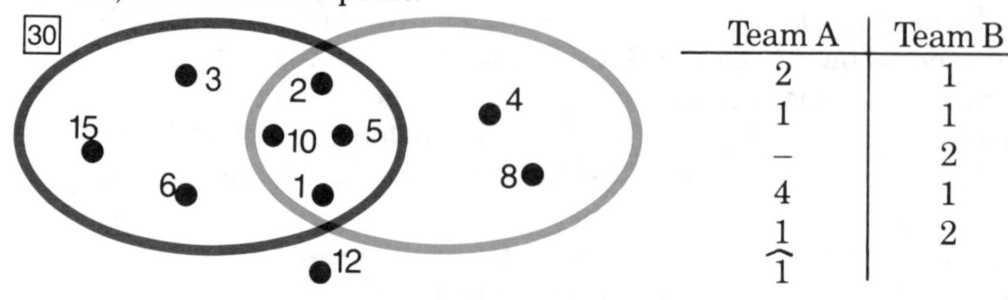

Team A	Team B
2	1
1	1
–	2
4	1
1	2
$\widehat{1}$	

12

S: *20.*
T:

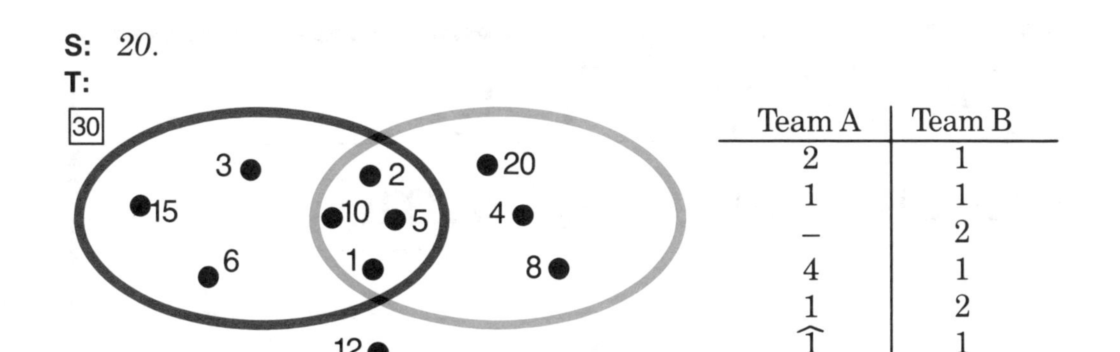

Team A	Team B
2	1
1	1
–	2
4	1
1	2
$\hat{1}$	1

The next four numbers selected are 30, 16, 40, and 50 (in that order).
S: *The blue string is for the positive divisors of 40.*
T: Correct!

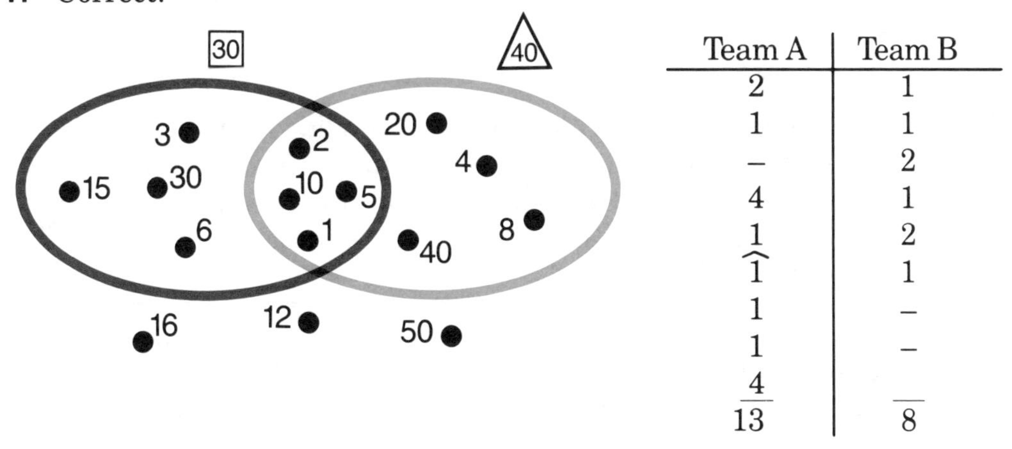

Team A	Team B
2	1
1	1
–	2
4	1
1	2
$\hat{1}$	1
1	–
1	–
4	
13	8

T: Team A wins with 13 points to team B's 8.

If there is enough time, play the game again, this time using the numbers 35 and 28 as the unknown contents of the square and triangle, respectively. The following is a crib sheet for this game.

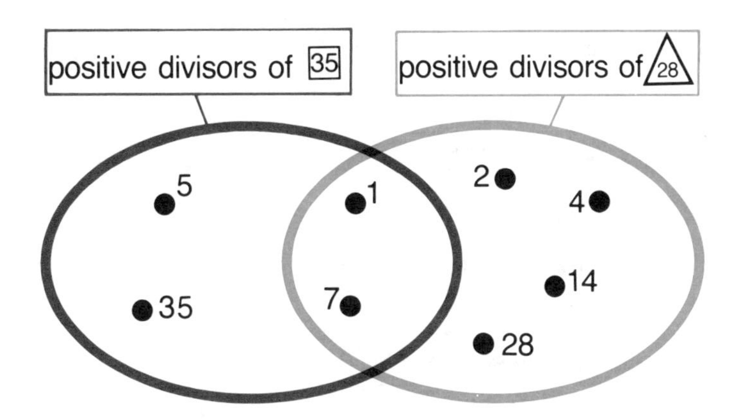

(All other whole numbers less than or equal to 50)

Resources Available

For out-of-class use: Any H-worksheet up through H24

ACTIVITY 13
Numerical String Game 1

Materials Needed
Teacher: Colored chalk, Numerical String Game kit
Students: None

Note to the Teacher

Before use, the label cards and playing pieces provided in the Numerical String Game kit need to be magnetized (or prepared by one of the alternative means suggested in the instructions included in the kit). Be sure to attach the magnetic material on the back of each playing piece, and on the front of each label card.

Depending on the time available, play the Divisors Game (Activity 12) once or twice. Use 24 and 42 for the square and triangle (respectively) for the first game, and 18 and 27 for the second. Crib sheets for these two games are provided below.

(1)

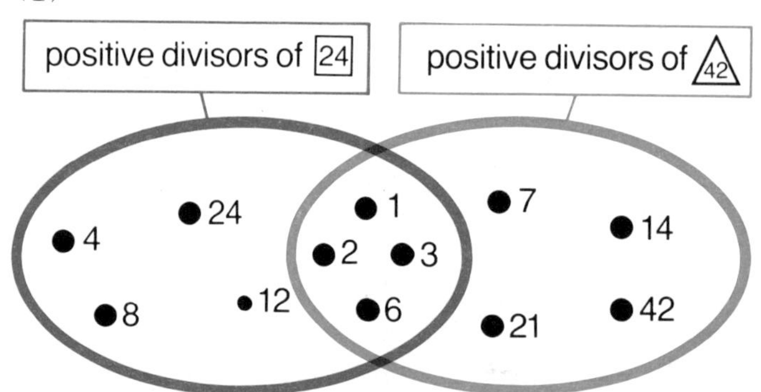

(All other whole numbers less than or equal to 50)

(2)

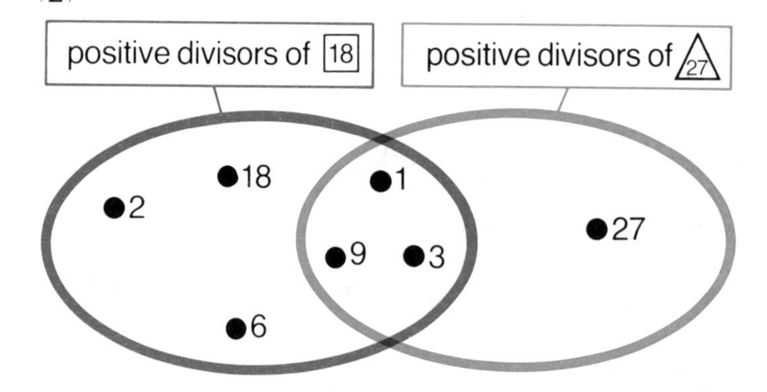

(All other whole numbers less than or equal to 50)

13

Draw the following diagram on the board:

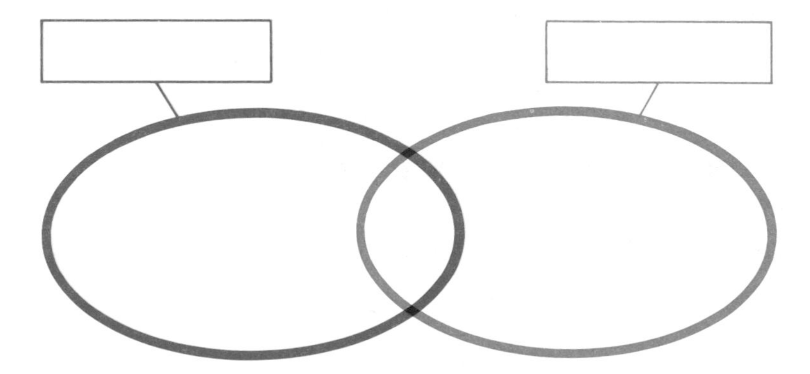

Tell the class that you are now going to show them a new String Game which is played with numbers rather than shapes. Tape a copy of Numerical String Game Poster 1 to the board.

MULTIPLES OF 2	MULTIPLES OF 3	MULTIPLES OF 4	MULTIPLES OF 5
MULTIPLES OF 10	POSITIVE DIVISORS OF 12	POSITIVE DIVISORS OF 18	POSITIVE DIVISORS OF 20
POSITIVE DIVISORS OF 24	POSITIVE DIVISORS OF 27	GREATER THAN 50	GREATER THAN $\widehat{10}$
LESS THAN 50	LESS THAN $\widehat{10}$	ODD NUMBERS	POSITIVE PRIME NUMBERS

T: These are the possible string labels in our new game. Just to make sure you know what each of them means, I'll point to some of them and I'd like you to tell me a number that belongs in a string labeled that way.

Point to several of the labels one by one and ask two or three students to tell you a number that has that attribute. To inject some variety into the situation, add a condition or two. For example, point to "multiples of 3" and ask for the smallest such number larger than 100, or point to "positive prime numbers" and ask for one between 60 and 70.

It is also interesting to ask for numbers that satisfy two or more of the conditions simultaneously. For example, you could ask for a number that is a multiple of 4, a positive divisor of 12, and a positive divisor of 24.

Occasionally ask for numbers that do not exist. For example, you could ask for a number that is a multiple of 10 and also a positive prime.

Continue the above activity until you think most of your students are comfortable with the 16 attributes. Then display the numerical playing pieces, explaining that they are the numbers with which the game is played. Also show the label cards to the students so they can see that there are two of each label. Point out that this means it is possible for the two strings to have the same label.

13

Choose two labels for the two strings, and write them in the boxes next to the strings. Then ask the students for numbers (chosen this time from among the playing pieces) that belong in regions you specify. For example, you could choose the following labels:

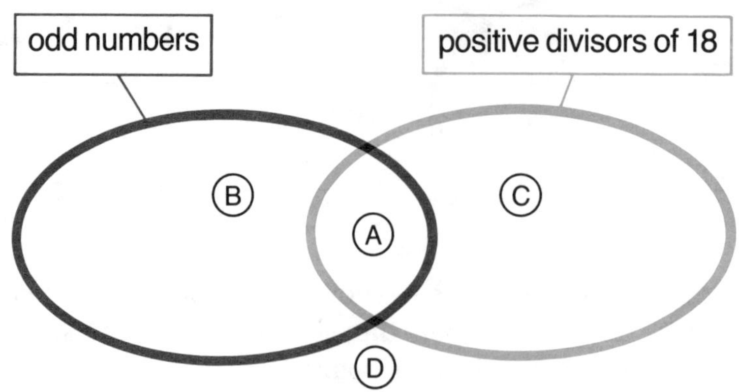

(Omit the circled letters.)
Point to region C.

T: Which of the playing numbers could go here?

Suppose a student comes to the board and places 6 in region C.

T: Is John correct? Does 6 go here? Explain your answer.

S: *Yes, because 6 is a positive divisor of 18.*

S: *But that's not enough. You also need to say that 6 is not an odd number.*

Continue this activity until you have two or three pieces in each region. Then let the students take turns to put the rest of the playing numbers where they belong, only stopping to discuss those that are incorrectly placed.

Resources Available

For out-of-class use: Any H-worksheet up through H26

ACTIVITY 14
Numerical String Game 2

Materials Needed
Teacher: Colored chalk, Numerical String Game kit
Students: None

Remind the students of the attributes by displaying Numerical String Game Poster 1. Also display all the playing pieces.

Play the game two or three times (depending on the time available). The game is played using the same rules as apply in the String Game with Shapes (see Volume 1, Activity 5). For the first few games, we recommend that you give four starting clues (two from each team's set of pieces) rather than the usual two.

To help students remember which numbers have been placed incorrectly during the course of the game, we recommend that you follow the procedure shown in the following diagram, where the incorrect number has been written on the board with chalk and then crossed out.

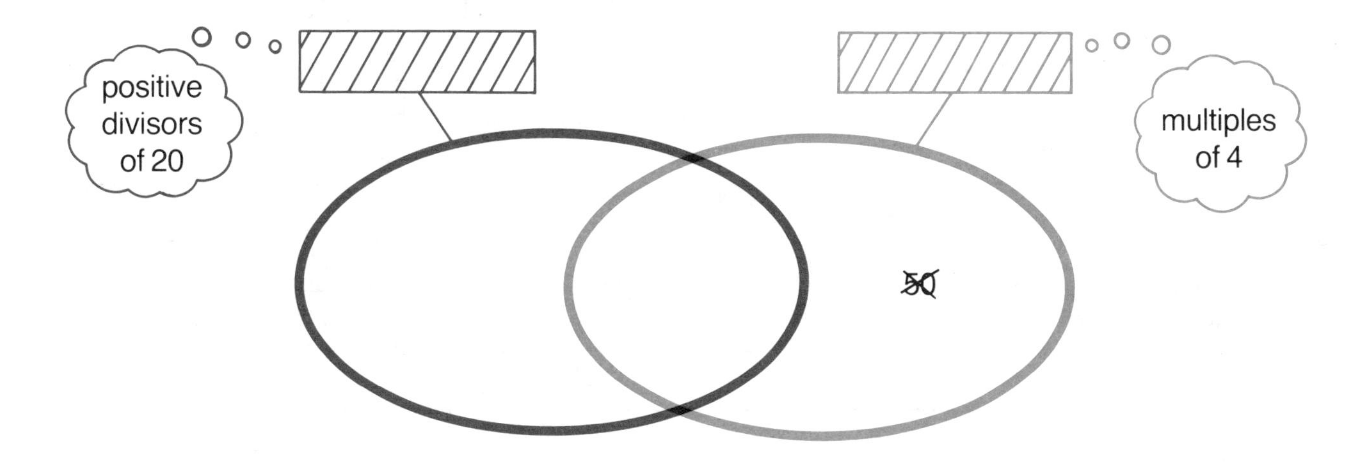

The crossed-out **50** indicates that a student played 50 in that region and you announced that it was not correct. Of course, the playing piece must be returned to the appropriate team's set of pieces as usual.

Here are two possible games; we have indicated the starting clues we recommend and have provided crib sheets.

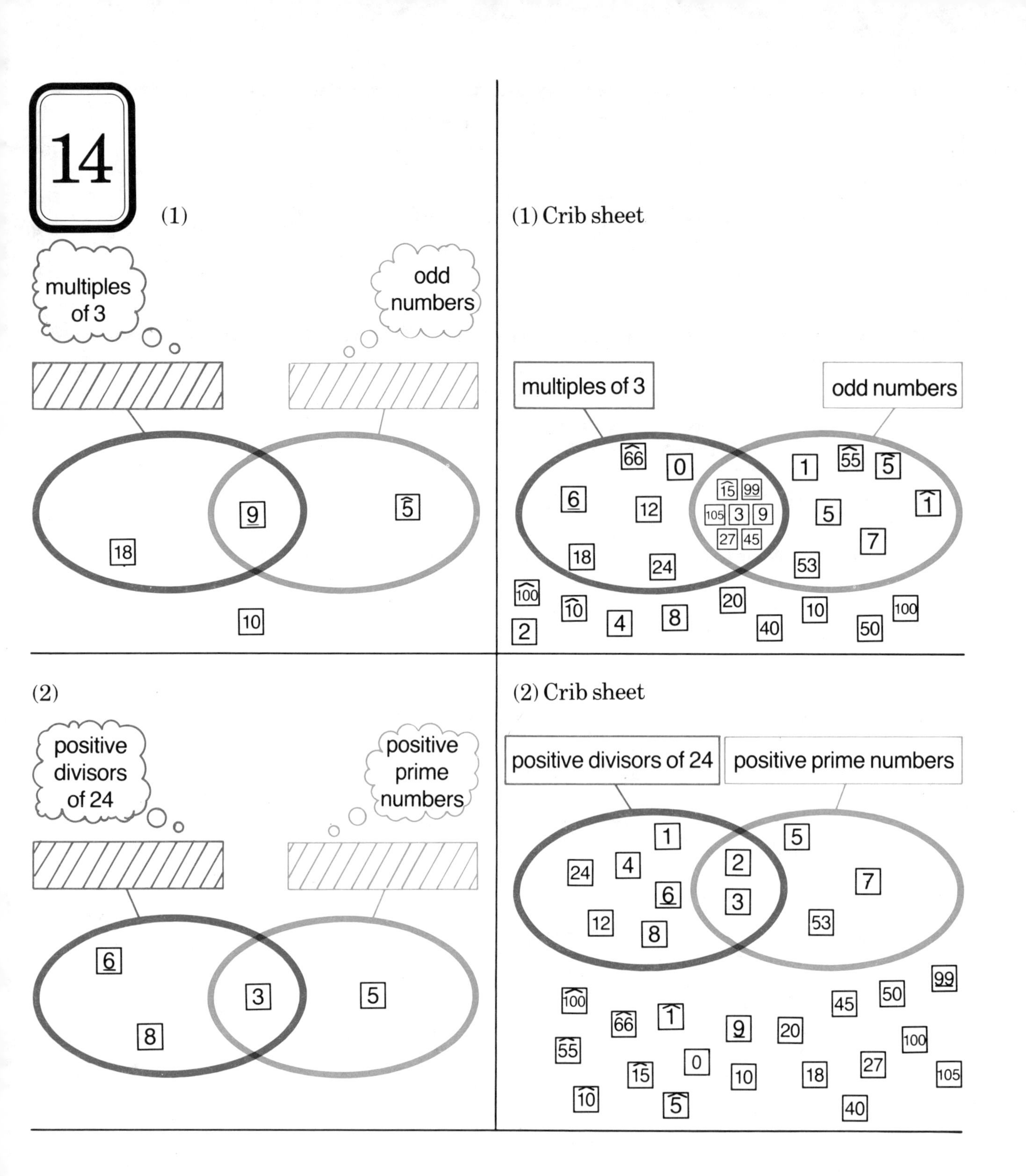

Resources Available

For out-of-class use: Any H-worksheet up through H26

ACTIVITY 15

Guess My Rule 1

Materials Needed
Teacher: Chalk
Students: Paper and pencils

Note to the Teacher

The secret rule $*$ in this lesson is given by this equation:

$$a * b = a + 2b$$

That is, add the first number to twice the second. This is for your information only. Do not divulge the rule to your students until they guess it.

T: Today we're going to play a new game called Guess My Rule. I'll use a secret sign, a star. Every time I "star" two numbers together I'll be doing the same thing, and your job is to find out what I'm doing. I'll start by giving you some clues.

One by one, write the following three calculations on the board. After each one give the students about 15 seconds to reflect on what you have written. Ask the students not to talk among themselves or call out what they think the rule is. Instead they should simply sit quietly and think for a while.

$$5 * 3 = 11$$
$$3 * 5 = 13$$
$$6 * 1 = 8$$

After a longer pause (about 30 seconds), add the following to your list:

$$1 * 6 =$$

Then ask the students who think they know the answer to write it on their papers, raise their hands and show their answers to you. Remind them not to call out or discuss their thoughts with anybody else. Circulate around the room, checking as many students' papers as you can and letting the authors know whether their answers are correct.

After a couple of minutes, ask someone who has the correct answer to announce it to the class. Complete the calculation on the board:

$$1 * 6 = 13$$

Repeat this procedure with the following calculations. The answers are given in parentheses.

$$4 * 2 = (8)$$
$$2 * 4 = (10)$$
$$7 * 5 = (17)$$

$$5 * 7 = (19)$$
$$0 * 9 = (18)$$
$$9 * 0 = (9)$$

By now it should be clear to you that at least one student knows the rule. Let such a student explain the rule to the class and go on to check all the calculations written on the board. If the student falls short of your expectations, ask another student for his or her opinion, and so on until the correct rule is given.

Distribute Worksheet L11 and let the students work on it individually. After the majority of the class has finished, check through the worksheet with the class.

Resources Available

For class use: Worksheet L11
For out-of-class use: Any H-worksheet up through H30

ACTIVITY 16
Guess My Rule 2

Materials Needed
Teacher: Colored chalk
Students: Paper and pencils

Note to the Teacher

If you are able to teach this activity immediately following Activity 15, then omit the first part of this activity and start instead at ■.

Remind the students of the special rule $*$ that they encountered in Activity 15. Do this by writing the following calculation on the board:

$$20 * 5 =$$

T: The star stands for the same rule we were using the other day. Write the answer to this calculation on your paper.

While you are giving the students sufficient time to do this, circulate among them, letting individuals know whether they have written down the correct answer. Ask one of those obtaining the correct answer to announce it to the class, and, for the sake of those who have forgotten, to explain what the rule is.

Write the following list of calculations on the board, and ask the students to copy and complete them on their papers. After a few minutes, go over the answer with the whole class, giving explanations when you think necessary. The answers are given in parentheses.

$$10 * 4 = (18)$$
$$4 * 10 = (24)$$
$$\hat{3} * 5 = (7)$$
$$4 * \hat{1} = (2)$$
$$11 * \hat{3} = (5)$$

■ Write the following equation on the board:

$$\square * 4 = 10$$

T: What number should go in the box to make this statement true? Explain your answer.

S: *2, because two times 4 is 8, and 2 + 8 = 10.*

Write the following problems on the board, and let the students work on them individually. The answers are given in parentheses.

$$\square * 8 = 20 \qquad (4)$$
$$4 * \square = 10 \qquad (3)$$
$$8 * \square = 20 \qquad (6)$$

Circulate around the room, checking students' work. When the majority has finished, discuss the solutions with the class.

Write the following equation on the board:

$\square * \square = 18$

T: In problems like this there's one other thing to remember: The same number must go in both boxes. Try this one by yourselves. When you think you have the answer, copy the problem onto your paper, write the same number in both boxes, raise your hand, and let me check your answer.

Give the students a minute or so to work on this problem, and then ask for the answer. Check it with the class.

$\boxed{6} * \boxed{6} = 18$

Write the following three problems on the board, and let the students work on them individually. The answers are given in parentheses.

$\square * \square = 30$ (10)
$\square * \square = 24$ (8)
$\square * \square = 39$ (13)

It is possible that certain students will notice that the answer is always one-third of the number on the right of the equals sign. If this is suggested, praise the student making the observation and ask for an explanation. If this discovery does not arise spontaneously, however, you should not attempt to provoke it.

Draw the following arrow picture on the board, omitting the letters.

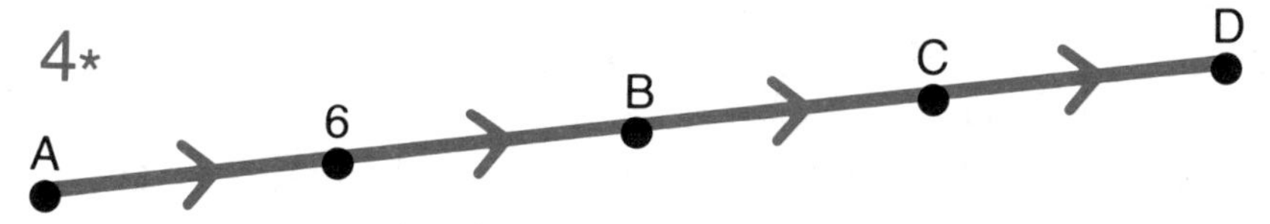

Point to the dot for 6.

T: Here is the number 6. The red arrows are for 4 *. So this number (point to dot B) is 4 * 6. What number is it?

S: *16.*

Label dot B **16**.

T: Now find the numbers here (point to dot C) and here (point to dot D).

S: *The first one is 36, because 4 * 16 = 36.*

S: *The last one is 76, because 4 * 36 = 76.*

T: How about this one? (point to dot A)

Ask the students to write their answers on their papers for you to check before asking one of them to announce it to the class.

S: *1, because 4 * 1 = 6.*

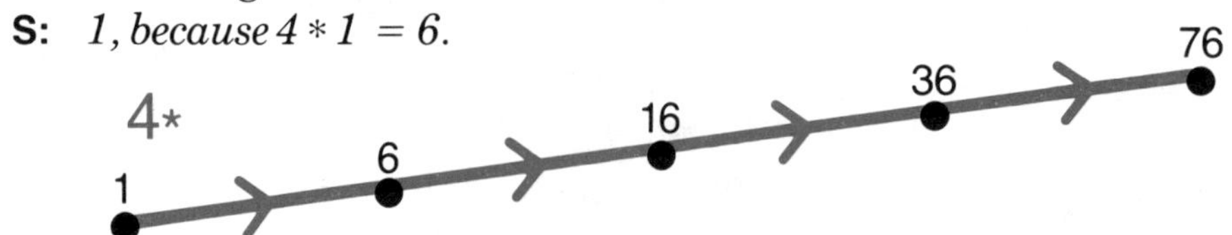

Resources Available

For class use: Worksheets L12 and L13
For out-of-class use: Any H-worksheets up through H30

ACTIVITY 17
Talkative Numbers 1

Materials Needed
Teacher: Colored chalk
Students: Paper and colored pencils

Tell the following story.

T: Did you know that the whole numbers have a club? Well, the president of the Whole Number Club is the number 0, and the secretary is the number 1. At each club meeting the president calls the meeting to order and the secretary reads the minutes of the last meeting. Lately, however, the numbers have been talking so loudly among themselves at the start of the meetings that 0 hasn't been able to make herself heard in order to ask for quiet for the secretary. To stop this chatter 0 posted a new rule for members of the Whole Number Club.

Write the following statement on the board as you say it out loud.

Two numbers in the Whole Number Club
may talk to each other
if and only if
one of them is a multiple of the other.

T: The whole numbers were confused by this new rule. At any rate, it certainly seemed to put a stop to the chatter. Do you think many numbers are still allowed to talk to each other under this new rule? Give me an example of two numbers that may still talk to each other.

S: *5 and 10.*

T: How do you know that 5 and 10 may talk to each other?

S: *Because 10 is a multiple of 5.*

T: So 5 may talk to 10 and 10 may talk to 5. I'll draw a red cord between dots for 5 and 10. To emphasize that they can talk in either direction, I won't put an arrowhead on the cord.

Draw the following on the board:

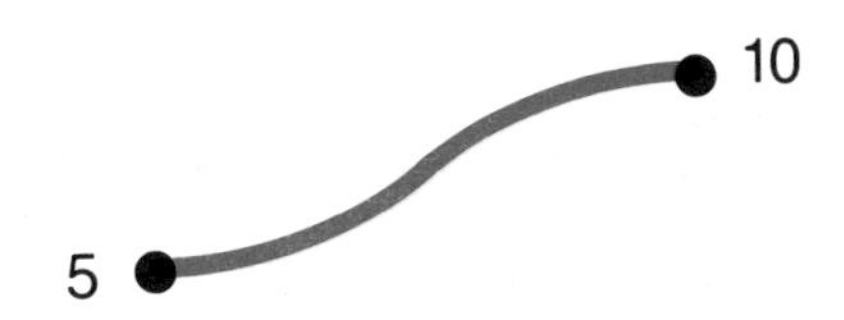

T: May 8 and 6 talk to each other?
S: *No; 8 is not a multiple of 6.*
T: And of course 6 is not a multiple of 8.
Continue asking for other suggestions of pairs of numbers that may talk to each other and pairs that may not. Record each suggestion on the board, which after a while might look like this:

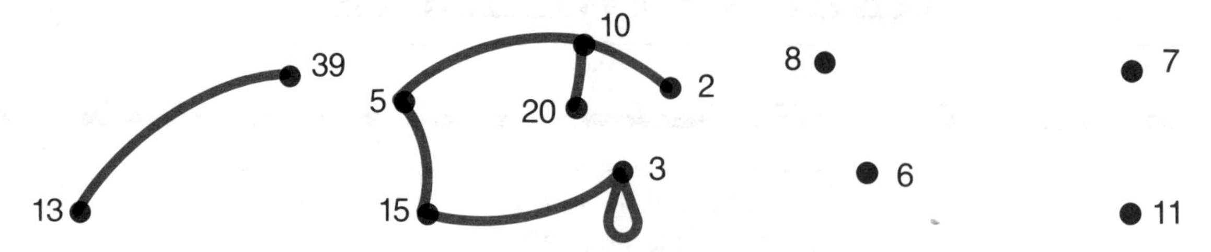

T: If you look at this picture, can you see any other cords that can be drawn between numbers?
The number of additional cords that can be drawn (which could well be large) will depend on your diagram. Let students draw a few of them without attempting to find all the possibilities. The following includes a few of the new cords that can be drawn in the above diagram.

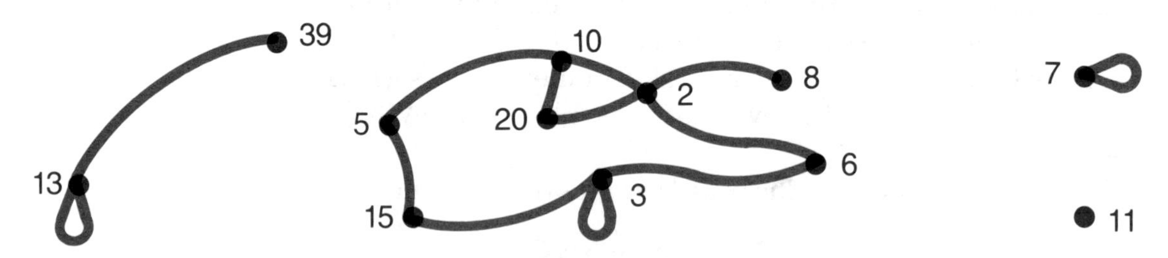

Erase the cord diagram and replace it with a dot for the club member 30:

30 ●

T: Suggest some numbers that may speak to 30.
As you receive suggestions, add them to the diagram on the board. If no one suggests a number less than 30, ask whether any such number may talk to 30. (Yes; 0, 1, 2, 3, 5, 6, 10, 12, and 15 may talk to 30 because 0 is a multiple of 30, and 30 is a multiple of each of the others.)

If necessary, review the notion of multiples by means of arrow roads. For example, 30 is a multiple of 6 because 30 is on the +6 arrow road that passes through 0:

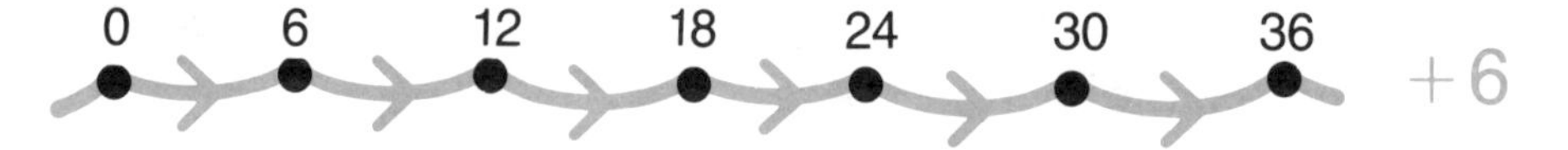

Zero is a multiple of 30 because 0 is on the +30 arrow road that passes through 0:

0 30 60 +30

The picture showing some of the club members that may talk to 30 might look like this:

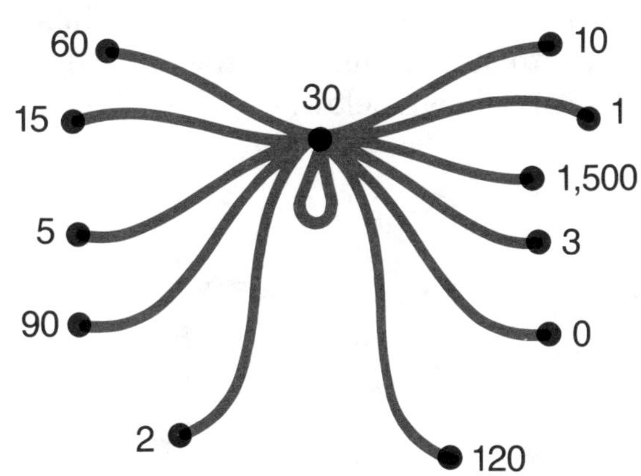

If it is not mentioned, call attention to the loop: 30 may talk to itself because 30 is a multiple of 30.

T: Can you tell me a number not already in the picture that 3 may talk to?

S: *6 or 9 or 12 or ...*

Add the suggested numbers to the diagram.

T: What about a number not in the picture that 10 may talk to?

S: *20 or 40 or 50 or ...*

Ask a few more such questions, and record all the answers:

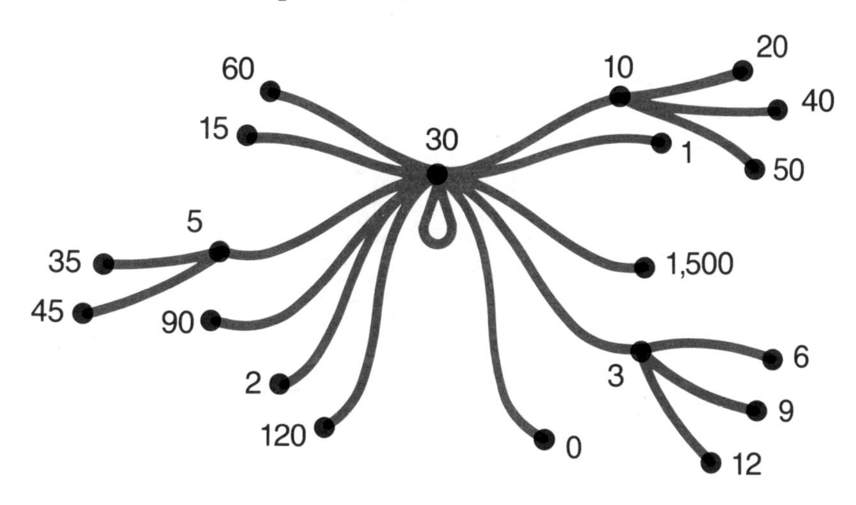

Erase the cord diagram and replace it with the following diagram.

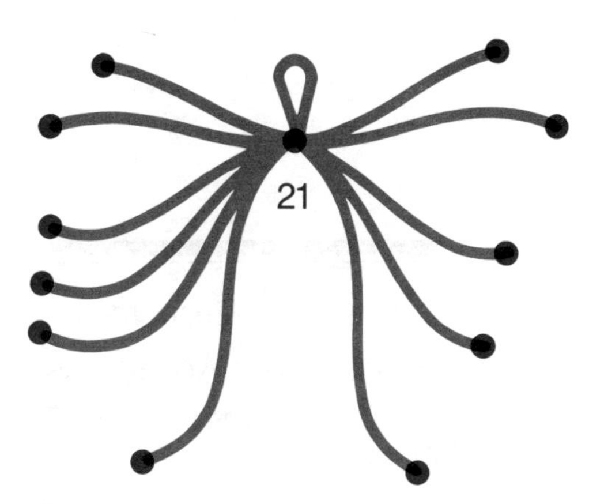

T: Copy this picture onto your paper and label some numbers that may talk to 21.

Walk around the room observing the students' work. Then ask volunteers, one at a time, to put a number on the diagram on the board. Some of the possibilities are shown below:

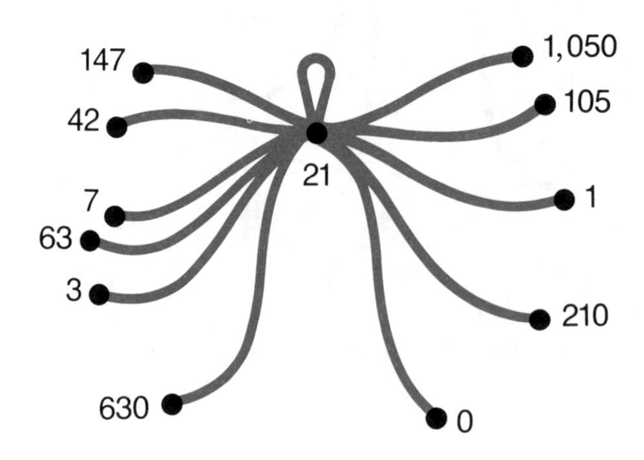

Resources Available

For class use: Worksheets L14 and L15

For out-of-class use: Any H-worksheet up through H31

ACTIVITY 18
Talkative Numbers 2

Materials Needed
Teacher: Colored chalk
Students: Paper and colored pencils

Briefly review the story of the Whole Numbers Club in Activity 17 and the new rule that the president, 0, imposed on the membership. Write the rule on the board:

Two numbers in the Whole Number Club
may talk to each other
if and only if
one of them is a multiple of the other.

T: Who can give me an example of two whole numbers that may talk to each other?
S: *6 and 18.*
T: Which is a multiple of which?
S: *18 is a multiple of 6.*
T: Another example?
S: *0 and 73.*
T: Which is a multiple of which?
S: *0 is a multiple of 73.*
S: *0 may speak to any whole number because 0 times any number is 0.*
T: Is there another number that may talk to every number in the club?
S: *Yes; 1, because every number is a multiple of 1.*
Continue this type of questioning for a few minutes. Then draw the following dot and label on the board:

42
●

T: How can we show that another number may talk to 42?
S: *Draw a red line between them.*
T: That's right. We call it a cord. It's like a two-way arrow with no arrowheads. Can you tell me some of the numbers that may talk to 42?

As students suggest numbers that may talk to 42, record them on the diagram on the board. Some possibilities are shown:

18

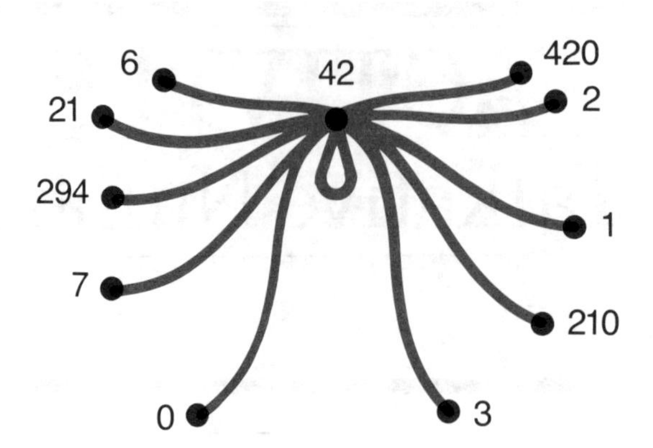

Point to a number in the diagram (other than 42) and draw two cords from that dot.

T: What are some numbers that may talk to this number?

Continue for some other numbers in the diagram. The result might look like this:

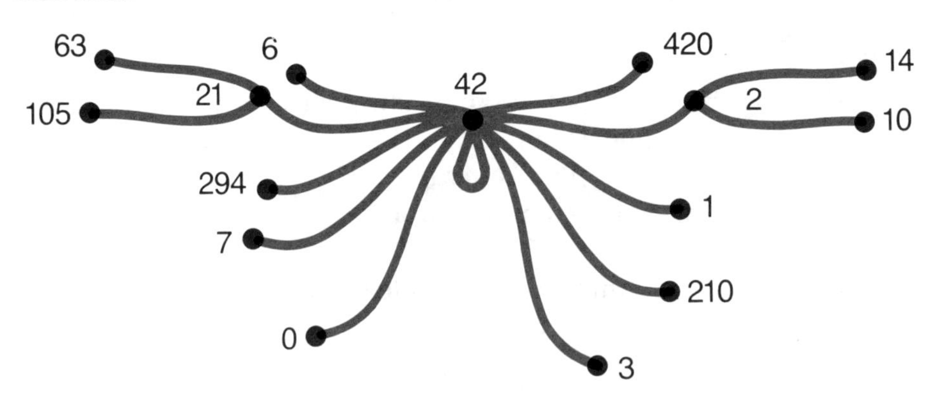

Erase the cord diagram from the board and replace it with the following:

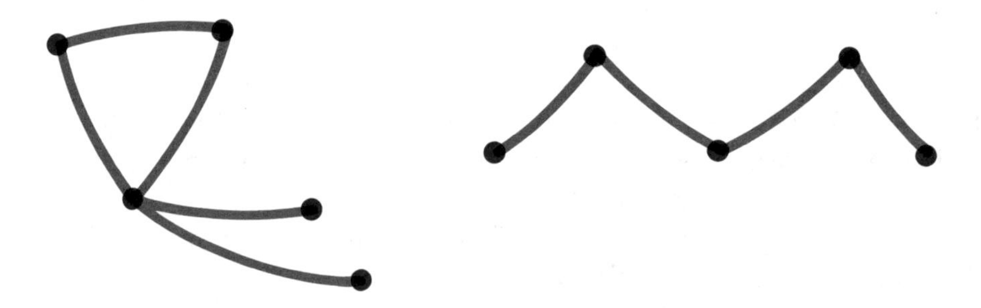

T: What numbers could these ten dots be for?

There are many possibilities for labeling these dots. Here is one of them:

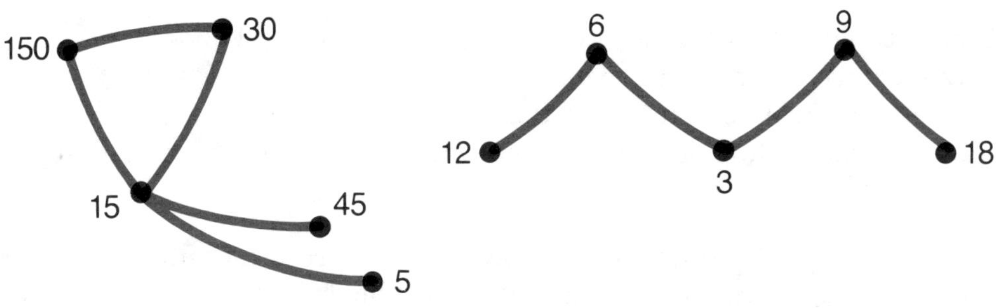

Do not insist that the labels chosen be such that no further cords may be drawn. That is, accept any labeling for which each red cord connects two numbers that may talk to each other, even though some pairs of numbers in the resulting diagram that may talk to each other do not have a cord between them. (See, for example, 3 and 12, 6 and 30 in the last diagram.)

Note to the Teacher

If your class is particularly quick with the preceding exercise, challenge them by repeating it with the new stipulation that the labels be chosen so that no further cords may be drawn. The students' first reaction will probably be, "That's impossible," but some students will eventually succeed in finding a solution, such as the one below.

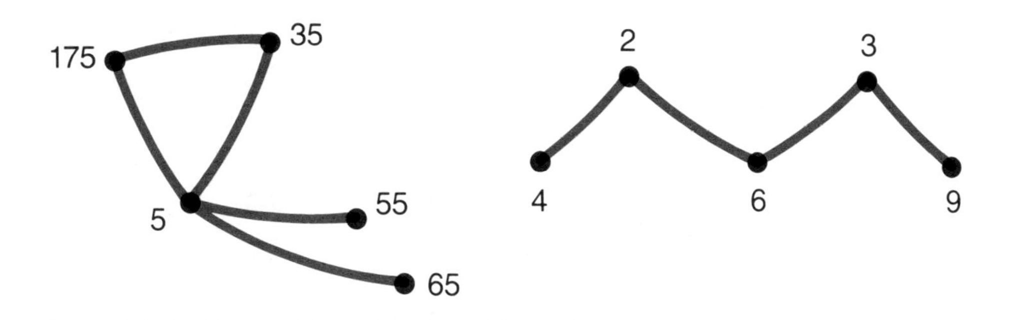

Erase the cord diagram from the board and replace it with the following dots and labels:

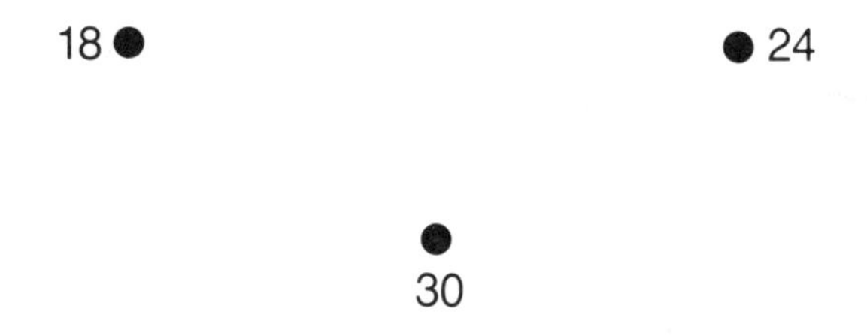

T: Are 18, 24, and 30 allowed to talk to each other?
S: *No; none is a multiple of any other.*
T: Well, these three numbers are very good friends, and they were very upset when they discovered that the new rule was going to prevent them from talking to each other. But then 24 had an idea. Why not send messages to 18 and 30 by talking to a number that could then talk to 18 and to 30? A number like that would have to be able to talk to 18, 24, and 30. Let's help them find such numbers.
S: *They may all talk to 6.*
S: *And to 3.*
S: *And 2.*
S: *And 0 and 1.*
T: But all the numbers you have suggested so far are less than 18. Are there any that are greater than 18?
S: *360.*
As this discussion proceeds, record the results on the board.

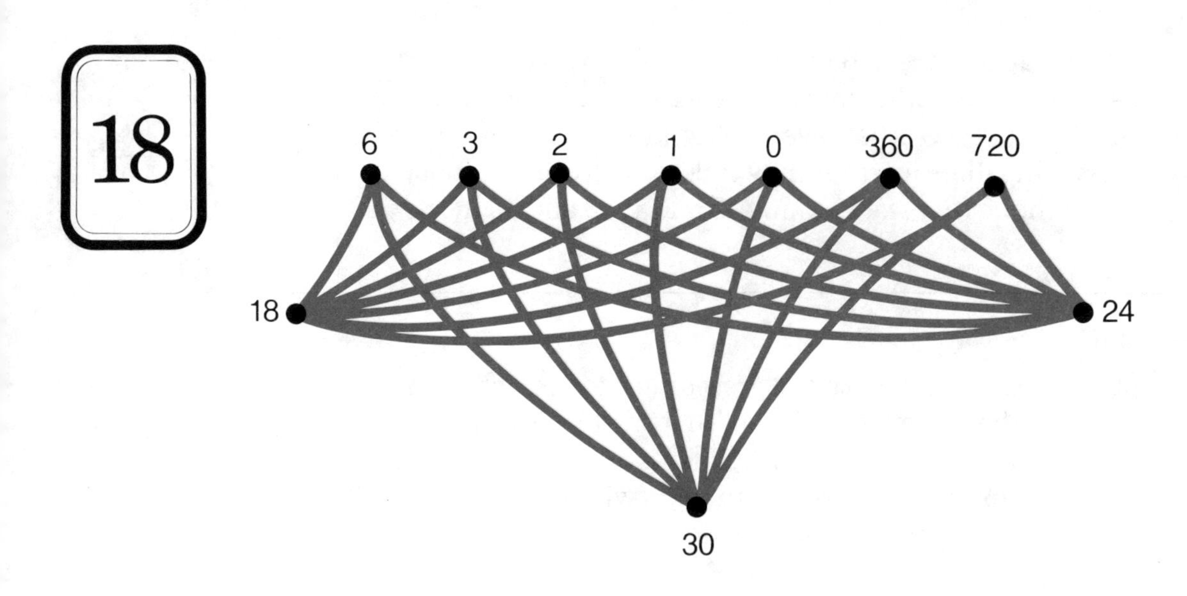

Resources Available

For out-of-class use: Any H-worksheet up through H35

ACTIVITY 19
Calculator Tug-of-War 1

Materials Needed
Teacher: Colored chalk
Students: One calculator each

T: Today we're going to play Calculator Tug-of-War.

Divide the class into two teams (Red and Blue) and give each student a calculator.

T: For this first game, the Red team will start at 267 and the Blue team will start at 935.

Write the following boxes and numbers on the board:

267		935

T: The Red team's number is less than the Blue team's number, so the Red team may only add and the Blue team may only subtract. When it's your turn you must choose a whole number and announce it to the class. Then, if you're on the Red team, the whole Red team must press [+] [your chosen whole number] [=], and if you're on the Blue team, the whole Blue team must press [−] [your chosen whole number] [=] . The teams take turns, and you take turns within your teams. I'll keep track of the play here on the board. The first team to meet the other team's number or to pass it will be the loser.

In this calculator version of Tug-of-War there's one more rule: You're not allowed to use paper and pencil, and the only time you're allowed to use your calculator is *after* a player on your team has announced a play.

Let the class play through the first game. After each play, check with the team concerned, and then amend the record of its current number on the board. Remember to insure that at the start of play each member of the Red team has 267 displayed on his or her calculator and that each member of the Blue team has 935 displayed.

Here is one possible development of the game:

Team	Play	Display Red	Display Blue
		267	935
Red	+ 67	334	935
Blue	− 40	334	895
Red	+ 70	404	895
Blue	− 200	404	695
Red	+ 20	424	695
Blue	− 40	424	655
Red	+ 100	524	655
Blue	− 55	524	600
Red	+ 60	584	600
Blue	− 10	584	590
Red	+ 5	589	590

S: *Red has won, because no matter what Blue does the Blue number will be 589 or smaller.*

Note to the Teacher

It is possible that a Blue player will suggest a play such as [+] [0.1] , which of course will keep the Blue number above 589. This is an excellent play and will be encouraged in later Calculator Tug-of-War activities and also in Calculator Golf activities. For the present, however, the rules as stated at the beginning of the activity restrict the numbers that may be added or subtracted to whole numbers only.

Play several more games. Suitable starting numbers are listed below. Notice that in alternate games the Red team has the larger and then the smaller starting number. This gives each team the experience of playing by adding as well as by subtracting.

Red	Blue
814	91
142	1151
75	92
127	206
52	607

Resources Available

For out-of-class use: Any H-worksheet up through H35

ACTIVITY 20
Numerical String Game 3

Materials Needed
Teacher: Colored chalk, Numerical String Game kit
Students: None

Begin the activity by playing a game with the following starting clues:

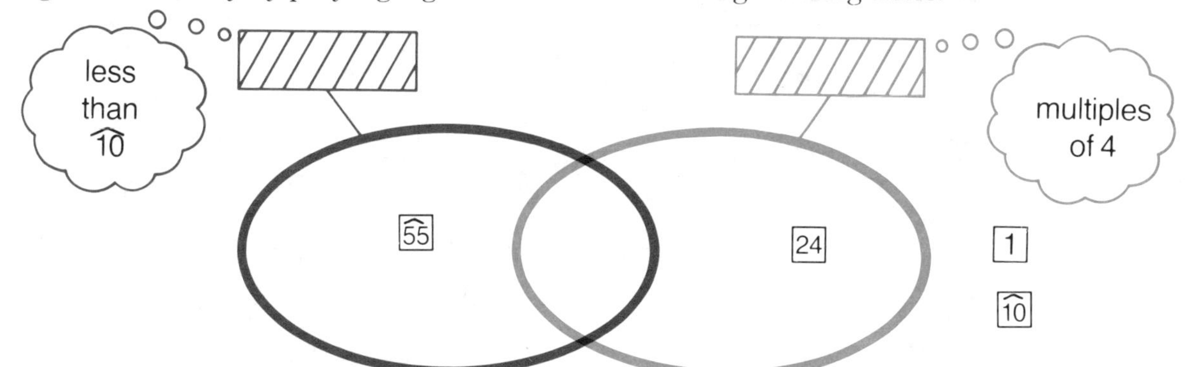

Here is a crib sheet for this game:

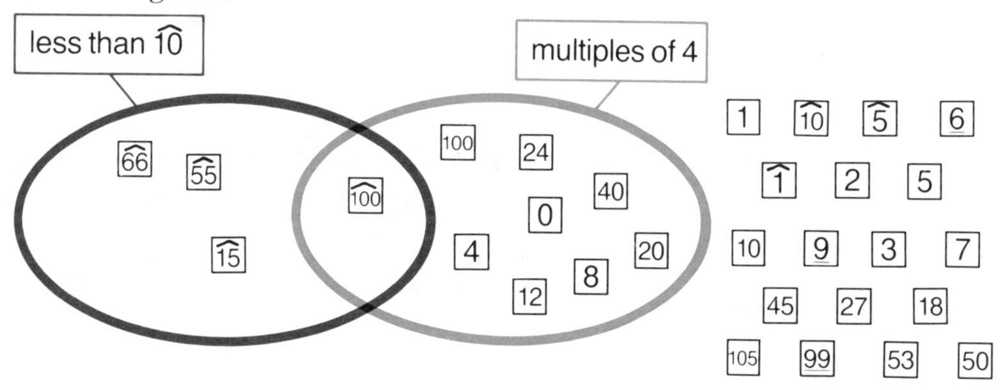

For the second game, use the following starting clues, which are different from any the class will have seen before.

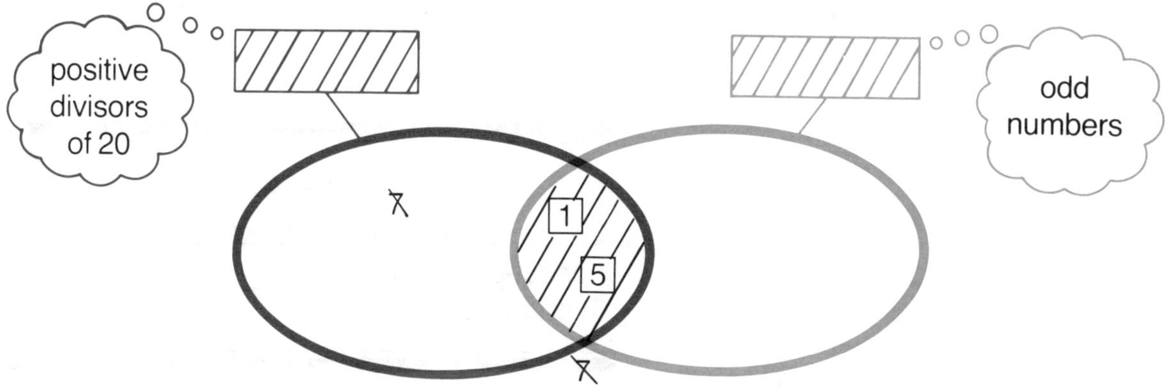

Here is one way in which you might alert the students to the new type of information being provided:

T: This time I've given you some new kinds of clues. What have I told you about the number 7?

S: *It doesn't go there (pointing to the region in the red string but outside the blue string), and it doesn't go there (pointing to the region outside both strings).*

T: And what does that hatching tell you?

S: *That 1 and 5 are the only numbers in the middle.*

S: *Then I know where 7 goes. It has to go here (pointing to the region in the blue string but outside the red string), because there's nowhere else for it to go.*

Here is a crib sheet for this game:

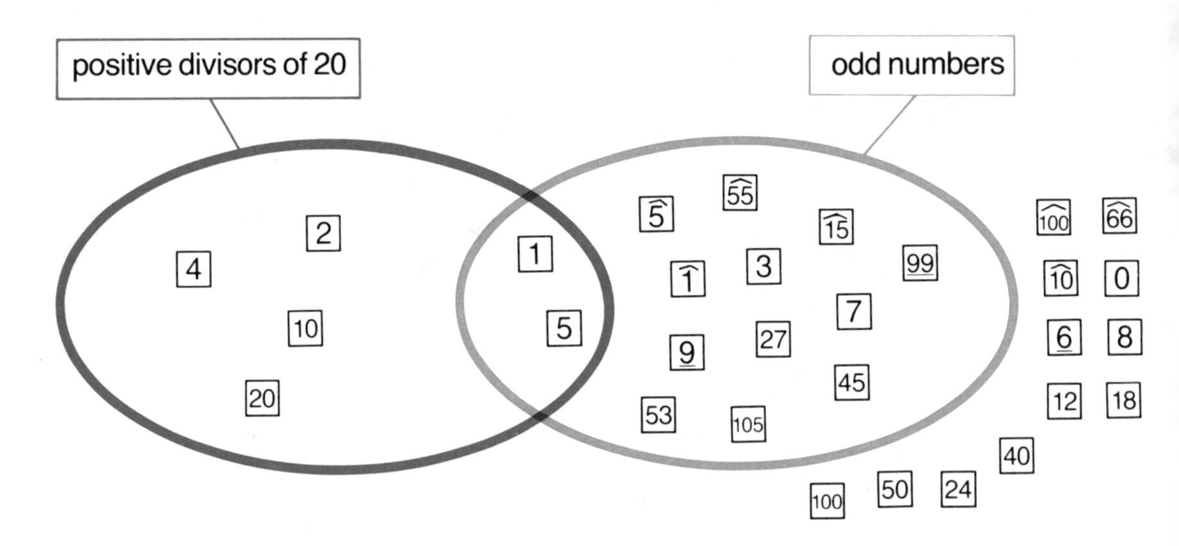

If time allows, Worksheets L16 and L17 are available for the students to work on individually. If not, the worksheets can be assigned for homework.

Resources Available

For class use: Worksheets L16 and L17
For out-of-class use: Any H-worksheet up through H37

ACTIVITY 21
Comparing Prices 1

Materials Needed
Teacher: Colored chalk
Students: None

Tell a story such as the following one, replacing "Bill" with the name of one of your students.

T: Bill has the job of buying special erasers for the students in the art classes. He compares prices at two stores. Kwiksave sells a package of three of the special erasers for 68 cents, and Doc's Dime Store charges 88 cents for a package of four of the same erasers.

As you tell the story, write the information on the board:

Kwiksave: 3 erasers for 68¢
Doc's Dime Store: 4 erasers for 88¢

T: Bill has to decide which erasers to buy. What should he do?

Let the students discuss all aspects of the problem. In all likelihood, some will quickly decide that erasers are cheaper at Doc's Dime Store because there each eraser costs 22 cents (a fourth of 88 cents), so that three would cost 66 cents (three times 22 cents). This is obviously cheaper than the 68 cents charged by Kwiksave. Other students (or you) should remind the class that Bill cannot buy three erasers at Doc's, because they are sold in packages of four.

T: Perhaps he could buy the same number of erasers at each store. Is that possible? (yes) What is the smallest possible number? (12) To get 12 erasers, how many packages would Bill have to buy at Kwiksave?

S: *Four packages, because Kwiksave sells them in packages of three.*

Draw the following picture on the board:

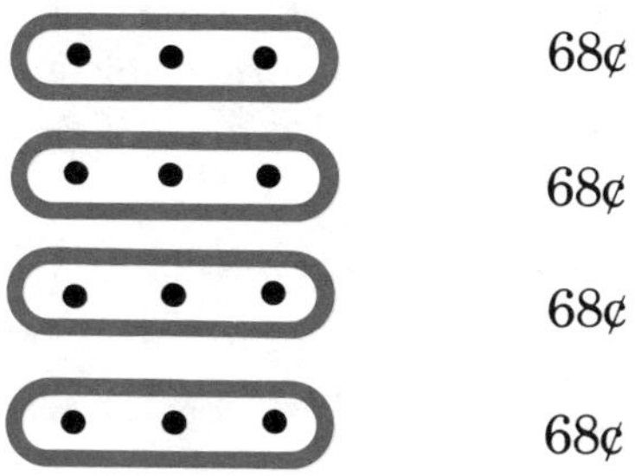

(• • •) 68¢
(• • •) 68¢
(• • •) 68¢
(• • •) 68¢

T: So how much would 12 erasers cost at Kwiksave?

S: *I've figured it out! 68 + 68 + 68 + 68 = 272, so they cost $2.72.*

Add this information to the prices listed on the board.

Kwiksave: 3 erasers for 68¢, or 12 for $2.72
Doc's Dime Store: 4 erasers for 88¢

T: How many packages would Bill have to buy at Doc's Dime Store to get 12 erasers? (3)

Draw the following picture on the board:

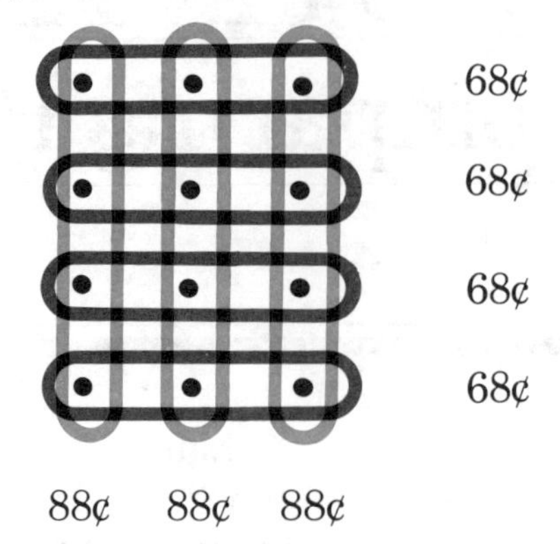

T: How much do three packages of erasers cost at Doc's?

S: *88 + 88 + 88 = 264; $2.64.*

Record this information:

Kwiksave: 3 erasers for 68¢, or 12 for $2.72
Doc's Dime Store: 4 erasers for 88¢, or 12 for $2.64

T: Which store sells 12 erasers for the lower price?

S: *Doc's Dime Store.*

T: How much would Bill save if he bought a dozen erasers at Doc's Dime Store rather than at Kwiksave? (8 cents) So if Bill has to buy one eraser for each student in the art classes, which store offers the better price?

At this point most students will say it is Doc's Dime Store because the price per dozen is lower there.

T: Would Bill ever consider buying erasers at Kwiksave?

S: *If he needed exactly three erasers.*

S: *If he only had 75 cents to spend.*

S: *If he needed exactly seven erasers, he ought to buy one package from each store.*

If your class seems to understand the problem, ask how Bill should shop for five erasers. Students will protest that Bill cannot buy exactly five erasers, so he will have to buy two packages of three, two packages of four, or one of each. They should conclude that if Bill needs only five erasers, then it is cheaper to buy two packages at Kwiksave for $1.36 (and have one extra eraser) than to buy one package at each store for $1.56 (and have two extras) or two packages at Doc's Dime Store for $1.76 (and have three extras).

T: Could Bill buy exactly six erasers? (yes) How? (He could buy two packages at Kwiksave.) Could he buy exactly seven? (Yes; one package at each store.) Could he buy exactly eight? (Yes; two packages at Doc's.)...

Could he buy exactly seventeen? (Yes; three packages at Kwiksave and two at Doc's.)

Continue the activity by telling another story dealing with the comparison of prices. This time replace "Sally" in the following problem with the name of another of your students.

T: Sally's assignment in the Botany Club is to order some special flower bulbs. She sees just what she wants in two catalogs, but one sells the bulbs in packets of five and the other in packets of four.

Erase all material relating to the first situation from the board, and replace it with the following information:

Seed and Bloom: 4 bulbs for $1.40
Green Thumb: 5 bulbs for $1.85

Then proceed as in the case of the first situation, helping the class to compare prices for the same number of bulbs (say, 20) and recording the results:

Seed and Bloom: 4 bulbs for $1.40, or 20 for $7.00
Green Thumb: 5 bulbs for $1.85, or 20 for $7.40

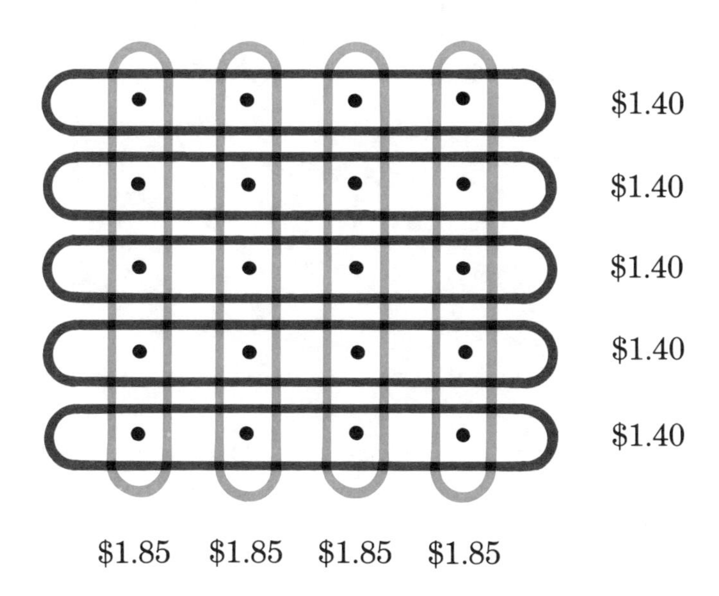

Ask questions similar to those asked in the first part of this activity:

- Which catalog offers the lower price for 20 bulbs? (Seed and Bloom)
- How much would Sally save by ordering 20 bulbs from Seed and Bloom rather than Green Thumb? (40 cents)
- Should Sally buy the bulbs from Seed and Bloom? (Yes; the cost per bulb is lower.)
- Should Sally ever buy bulbs from Green Thumb? (Yes; if she needed only five or ten bulbs.)
- How should she buy seven bulbs? (Two packets from Seed and Bloom will cost $2.80, with one bulb extra, whereas one packet from each catalog will cost $3.25, with two bulbs extra.)
- Can she buy exactly nine bulbs? (Yes; one packet from each catalog.)
- Can she buy exactly ten bulbs? (Yes; two packets from Green Thumb.)

  exactly eleven bulbs? (no)
  exactly twelve bulbs? (yes)
  exactly thirteen bulbs? (yes)
  ...
  exactly 23 bulbs? (yes)

To summarize the activity, if time allows, ask students to help you complete the following table drawn on the board:

21

Number of Bulbs Needed	Number of packets from: Seed and Bloom	Green Thumb
4	1	0
5	0	1
6	–	–
7	–	–
8	2	0
9	1	1
10	0	2
11	–	–
12	3	0
13	2	1
14	1	2

Resources Available

For out-of-class use: Any H-worksheet up through H39

ACTIVITY 22
Detective Story 1

Materials Needed
Teacher: Colored chalk, Minicomputer kit
Students: None

Before class choose a boy and a girl in your class (in this description we suppose they are called "John" and "Patty"). Write the numbers 21 and 8 on separate pieces of paper, and fold each of them so that what you have written cannot be seen. Give John the piece of paper with **21** written on it, and give Patty the one with **8** written on it. Ask them to hold the pieces of paper throughout the activity without looking at them. (It is of course important not to mix the papers up before you give them to John and Patty.)

T: Today we are looking for two numbers called John and Patty. To help us remember which is which, I've given a folded-up piece of paper with the real identity of the number John written on it to John. And Patty is holding another folded-up piece of paper with the number Patty's real identity written on it. At the end of the lesson we'll ask them to unfold their pieces of paper so that we can check if we really have managed to figure out what numbers John and Patty are. Before I give you the first clue, I should tell you that John and Patty are both whole numbers. Here's the first clue.

Draw the following diagram on the board:
Clue 1:

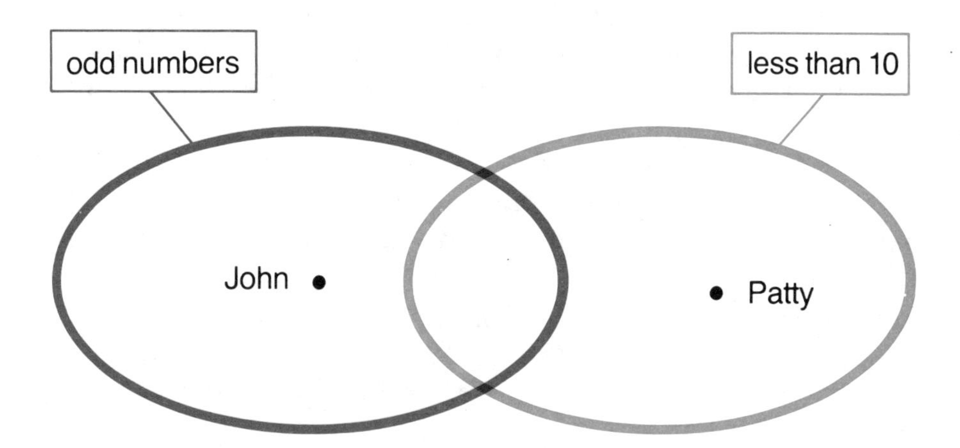

T: What does this string picture tell us?
S: *Patty could be 4.*
S: *John could be 15.*

T: Let's write down some of these possibilities.
Start a table on the board such as the following:

John	Patty
15	4

S: *Patty can only be 0, 2, 4, 6, or 8, because those are the only whole numbers that are less than 10 and not odd.*
Add these numbers to the table on the board.
T: Is there a smallest number that John could be?
S: *Yes, 11.*
Add this and a few more possibilities for John to the table on the board.
T: Good. Now for the second clue: Both Patty and John are in this arrow diagram.
Draw the following diagram on the board:

Clue 2:

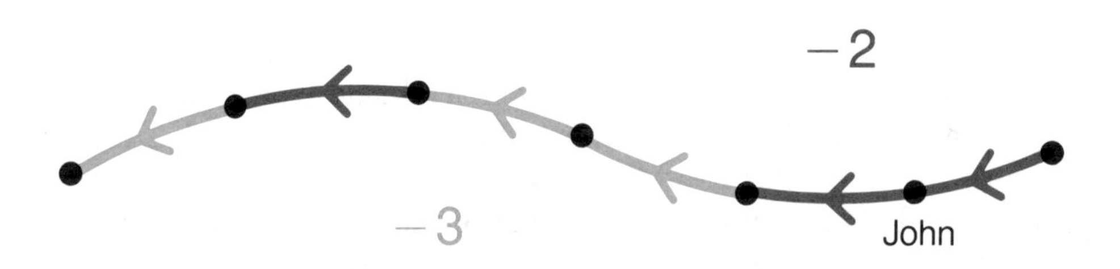

S: *But Patty's not mentioned in that diagram.*
S: *There aren't any numbers to work from.*
T: You're right. But we can still find out some important information from this diagram. To begin with, let's try to figure out which of these dots could be for Patty.
The students will probably need plenty of time at this stage to think. If no answer is forthcoming after a suitable interval, refer the class to Clue 1.
S(Bill): *Patty couldn't be either of the numbers with dots next to John's dot, because John is odd and so are they.*
T: Excellent. Does everyone see that? Let's check by trying a couple of numbers for John.
S: *If John is 35, then the dots next to his dot are for 33 and 37. If John is 1,001, then those dots are for 999 and 1,003.*
T: Good. Now can we go on using Bill's idea to help us discover which dots could be for Patty?
S(Amy): *Yes. The next dot could be for Patty because when you take 3 away from an odd number you get an even number.*
T: Fine. I'll mark that on the board. While I'm doing that, Amy, could you check what you've just said when John is 35?

Modify the arrow diagram as follows:

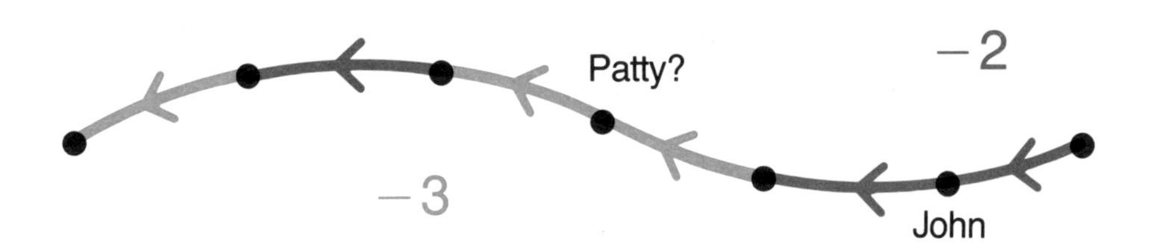

S(Amy): *If John is 35, the next dot to the left is for 33, and the next dot is for 30, which is even.*

S: *Yes, but Patty can't be that big.*

T: You're right, but at the moment we're just worried about whether the numbers are odd or even. Is there another dot in the diagram that stands for an even number, and so could be for Patty?

S: *The last dot on the left, because after the dot you marked "Patty question mark" the next two are odd, and then it changes back to even again.*

T: Excellent. I'll mark that, too.

Label the left-most dot "Patty?".

If the students seem to be having difficulty with the odd-even arguments, you might ask them to help you write "even" or "odd" next to each of the dots in the arrow diagram, starting with John and asking for reasons as you go.

T: Let's move on to the next clue.
Clue 3: Patty is the smallest even number in the arrow diagram.

S: *Well, that means that Patty's dot is the one on the far left.*

T: Does everyone agree? OK, I'll cross out the other possibility and the question mark.

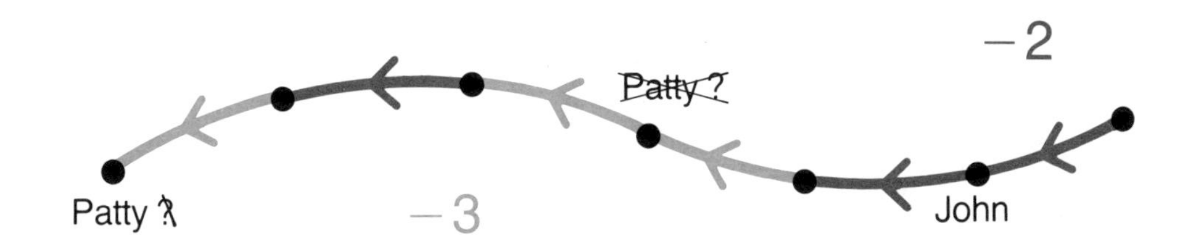

T: We still don't have any numbers, but we do know more about John and Patty. What can you tell me?

S: *They're 13 apart.*

T: Right. Let's use that information and make a more accurate list.

Erase the numbers recorded in the table on the board, leaving just the column headings.

T: Can anyone give me a pair of numbers that would fit all the clues so far?

S: *35 for John, 22 for Patty.*

S: *No. Patty must be less than 10.*

S: *13 for John, 0 for Patty.*

Record the five possibilities in the table as they are discovered.

John	Patty
13	0
17	4
21	8
19	6
15	2

T: Here's the last clue.
Clue 4: John may be shown on two Minicomputer boards with fewer than three regular checkers.

By working their way through the five possible values of John, the students will come to realize that John must be 21; this then implies that Patty must be 8. Finish the activity by asking the two students with the folded pieces of paper to disclose what they have been guarding throughout the lesson.

Resources Available

For out-of-class use: Any H-worksheet up through H39

ACTIVITY 23
Comparing Prices 2

Materials Needed
Teacher: Colored chalk
Students: None

Tell a story such as the following, replacing "Joe" with the name of one of your students.

T: Joe's brother goes to and from work on the city bus five days a week. Each time he gets on the bus, the driver punches his ticket. Joe's brother can buy a 30-ride ticket for 13 dollars or a 50-ride ticket for 21 dollars. How many times a week does he ride the bus as he goes to and from work?
S: *Ten times: twice a day for five days.*
T: So how many weeks will a 30-ride ticket last?
S: *Three weeks, and a 50-ride ticket will last five weeks.*

Record this information on the board:

30-ride ticket: 3 weeks for $13
50-ride ticket: 5 weeks for $21

T: Which ticket should Joe's brother buy?

The students will probably remember their past experiences in comparing prices and will decide to compare the costs of the same number of weeks; in this case, say 15 weeks.

Allow students to explain how the calculations are made, and then add the information to what is already recorded on the board:

30-ride ticket: 3 weeks for $13, or 15 weeks for $65
50-ride ticket: 5 weeks for $21, or 15 weeks for $63

S: *He should buy the 50-ride ticket.*
S: *Not if he only needs 30 rides!*
T: Joe's brother plans to ride the bus for 18 weeks until his new car is delivered. Can he buy exactly 18 weeks' worth of tickets?
S: *Yes, he can. He just has to buy six three-week tickets.*
T: What would that cost him?
S: *78 dollars: $6 \times 13 = 78$*

If your students have difficulty with this calculation, let them add $13 + 13 + 13 + 13 + 13 + 13$ or think "$(6 \times 10) + (6 \times 3)$" or actually use a multiplication algorithm to calculate 6×13.

T: Is there another way to buy tickets for 18 weeks?
S: *I've got it; he could buy one three-week ticket and three five-week tickets.*

T: What would that cost?

S: *76 dollars: 13 + 21 + 21 + 21 = 76. That's cheaper than six three-week tickets.*

T: Are we sure there are no other ways to buy 18 weeks' worth of tickets?

Let the students try various combinations of tickets until they are satisfied that these are the only ways.

T: So the cheapest thing for Joe's brother to do is to buy one three-week ticket and three five-week tickets.

Record the results of this activity in a table on the board as follows:

Number of Weeks	Number of 3-week Tickets	Number of 5-week Tickets	Total Cost
18	6	0	$78
18	1	3	$76

In the time remaining, let the students work individually or in groups on determining the lowest costs of buying tickets for:

- 38 weeks
  (Answer: One three-week ticket and seven five-week tickets; cost 160 dollars.)
- One year (52 weeks)
  (Answer: Four three-week tickets and eight five-week tickets; cost 220 dollars.)

As students solve these problems, ask them to record in the table on the board all the ways they have found to buy the required number of tickets and then to indicate which is the cheapest.

Resources Available

For out-of-class use: Any H-worksheet up through H40

ACTIVITY 24

Calculator 1

Materials Needed
Teacher: Chalk
Students: One calculator each

Note to the Teacher

In this and all subsequent lessons involving calculators, it is assumed that each student has an electronic calculator with the following two features.

- Chain operation –The calculator responds to instructions in the order in which they are given. For example, pressing

  [2] [+] [3] [×] [4] [=]

  results in 20 appearing on the display. That is, pressing any of the keys [+], [−], [×], [÷], or [=] causes any pending operation to be completed. (Notice that this implies that the normal hierarchy of operations is *not* obeyed. Some calculators incorporate that hierarchy, in which multiplication has precedence over addition. On such calculators the above sequence of keystrokes would produce an answer of 14.)

- Constant mode –Continuing to press [=] after performing any of the four operations causes that operation to be repeated. For example, pressing

  [5] [+] [3] [=] [=] [=] [=]

  results in 17 appearing on the display. (The operation being repeated is +3.)

If your calculators do not operate in constant mode, then they may still be used for these activities provided you interpret

[2] [+] [3] [=] . . . as
[2] [+] [3] [=] [+] [3] [=] [+] [3] [=] and so on.

Similarly, you should interpret

[×] [5] [=] . . . as
[×] [5] [=] [×] [5] [=] [×] [5] [=] and so on.

Be warned! Some calculators operate only in constant mode for addition. Test yours before using them in class so that, if necessary, you can modify these activities to suit your equipment.

Distribute the calculators, one for each student.
Write on the board:

T: You have to find out which of the signs +, −, ×, and ÷ should go in each of the empty boxes to make the sentence true. You may use the same sign in both boxes or different signs. Copy the problem and then try to solve it.

Give the students some time to solve the problem. Encourage them to use their calculators to check their solutions before showing them to you. When at least half the class has solved the problem, let a student complete the sentence on the board.

T: Now copy these problems and try to solve them.

Write the following problems on the board. (The solutions are given above the empty boxes for your information.)

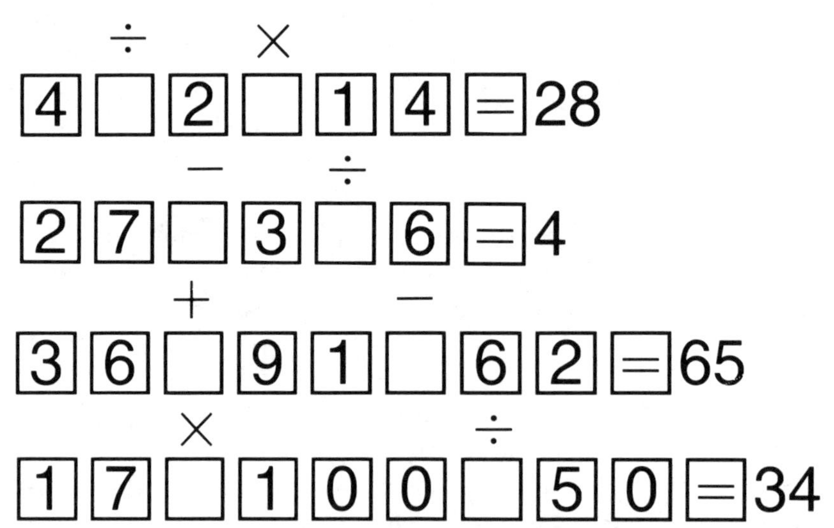

Resources Available

For class use: Worksheet L18
For out-of-class use: Any H-worksheet up through H40

ACTIVITY 25
Guess My Rule 3

Materials Needed
Teacher: Chalk
Students: Paper and pencils

Note to the Teacher

The secret rule $*$ in this lesson is given by this equation:

$$a * b = 2a + \tfrac{1}{2}b$$

That is, add double the first number to half the second number. This is for your information only. Do not divulge the rule to your students until they guess it.

T: Today we're going to play another Guess My Rule game. I'll use the same secret sign as I used last time, a star, but it will mean something different today. You have to figure out what it means today. I'll begin by giving you some clues, and then you'll have a chance to guess the rule.

One by one, write the following four calculations on the board. After each one, give the students about 15 seconds to reflect on what you have written. Ask the students not to talk among themselves or call out what they think the rule is. Instead they should simply sit quietly and think for a while.

$$\begin{aligned} 5 * 4 &= 12 \\ 6 * 10 &= 17 \\ 10 * 6 &= 23 \\ 12 * 8 &= 28 \end{aligned}$$

After a longer pause (about 30 seconds), add the following to your list:

$$7 * 2 =$$

Then ask the students who think they know the answer to write it on their papers, raise their hands, and show their answers to you. Remind them not to call out or discuss their thoughts with anybody else. Circulate around the room, checking as many students' papers as you can and letting the authors know whether their answers are correct.

After a couple of minutes, ask someone who has the correct answer to announce it to the class. Complete the calculation on the board:

$$7 * 2 = 15$$

Repeat this procedure with the following calculations. The answers are given in parentheses.

$$9 * 4 = (20)$$
$$16 * 20 = (42)$$
$$20 * 16 = (48)$$
$$0 * 14 = (7)$$
$$14 * 0 = (28)$$
$$10 * 3 = (21.5)$$

By now it should be clear to you that at least one student knows the rule. Let such a student explain the rule to the class and go on to check all the calculations written on the board. If the student falls short of your expectations, ask another student for his or her opinion, and so on until the correct rule is given.

Distribute Worksheet L19 and let the students work on it individually. After the majority of the class has finished, check through the worksheet with the class.

Resources Available

For class use: Worksheet L19
For out-of-class use: Any H-worksheet up through H40

ACTIVITY 26

Guess My Rule 4

Materials Needed
Teacher: Colored chalk
Students: Paper and pencils

Note to the Teacher

If you are able to teach this activity immediately following Activity 25, then omit the first part of this activity and start instead at ■.

Remind the students of the special rule $*$ that they met in Activity 25. Do this by writing the following calculation on the board:

$$8 * 14 =$$

T: The star stands for the same rule we were using the other day. Write the answer to this calculation on your paper.

While you are giving the students sufficient time to do this, circulate among them, letting individuals know whether they have written down the correct answer. Ask one of those obtaining the correct answer to announce it to the class, and, for the sake of those who have forgotten, to explain what the rule is.

Write the following list of calculations on the board, and ask the students to copy and complete them on their papers. After a few minutes, go over the answers with the whole class, giving explanations when you think necessary. The answers are given in parentheses.

$$30 * 20 = (70)$$
$$19 * 42 = (59)$$
$$\widehat{4} * 8 = (4)$$
$$\widehat{5} * \widehat{6} = (\widehat{13})$$
$$4 * 9 = (12.5)$$

■ Write the following equation on the board:

$$\square * 6 = 21$$

T: What number should go in the box to make this statement true? Explain your answer.

S: *9, because* $2 \times 9 = 18$, $\frac{1}{2}$ *of* $6 = 3$, *and* $18 + 3 = 21$.

Write the following problems on the board and let the students work on them individually. The answers are given in parentheses.

$\square * 10 = 19$ (7)
$5 * \square = 24$ (28)
$2 * \square = 5.5$ (3)

Circulate around the room, checking students' work. When the majority has finished, discuss the solutions with the class.

Write the following on the board:

$\square * \square = 15$

T: Remember that in problems like this, the same number must go in both boxes. Copy this problem onto your papers and write the same number in both boxes so that the statement is true. Raise your hand when you think you have a solution.

Give the students a minute or so to work on this problem, and then ask for the answer. Check it with the class.

$\boxed{6} * \boxed{6} = 15$

Write the following three problems on the board, and let the students work on them individually. The answers are given in parentheses.

$\square * \square = 30$ (12)
$\square * \square = 250$ (100)
$\square * \square = 12.5$ (5)

Erase what is written on the board, and replace it with the following:

$\square * \triangle = 10$

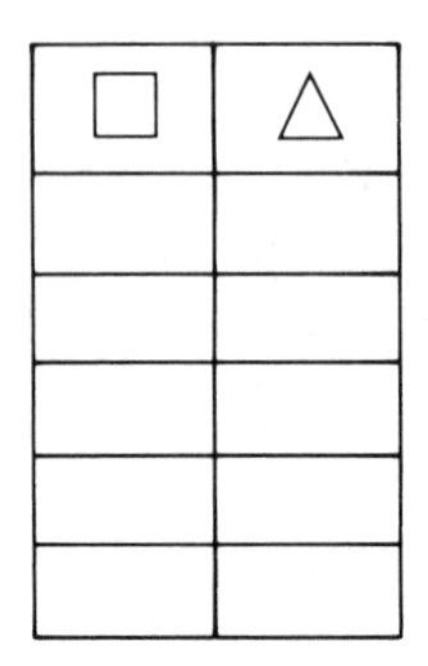

T: This time we have two different shapes, so we don't have to use the same number in both boxes; we *may*, but we don't have to. There are many solutions to this problem. Try to find some of them.

Record some of the solutions that are suggested by your students in the chart on the board. For example:

□	△
4	4
2	12
10	20
3	8
5	0

Ask the students to copy the chart and try to find at least three more solutions. Draw the following arrow picture on the board, omitting the letters.

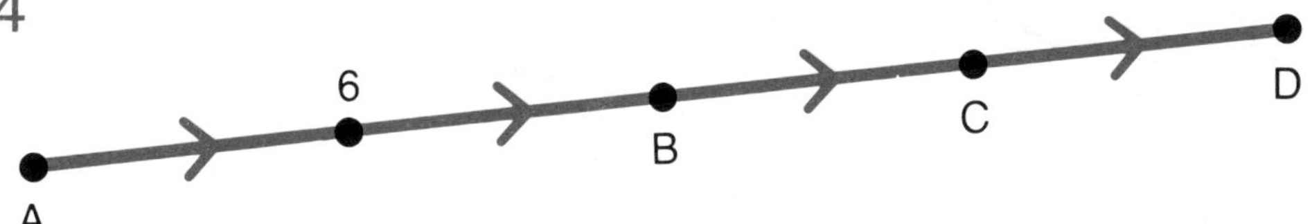

Point to the dot for 6.

T: Here is the number 6. The red arrows are for $*4$. So this number (point to dot B) is $6 * 4$. What number is it?

S: *14.*

Label dot B **14**.

T: Now find the numbers here (point to dot C) and here (point to dot D)

S: *The first one is 30 because* $14 * 4 = 30$.

S: *The second one is 62 because* $30 * 4 = 62$.

Label dots C and D.

T: How about this one (point to dot A)?

Ask the students to write their answers on their papers for you to check before you ask one of them to announce it to the class.

S: *2, because* $2 * 4 = 6$.

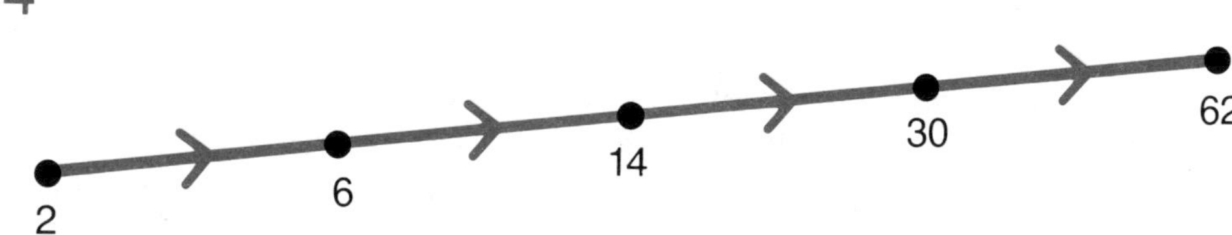

Resources Available

For class use: Worksheets L20 and L21
For out-of-class use: Any H-worksheet up through H42

ACTIVITY 27
Logical Thinking 1

Materials Needed
Teacher: Colored chalk
Students: None

Draw the following picture on the board:

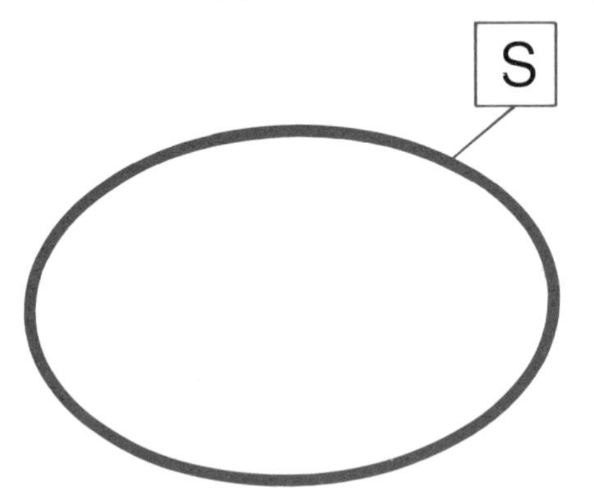

T: How many of you have older sisters?

Count the number and announce it to the class.

T: This red string, which I've labeled ***S***, is for all of you who have older sisters. Raise your hands again and keep them up until I have drawn a dot for you in the string *S*.

Draw and label a dot for each student having an older sister. For the rest of this exercise we suppose that the situation is as shown below. (Obviously, you will need to adjust the following dialog to your own string picture.)

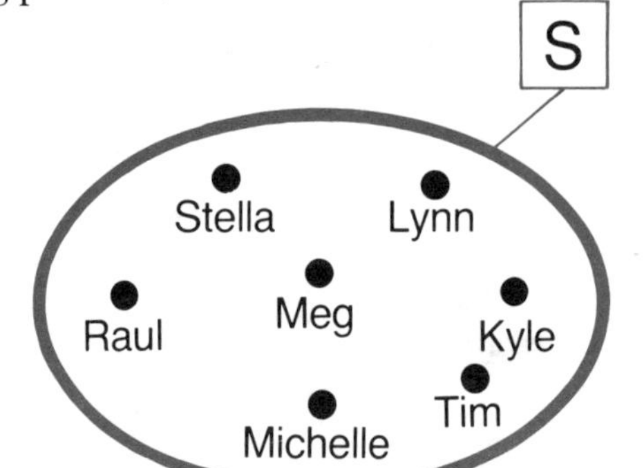

T: I'm now going to make some statements about this situation, and I want you to tell me whether what I say is true or false. Here's the first statement:

Everybody in S is a boy.

S: *False; Stella, Meg, Lynn, and Michelle are girls.*
T: Nobody in S is a boy.
S: *False; Raul, Tim, and Kyle are boys.*
T: At least one person in S is a boy.
S: *True.*
T: Why?
S: *Because "at least one" means one or more than one, and here we have three boys in S.*
T: There are at least five boys in S.
S: *False.*
T: What does "at least five" mean?
S: *Five or more than five, and three is obviously not more than five.*
T: So you were correct to say "False."

There are at least two boys in S.

S: *False; there are at least three boys in* S.
T: I agree that there are at least three boys in S, but does that make my statement false?
S: *No; "at least two" means two or more than two, and three is certainly more than two.*
T: That's a very good explanation. Now be careful with this one:

At most one person in S is a boy.

S: *False.*
T: First explain what "at most one" means, and then explain your answer.
S: *"At most one" means one or less than one, that is, one or none. But there is more than one boy in* S, *so it's false.*
T: There are at most four boys in S.
S: *True, because "at most four" means four, three, two, one, or none, and there are three boys in* S.

Note to the Teacher

The phrase "at most" is very difficult for some students when they meet it for the first time. Gradually, however, most of them will come to understand this concept through experience and exposure to many different contexts in which it is used. Have patience, and take every opportunity to remind students of the meaning of this phrase whenever it appears.

T: There are exactly seven people in S.
S: *True.*
S: *But Kevin should be in* S *because he has an older sister. Kevin is absent today, but he belongs there. So there are definitely more than seven, and what you said is false.*
T: That's a good remark, but I should have said that S includes only students who are in class today and have an older sister. That means that Kevin is not in S, and so what I said is true.

27

Erase the string picture on the board, and replace it with the following:

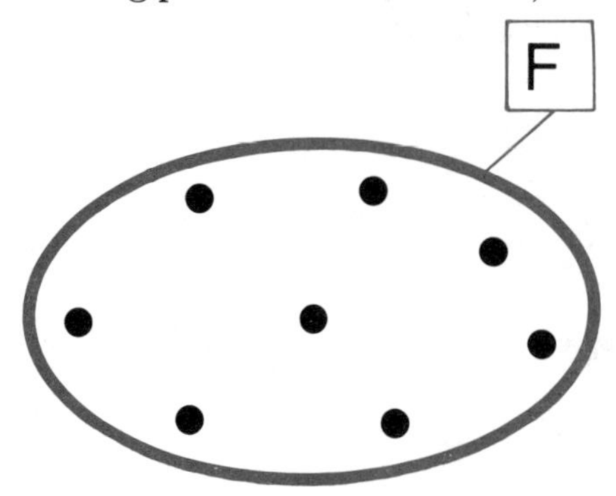

T: These dots are for whole numbers. I will now write on the board a statement that tells you something about these numbers.

Write the following statement on the board:

Each member of *F* is a whole number that is both greater than 50 **and** a multiple of 4.

T: What are some numbers that could be in *F*?

S: *24, because it's a multiple of 4.*

S: *But 24 is not greater than 50, so it's not in* F.

S: *60.*

T: Is it greater than 50? (yes) Is it a multiple of 4? (yes) Explain.

S: $60 = 15 \times 4$.

S: *64, 68, 72, 76, …*

S: *400, 404, 408, …*

S: *4,000, 4,004, 4,008, …*

T: Give me a number between 90 and 95 that is in *F*.

S: *92.*

T: How can you be sure?

S: *Well, 100 is in* F *because* $100 = 25 \times 4$, *96 is four less than 100, and 92 is four less than 96.*

T: How about 410?

S: *No, because 400 is in* F, *and then so is 404, 408, and 412, and we miss 410.*

T: Let's label the dots in the string picture. Try to use numbers we haven't mentioned so far.

Let several students come to the board to label the dots. Be sure the class is in agreement about each label. In case of disagreement, ask the student who labeled the dot to explain his or her answer. For the rest of this exercise we suppose that the dots are labeled as shown below. (Obviously, you will need to adjust the following dialog to your own string picture.)

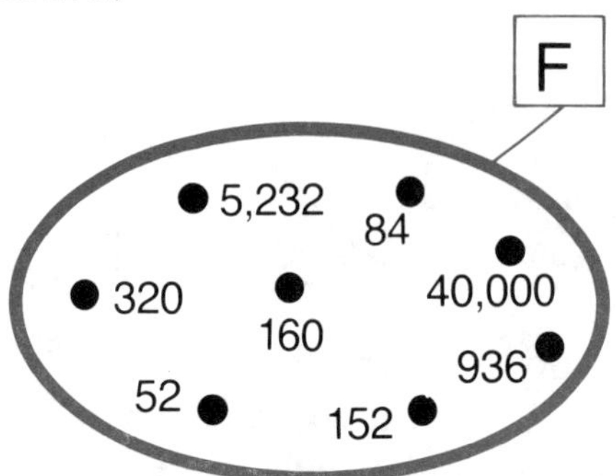

T: *F* is this set of exactly eight numbers. Nothing else is in *F*. I'm now going to make some statements about *F*, and I want you to tell me whether what I say is true or false, and explain why you think that.

27

T: **All** numbers in *F* are even.
S: *True; every multiple of 4 is also a multiple of 2 and so must be even.*
T: **No** number in *F* is odd.
S: *True; that just says the same thing as before.*
T: **At least** three numbers in *F* are greater than 100.
S: *True; there are six numbers in F* that are greater than 100, and "at least three" means three or more than three.
T: **At least** four numbers in *F* are greater than 800.
S: *False; only three numbers in* F *are greater than 800 and "at least four" means four or more than four.*
T: **At most** two numbers in *F* are even.
S: *False; "at most two" means two, one, or none. But all eight numbers in* F *are even.*
T: **At most** six numbers in *F* are odd.
S: *True; "at most six" means six, five, four, three, two, one, or none, and there are no odd numbers in* F.
T: **At most** seven numbers in *F* are less than 1,000.
S: *True; there are six numbers in* F *that are less than 1,000, and "at most seven" includes six.*
T: **At most** six numbers in *F* are less than 4,000.
S: *True; exactly six numbers in* F *are less than 4,000, so it's true that at most six are less than 4,000.*

If time allows, distribute Worksheets L22 and L23 and let the students work on them individually. As they do so, move around the room observing the students' work. From time to time ask one of the students to explain his or her answers to you. This may reinforce the attitude that students need to think about their answers rather than simply guess. If a question is answered incorrectly by quite a number of students, it may be useful to stop everyone for a moment and have a collective discussion about that question.

If there is insufficient time for the students to work on these worksheets in class, issue them for homework.

Resources Available

For class use: Worksheets L22 and L23
For out-of-class use: Any H-worksheet up through H44

ACTIVITY 28
Logical Thinking 2

Materials Needed
Teacher: Colored chalk
Students: Paper and pencils

Draw the following diagram on the board:

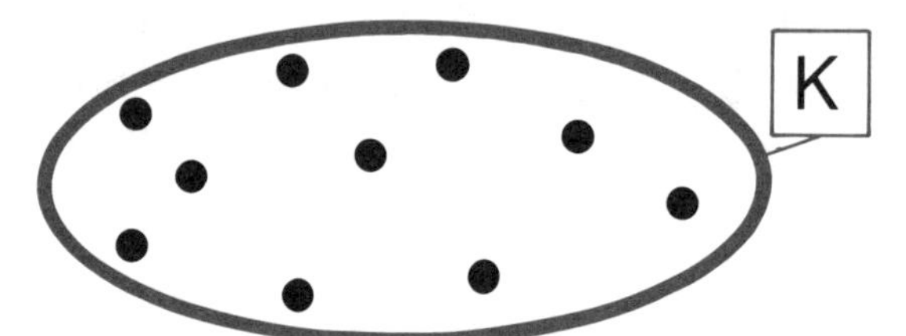

T: *K* contains exactly ten numbers. I'm going to tell you something about these numbers, and then we'll try to label the dots to agree with the information.

Write on the board:

There are at least three multiples of 5 in *K*

and

There are at most four odd numbers in *K*

and

There are exactly two positive prime numbers in *K*

and

There are at least five numbers in *K* that are less than $\widehat{7}$.

T: Copy the picture onto your piece of paper. Then try to label the dots so that everything on the board is true.

Let the students work on the problem for a while. Circulate among them, giving encouragement when necessary. When a student thinks he or she has solved the problem, ask him or her to record the proposed solution on the board, and then discuss it collectively. If it is not entirely correct, try to modify it as little as possible so as to arrive at a correct solution. The following dialog provides some idea about how the discussion might proceed.

T: Sasha, please put your solution on the board.

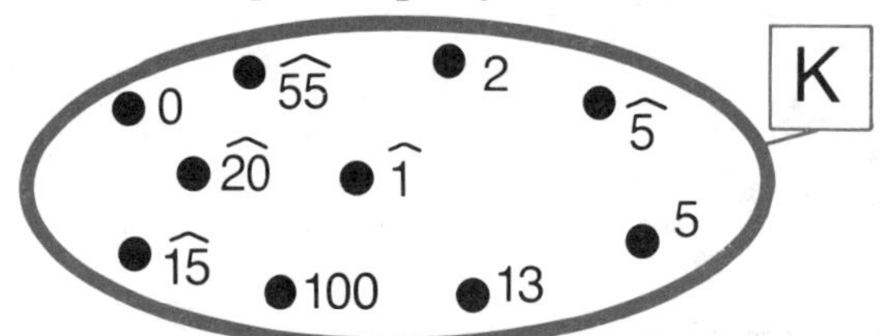

T: What do you think of Sasha's solution?

S: *It's wrong. She has six odd numbers, and there are at most four odd numbers in* K.

T: Which are the six odd numbers?

S: $\widehat{15}, \widehat{55}, \widehat{1}, 13, \widehat{5}$, *and* 5.

S: *And* K *is supposed to have exactly two positive primes, but there are three here:* 2, 5, 13.

S: *She has only three numbers less than* $\widehat{7}$: $\widehat{15}, \widehat{20}$, *and* $\widehat{55}$; *and there are supposed to be at least five.*

T: Does *K* have at least three multiples of 5?

S: *Yes, it has seven multiples of* 5: $\widehat{15}, 0, \widehat{55}, \widehat{20}, 100, \widehat{5}$, *and* 5; *and seven is at least three.*

T: Can someone fix Sasha's solution so that it's correct? Don't change the labels of any more dots than you have to.

S: *I can do it by changing only two dots. Change* **13** *to* $\widehat{\mathbf{8}}$ *and* $\widehat{\mathbf{5}}$ *to* $\widehat{\mathbf{12}}$.

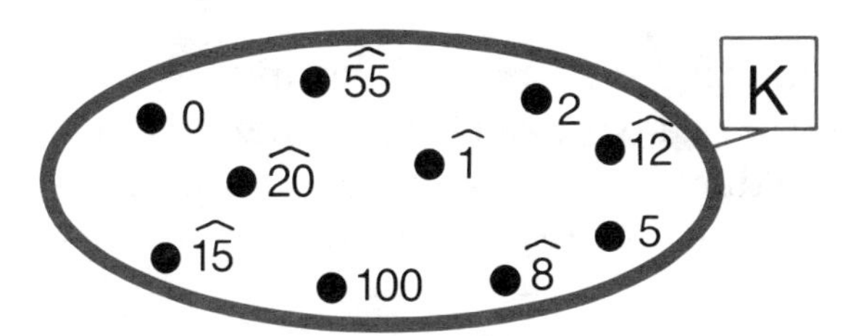

T: Who can explain why it is correct now?

S: *There are six multiples of* 5: $0, \widehat{15}, \widehat{55}, \widehat{20}, 100$, *and* 5; *and so there are at least three.*

There are exactly four odd numbers: $\widehat{15}, \widehat{55}, \widehat{1}$, *and* 5; *and so there are at most four.*

There are exactly two positive prime numbers: 2 *and* 5.

There are exactly five numbers less than $\widehat{7}$: $\widehat{15}, \widehat{55}, \widehat{20}, \widehat{8}$, *and* $\widehat{12}$; *so there are certainly at least five numbers less than* $\widehat{7}$.

If time allows, distribute Worksheets L24 and L25 and let the students work on them individually. Remind students that they will probably each find a different solution. When they think they have a solution, they should raise their hands so you can check it. If they have to wait while you check other students' papers, they may go on to the second worksheet. After most students have finished the first worksheet, ask for one or two solutions to be transferred to the board. Allow the class to decide if the displayed solutions are correct, and discuss any objections that are raised. If interest continues, you might make up a few true/false questions involving "at least," "at most," "exactly," and so on, about the solutions on the board, and answer them collectively. The worksheets may be completed at home if there is not sufficient time in class.

Resources Available

For class use: Worksheets L24 and L25

For out-of-class use: Any H-worksheet up through H45

ACTIVITIES 29 and 30
Order in the Decimals

Materials Needed
Teacher: Minicomputer kit plus some extra checkers
Students: Pencils

Review the decimals by posing a question such as the following:

T: Four friends see a super skateboard advertised for 55 dollars. They really want that skateboard, so they decide to save their allowances until they have enough money to buy it. How much must each one save?

Let the class decide that the friends should contribute equally to the purchase, that is, that the problem amounts to calculating $\frac{1}{4} \times 55$. Ask for estimates, and then suggest using the Minicomputer to do the calculation.

Ask a student to put 55 on the Minicomputer and invite someone to remind the class how to find one-fourth of a number on the Minicomputer. (Make backward robot moves until checkers are grouped in fours on squares.) Give as many students as possible an opportunity to come forward and make robot moves such as the following:

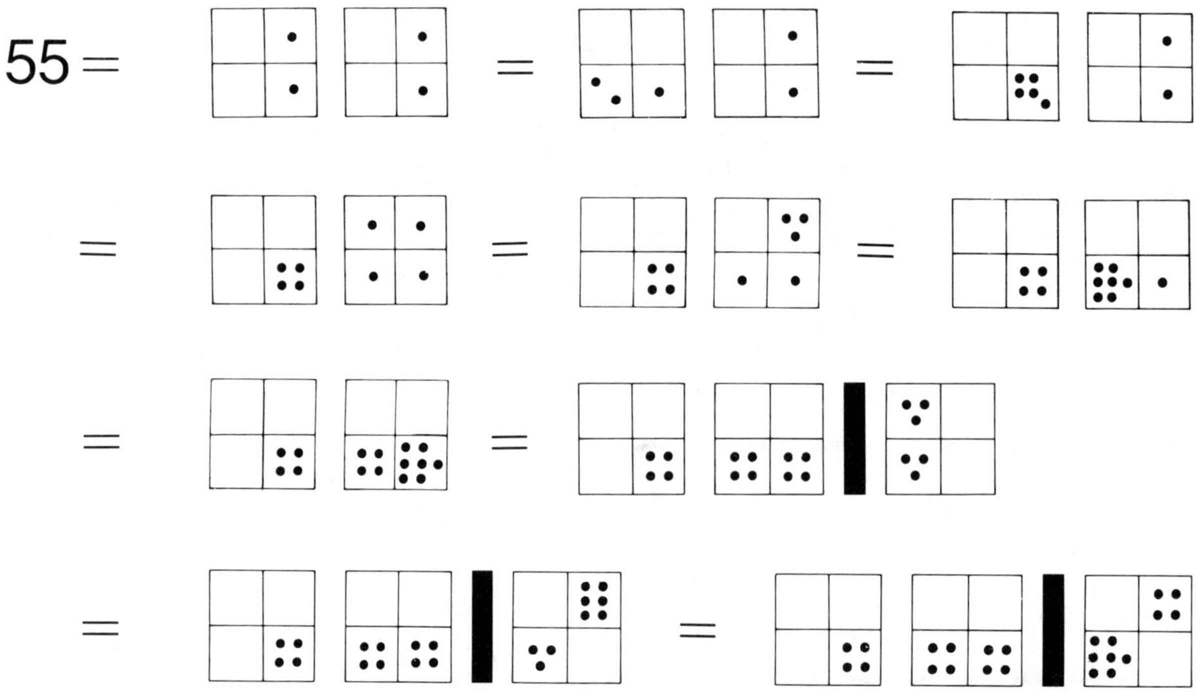

55 = = =

= = =

= =

= =

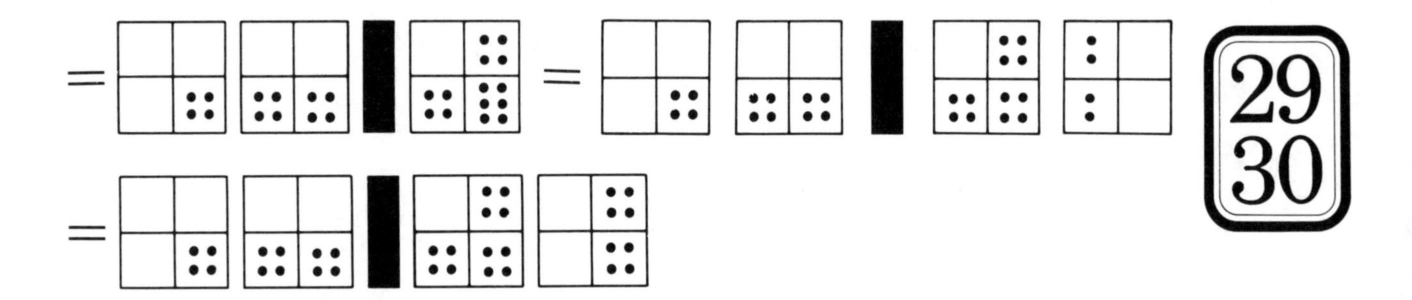

Then:

$\frac{1}{4} \times 55 =$ $= 13.75$

That is, each friend must save \$13.75, and $4 \times \$13.75 = \$55.00$.

Encourage students to compare their estimates with the result, steering the discussion toward whether they were too low or too high. For example:

S: *My estimate was 14 dollars, because I know that* $\frac{1}{4} \times 40 = 10$ *and* $\frac{1}{4} \times 16 = 4$*, and 56 dollars is close to 55 dollars. But 14 dollars is too big because 56 is greater than 55.*

As further experience with the comparison of decimals, engage the class in a discussion such as this:

Write **0.37** on the board.

T: This is the number zero point three seven. Joan, please name a number that is less than 0.37.

(If Joan has any difficulty with this request, remind her that she can think of 0.37 as 37 cents.)

S: *Fifteen cents; I mean 0.15.*

T: Correct; 0.15 is less than 0.37.

As you say this, write on the board:

$$0.15 < 0.37$$

T: George, please name a number that is greater than 0.37.

S: *0.61.*

Write on the board:

$$0.61 > 0.37$$

Then say:

T: 0.61 is greater than 0.37. Diego, what is a number between 0.37 and 0.61?

S: *0.45.*

T: Is 0.37 less than 0.45, and is 0.61 greater than 0.45? (yes; yes)

Write $\mathbf{\widehat{0.23}}$ on the board.

T: This is the number negative zero point two three. Bill, please name a number that is less than $\widehat{0.23}$.

S: $\widehat{0.15}$.

T: It is true that 0.15 is less than 0.23, because 15 cents is less than 23 cents. But *negative* 15 is bigger than *negative* 23, so negative 0.15 is bigger than negative 0.23.

Write on the board $\mathbf{\widehat{0.15} > \widehat{0.23}}$.

T: Bill, now name a number that is less than $\widehat{0.23}$.
S: $\widehat{0.35}$.
T: Good.

Write on the board beside the other inequality:

$$\widehat{0.15} > \widehat{0.23} \text{ and } \widehat{0.35} < \widehat{0.23}$$

T: Alice, please name a number between $\widehat{0.35}$ and $\widehat{0.23}$.
S: $\widehat{0.29}$.
T: Is $\widehat{0.29}$ greater than or less than $\widehat{0.35}$? (greater than) Is $\widehat{0.29}$ greater than or less than $\widehat{0.23}$? (less than)
T: So, $\widehat{0.29}$ is between $\widehat{0.35}$ and $\widehat{0.23}$.

Continue this type of questioning for as long as you think necessary. Then let the students spend the remaining time working on Worksheets L26 and L27.

Resources Available

For class use: Worksheets L26 and L27
For out-of-class use: Any H-worksheet up through H47

ACTIVITY 31
Calculator Golf 1

Materials Needed
Teacher: Colored chalk
Students: One calculator each

Provide each student with a calculator, and then divide the class into two teams, the Red team and the Blue team.

T: Today we're going to play a different kind of golf game. Instead of using the Minicomputer we're going to use calculators. In many ways Calculator Golf is just like Minicomputer Golf. We have a starting number (today we'll start with 351) and we have a goal (today it'll be 1,000).

Draw the following dots and labels on the board:

351 ● ● 1,000

T: Just as in Minicomputer Golf, the teams take turns to play and the members of the teams take turns too. When it's your turn, I'll tell you whether you have to add or subtract as well as any other information you need to know, and you have to say what number you're going to add or subtract. Then everybody adds or subtracts that number on their calculators. You're not allowed to use paper and pencil, and no one should touch a calculator until I say so after the player has announced his or her number.

Play the game. Begin by applying

Rule 1: The first player must add.

Then go on, applying

Rule 2: If the result is less than the goal, the next player must add.

Apply these rules until the goal is reached or is overshot for the first time. In the first case, the team reaching the goal is the winner. In the second, apply

Rule 3: If the result is greater than the goal, the next player must subtract. *But* the number subtracted must be small enough that the result of the subtraction is greater than the greatest previously obtained number below the goal.

Go on applying rule 3 until the goal is reached or is overshot again in the opposite direction. In the first case, the team reaching the goal is the winner. In the second, apply

Rule 4: If the result is less than the goal, the next player must add. *But* the number added must be small enough that the result of the addition is less than the smallest previously obtained number above the goal.

Subsequent play is governed entirely by rules 3 and 4. At each stage, before each play you should tell the next player exactly what he or she must do, specifying any conditions that may be in force on the size of the result of the play.

The dialog that follows is artificially long so that all aspects of these rules may be exemplified. In practice, your classes will probably reach the goal much more quickly than this.

T: Everybody enter the starting number, 351, into your calculators. Then put the calculators on the desks and don't touch them. Ann, you're the first player. You must add some number. What number would you like to add?

Ann: *400.*

T: Everybody press [+] [4] [0] [0] [=]. What do we get?

S: *751.*

Record this first play by drawing an arrow on the board in the appropriate color for the first player's team. (Let's say Ann is on the Red team.)

T: Bill, you're next. You must add some number as well. What number would you like to add?

Bill: *238.*

Calculate the result together, and record it on the board as in the previous case. This play and the next are as follows:

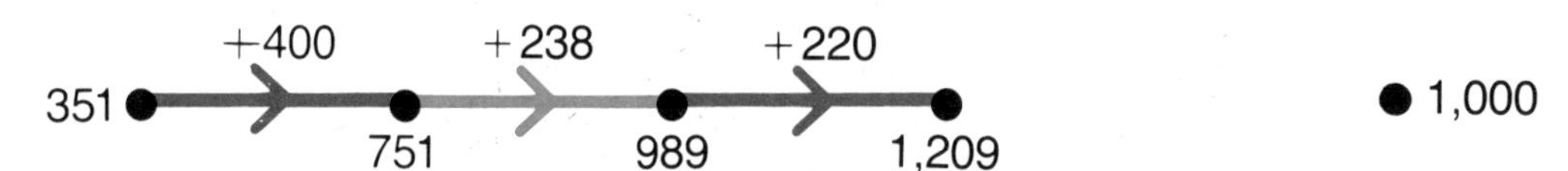

(Rule 3 now comes into force.)

T: Donna, now it's your turn. We've just gone past the goal, so this time you must subtract some number. *But* to make sure we keep getting closer to the goal, your answer must be greater than 989. (Point to the dot for 989.) What number would you like to subtract?

Donna: *300.*

Chris: *Hey, wait a minute! I added 220 to get to 1,209. If Donna subtracts 300 (which is more than 220), she's going to end up lower than 989.*

T: Very good, Chris. I'm sorry, Donna, he's right. You're wanting to subtract too much. You'll have to forfeit your turn.

Erma, you're next. We're still above the goal, so you must subtract some number. Don't forget: your answer must be greater than 989.

Erma: *I'll subtract 218.*

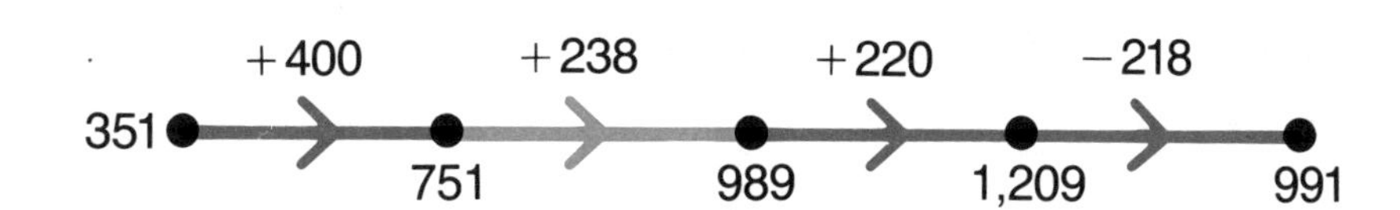

(Rule 4 now comes into force.)

T: OK, Frank, your turn. We've come down below the goal again, so you have to add some number. Make sure your answer is less than 1,209, though. (Point to the dot for 1,209.)

Frank: *I'll add 234.*

T: What do you think of that?

Erma: *Well, it's more than I subtracted, so it's bound to end up higher than 1,209.*

T: She's right, Frank. I'm afraid you'll have to forfeit your turn as well. George, what number do you want to add? Remember, your answer must be less than 1,209.

George: *19.*

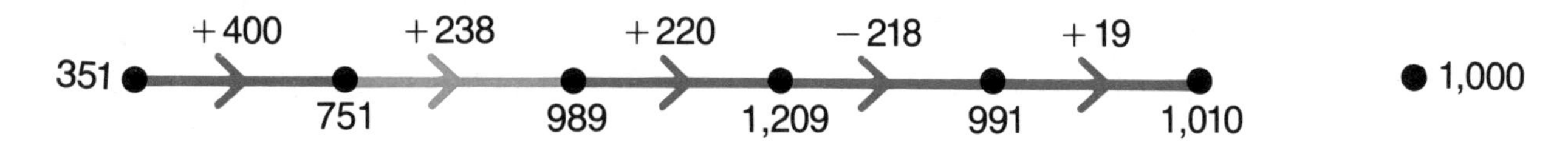

(Rule 3 is now in force again.)

T: Now we're above the goal again. Harriet, what number would you like to subtract? Your answer has to be greater than 991. (Point to the dot for 991.)

Harriet: *Subtract 10.*

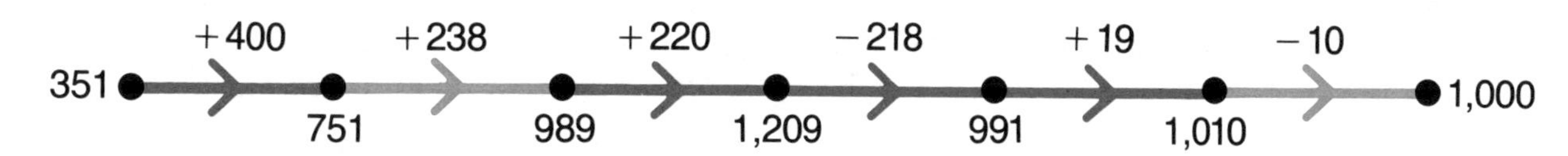

T: Harriet's reached the goal. So the Blue team wins.

Because your game will have been far less excruciating and time-consuming than the foregoing one, you will have time to play the game several more times. Use the following starting numbers and goals:

Starting Numbers	Goals
277	813
564	1,131
817	94*
$\widehat{17}$	179
82	$\widehat{96}$*

* For this game, interchange "add" and "subtract," "greater" and "less," "greatest" and "smallest," and "above" and "below" in the statements of the four rules.

Resources Available

For out-of-class use: Any H-worksheet up through H47

ACTIVITY 32

Decimal Tug-of-War

Materials Needed
Teacher: Minicomputer kit, colored chalk
Students: None

Display four demonstration Minicomputer boards and place four red and four blue checkers as shown below. Draw a red box on the board to the left of the Minicomputer and a blue box to the right.

Divide the class into two teams, the Red team and the Blue team, and say:

T: We are going to play Decimal Tug-of-War today. Here's the starting position. Red team, what's your starting number? (150) Blue team, what's yours? (0.15)

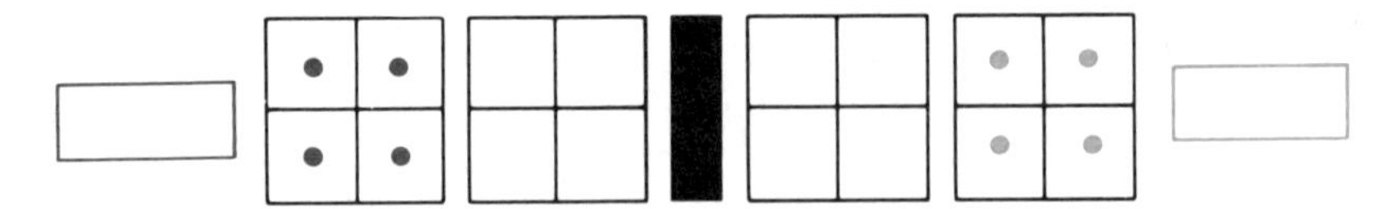

Record the teams' numbers in the appropriate boxes, and, if necessary, review the rules of the game (see Volume 1, Activity 50).

A possible game, with Red taking the first step, might go like this:

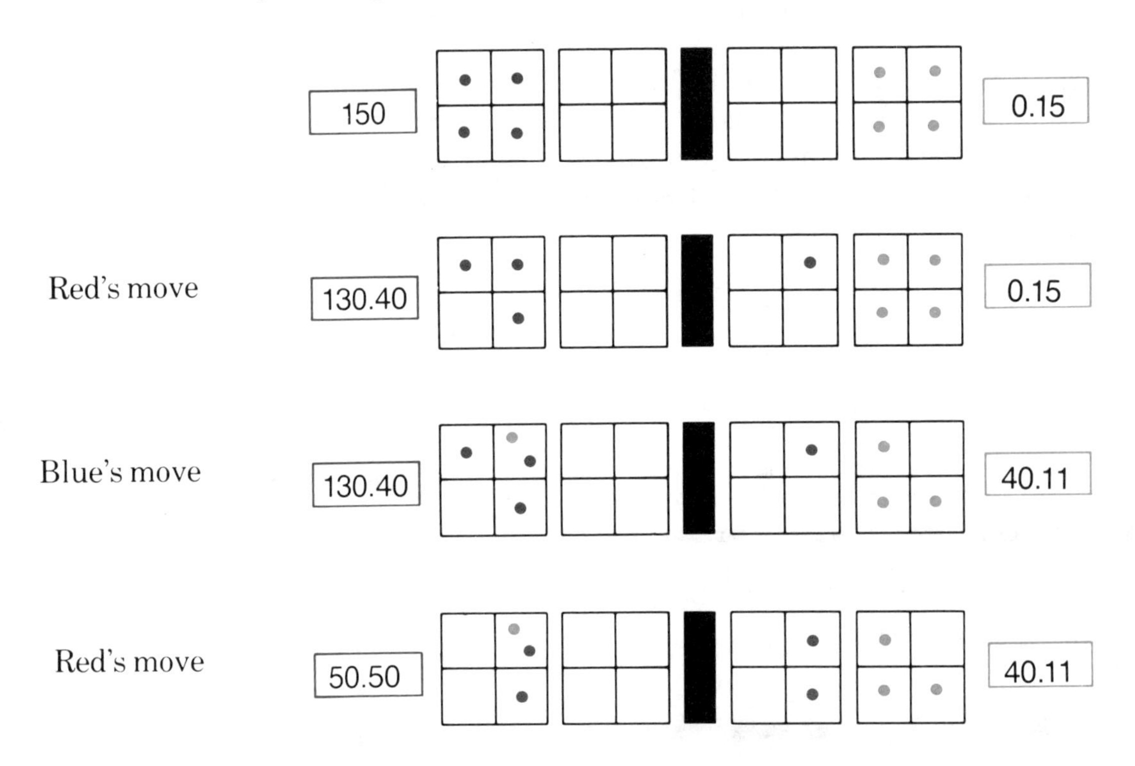

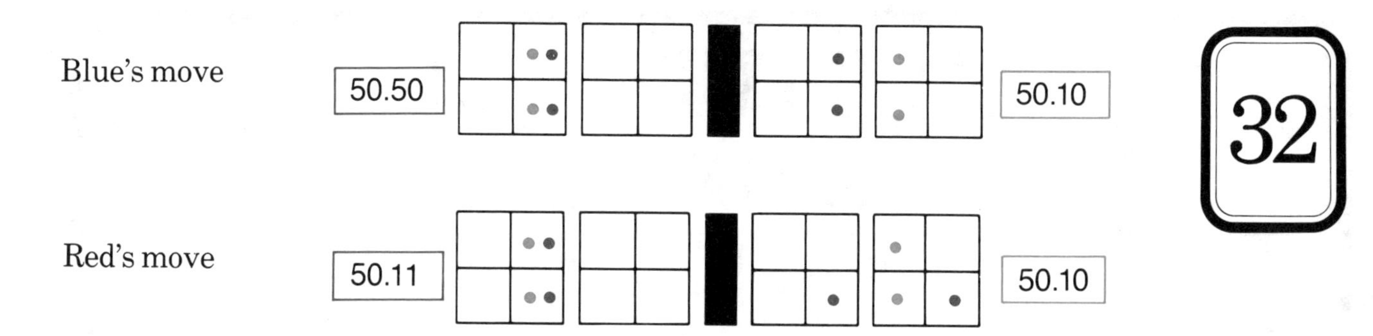

At this point in the game, Blue cannot make a move without making its number the same as or greater than the Red number. So the Red team is the winner.

Return the checkers to their original positions and play the game again, but with the members of the Red and Blue teams interchanged.

Resources Available

For out-of-class use: Any H-worksheet up through H49

ACTIVITY 33
Tag the Arrow Pictures 1

Materials Needed
Teacher: Colored chalk
Students: Paper and colored pencils

Note to the Teacher

To ensure that the activity runs smoothly, draw the pictures on the board in advance.

Draw the following pictures and tags on the board:

−10	×6	−4	÷2	×3

(1)

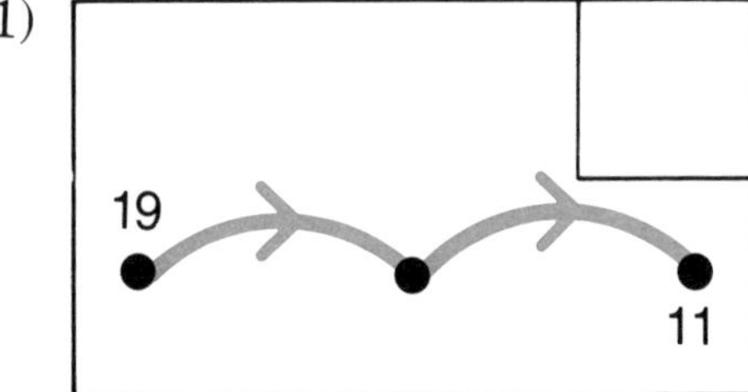

(2)

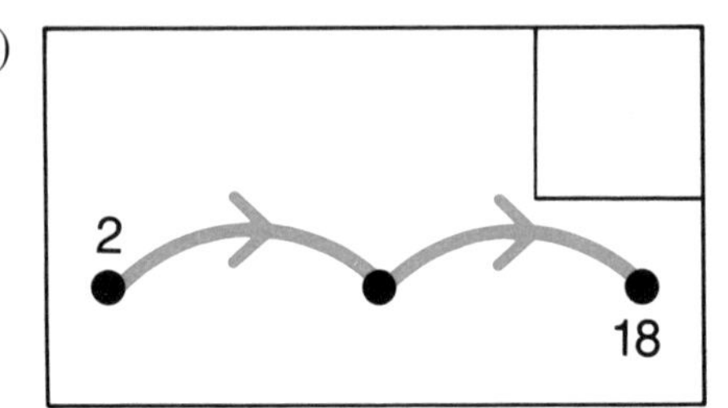

(3)

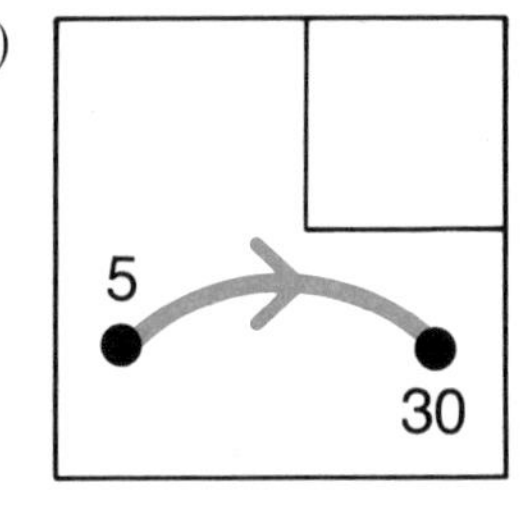

(4)

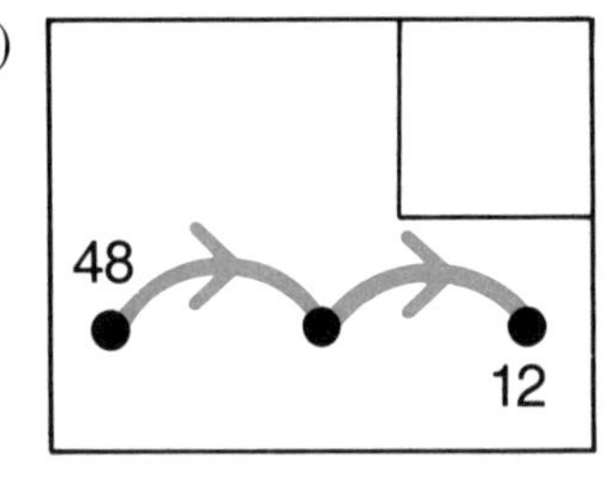

(5)

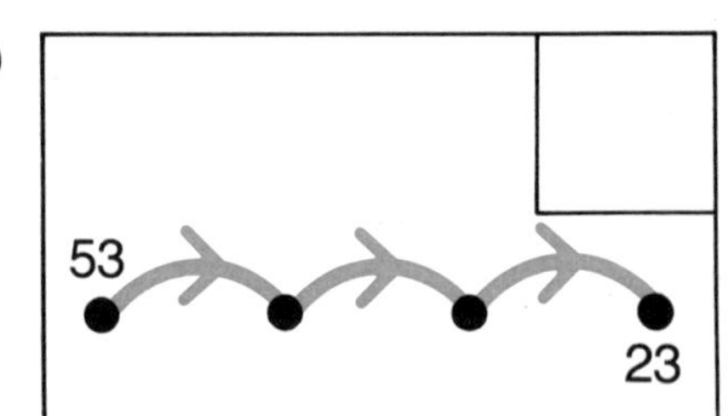

T: There are five arrow pictures and five tags on the board. Each tag is for one of these pictures. No tag can be used more than once, and no picture has more than one tag. Your job is to match the tags and the pictures.

Point to the first picture.

T: Which is the tag for this picture?

Let a number of students whisper their answers to you. Then ask one of those giving the correct answer to write **−4** in blue on the blank tag and label the middle dot with the correct answer **15.**

Proceed similarly for the other pictures.
Answers:

(1)

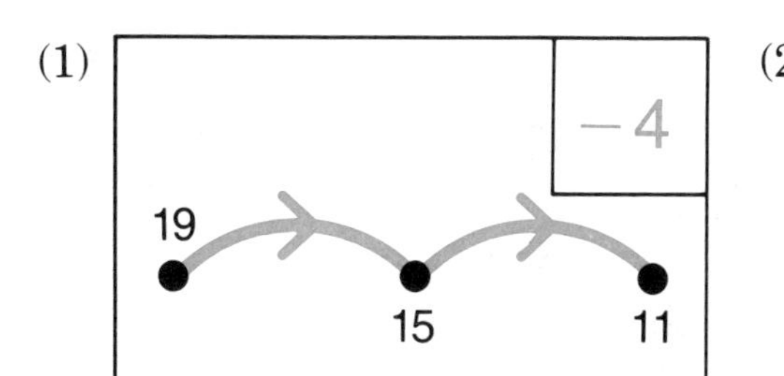

(2)

×3
2
6
18

(3)

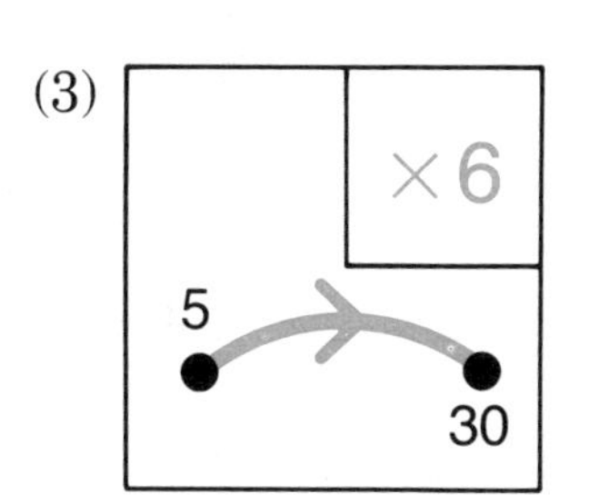

(4)

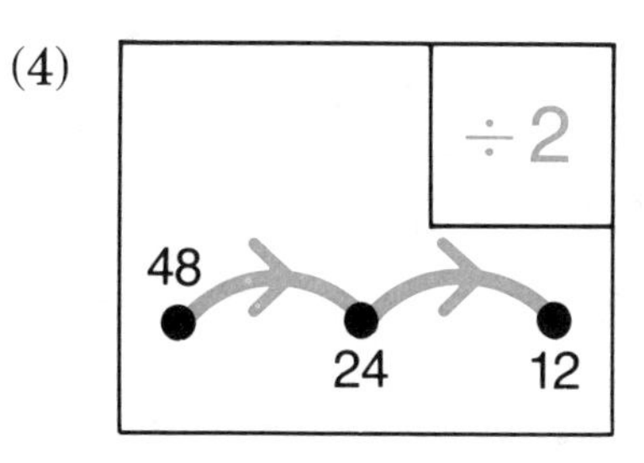

(5)

−10
53
43
33
23

Follow the same procedure for this collection of pictures and tags:

(1)

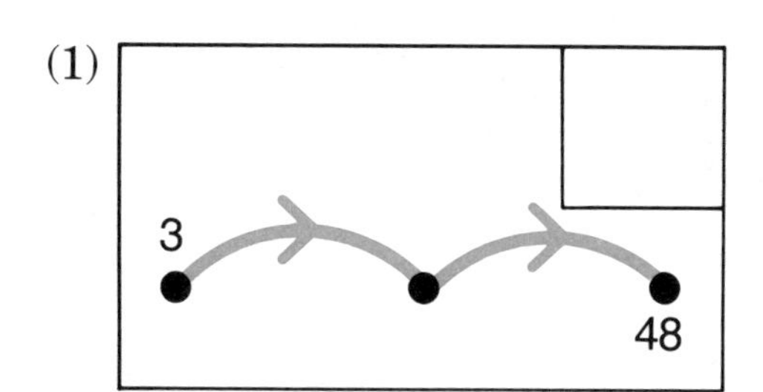

(2)

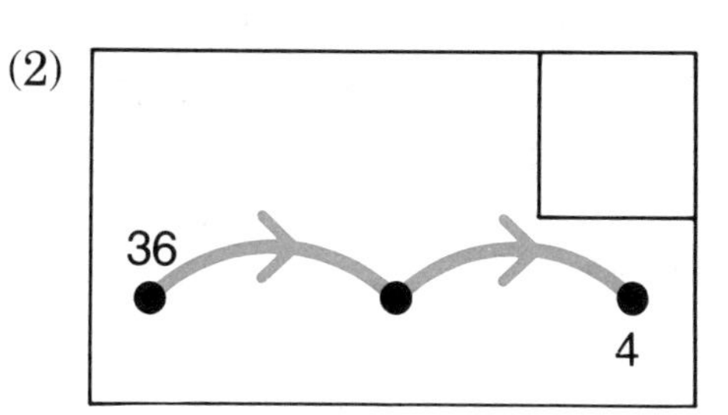

(3)

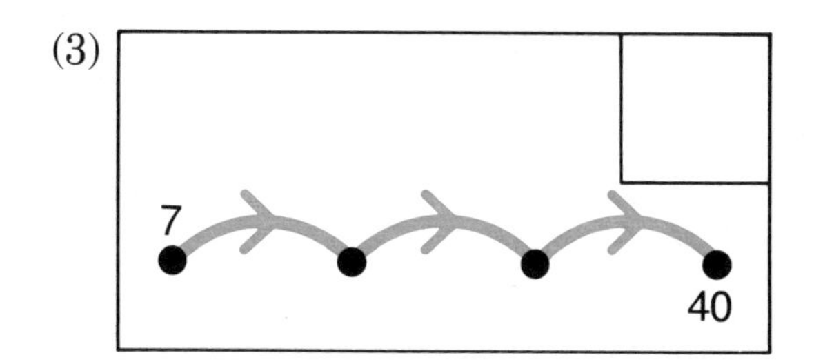

(4)

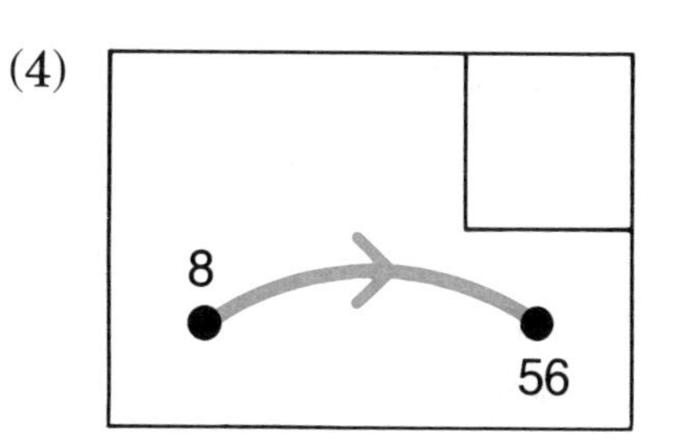

(5)

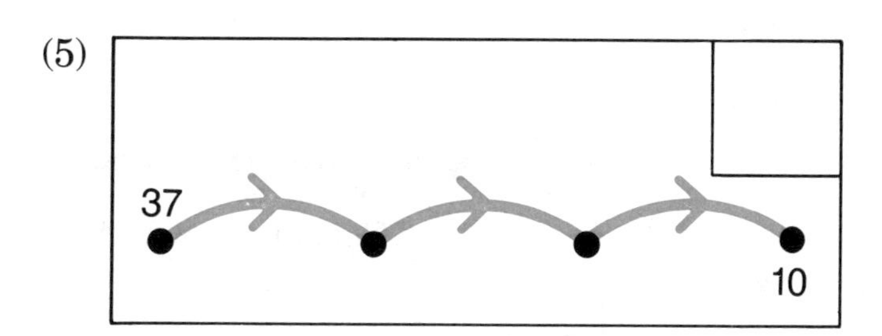

−9 ×7 ÷3 +11 ×4

33

Answers:

(1)

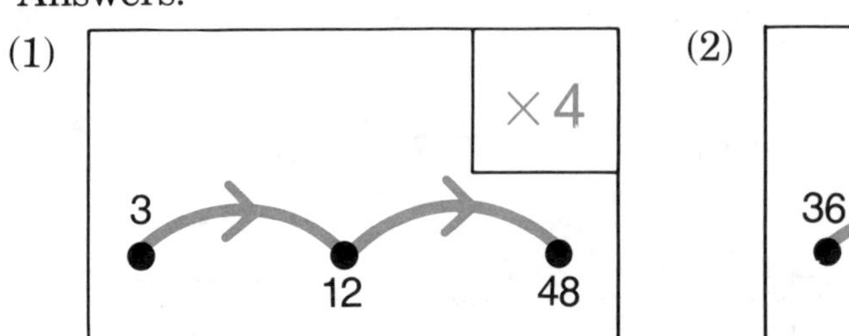

(2)

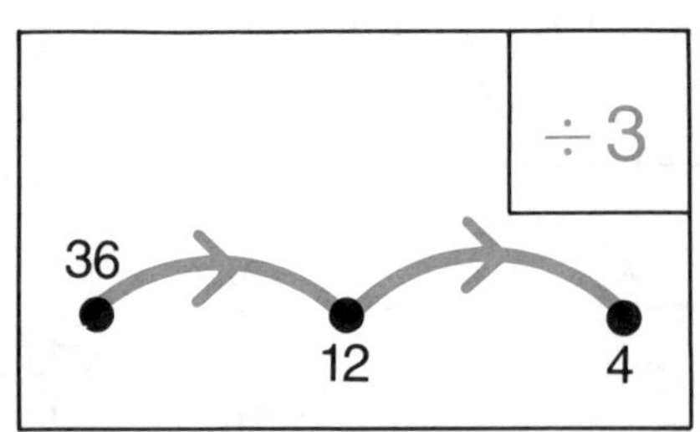

(3)

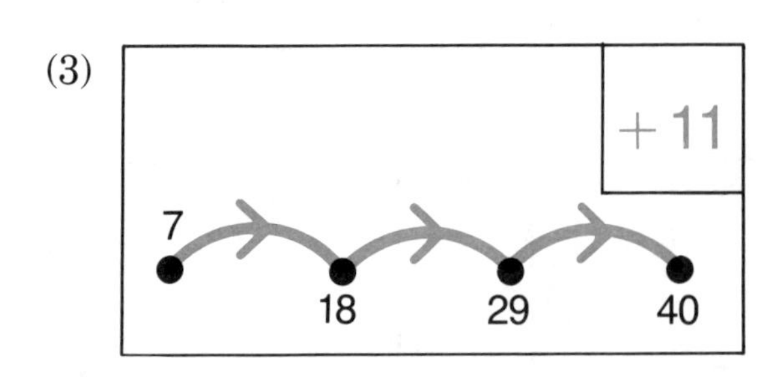

(4)

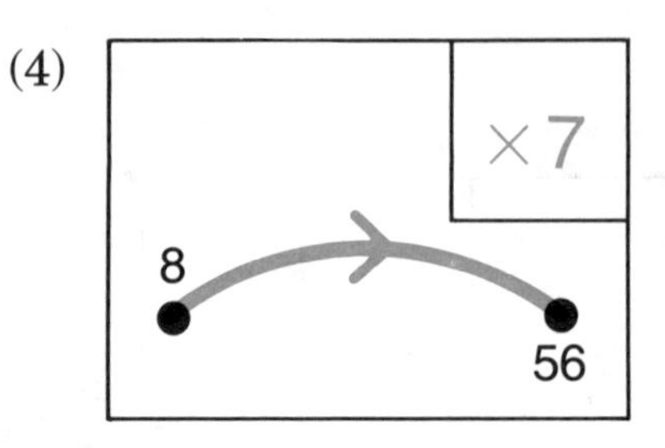

(5)

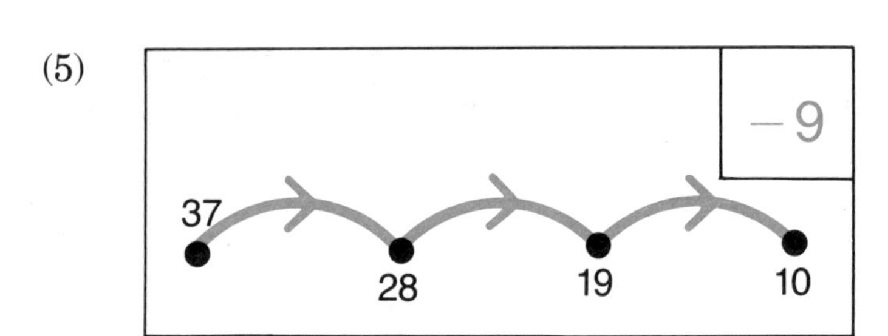

Resources Available

For class use: Worksheets L28 and L29, and for those who finish early, Worksheets A1 and A2

For out-of-class use: Any H-worksheet up through H49

ACTIVITY 34
Tag the Arrow Pictures 2

Materials Needed
Teacher: Colored chalk
Students: Paper and colored pencils

Draw the following picture on the board, and ask your students to copy it onto their papers.

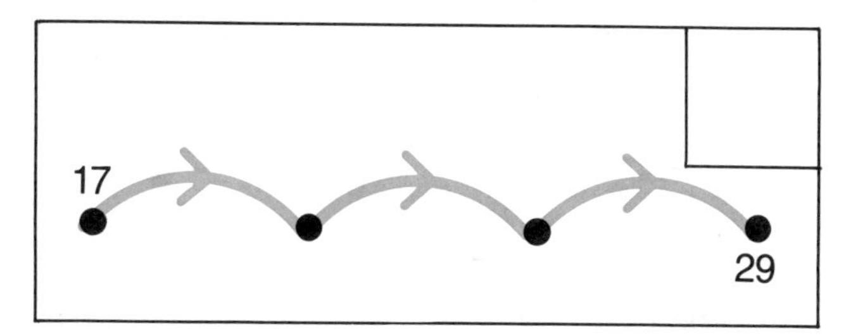

T: What could these blue arrows be for? Write the answer in blue in the little box in the corner of the picture. Then label the dots.

After a few minutes ask a student who has found correct answers to explain that the blue arrows could be for +4, in which case the other two dots would be for 21 and 25.

Draw the following five pictures on the board and ask the class to deal with them in a similar fashion. Warn students that in some cases it is possible to find more than one solution. If they do find a second answer for a particular picture, they should label above the dots for one of the tags and below the dots for the other. (See the answers below for the format suggested.)

(1)

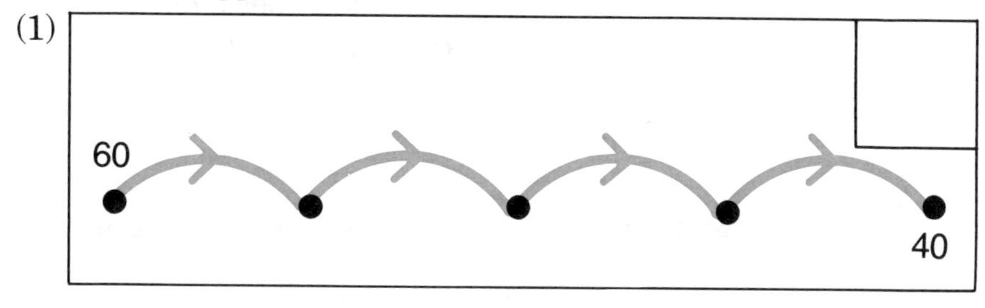

(2) (3)

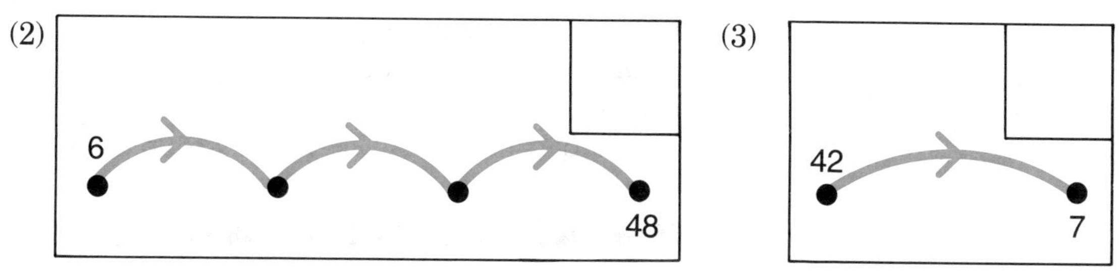

34

(4)

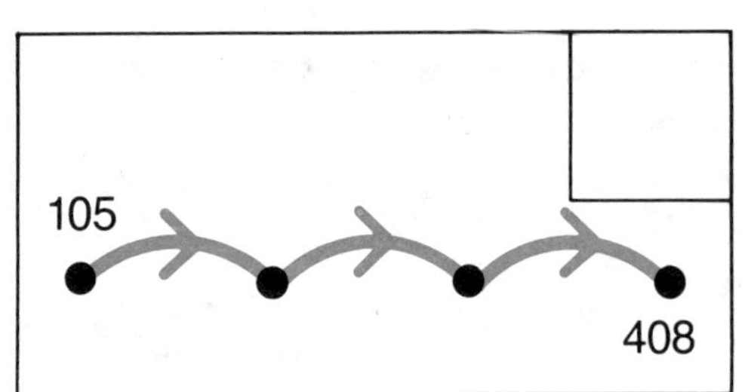

(5)

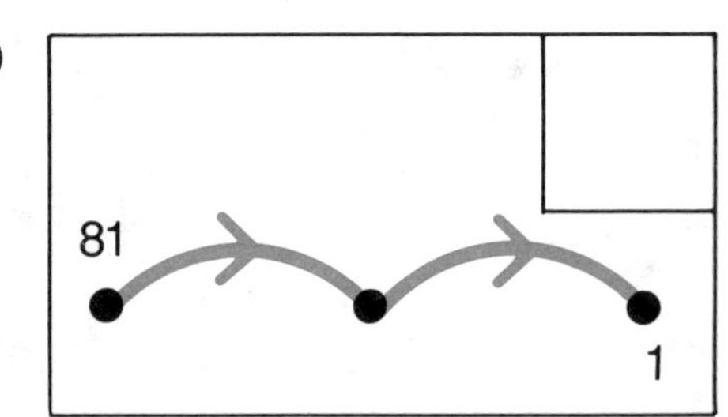

Answers:

(1)

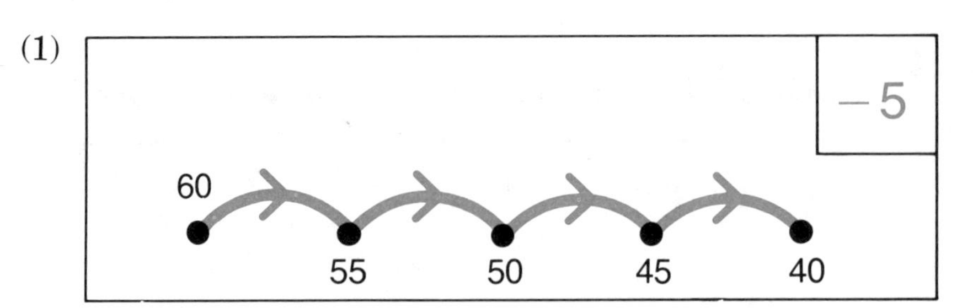

(2)

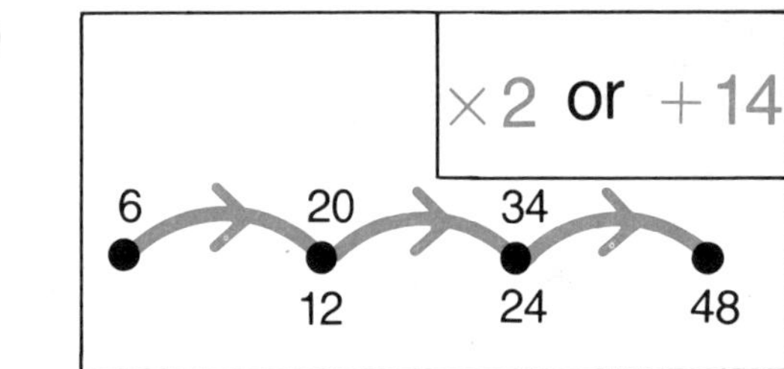

(3)

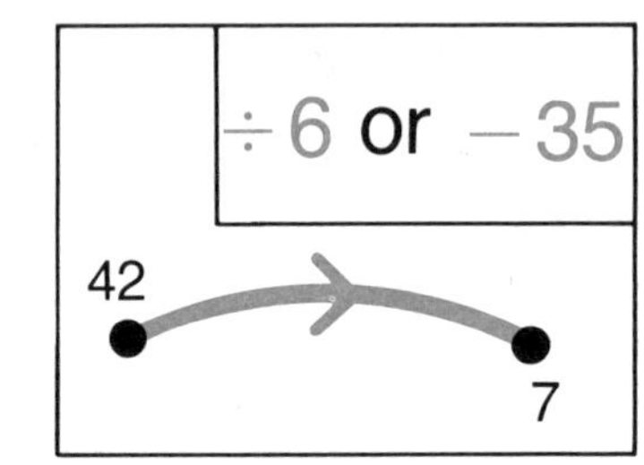

Note: The lower labels correspond to $\times 2$. The upper labels correspond to $+14$.

(4)

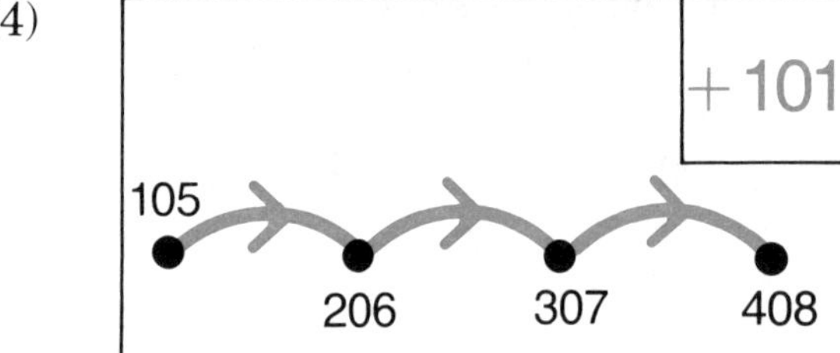

(5)

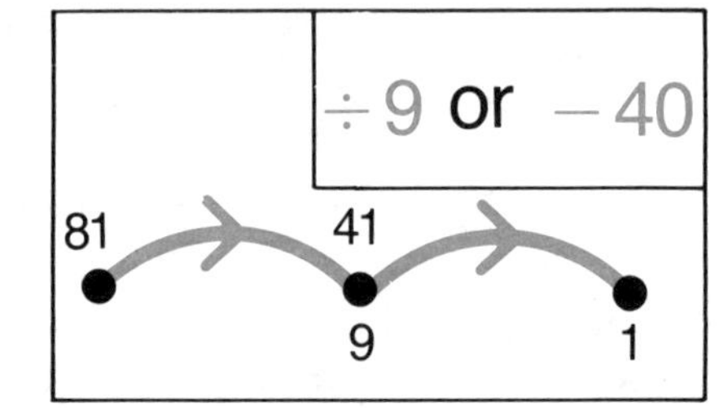

Note: The lower labels correspond to $\div 9$. The upper labels correspond to -40.

Resources Available

For class use: Worksheets L30 and L31, and for those who finish early, Worksheets A3 and A4
For out-of-class use: Any H-worksheet up through H51

ACTIVITY 35
Composition Games 1

Materials Needed
Teacher: Colored chalk, seven student chairs
Students: Pencils

Note to the Teacher

We draw your attention to theNote to theTeacher at the beginning of Volume 1,Activities 53 and 54 (composition of relations). In particular, we emphasize that there is absolutely no need to use with the students the technical vocabulary in the title of this activity.

Before you begin the activity, place at the front of the class seven student chairs in two groups, one of four and one of three. Within each group the chairs should be arranged in a circle facing inward, about 1 to $1\frac{1}{2}$ meters apart.

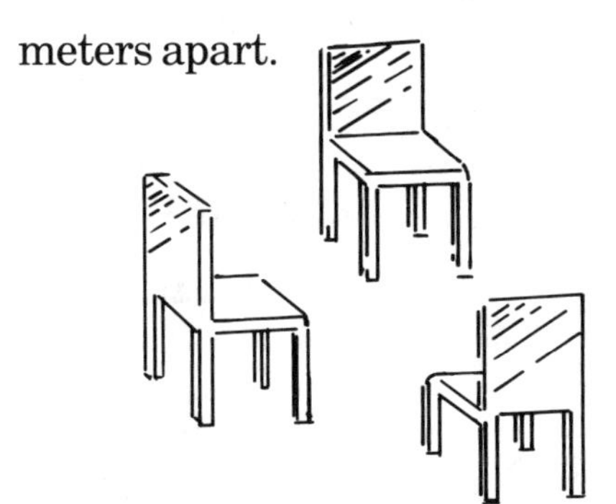

T: Will these seven students please come up and sit in these seven chairs without moving them: Alan, Bella, Carlos, ... (choose seven) Now I want these seven to follow instructions carefully, and I want the rest of you to help me make sure they do. Here is what I want you seven to do:

- Each time I clap my hands I want you to move to the next chair to your right. Please point to the chair on your right as a check that we all agree on the direction.
- Remember which chair you start on. Whenever you come back to that same chair, raise your hand.

Now let's try. Everybody else watch as I signal.

Clap. As the students move, write **1** on the board.
Clap. Write **2** after the **1**.
Clap. Write **3** after the **2**. The group of three should have their hands raised. Draw a red triangle around the **3**, and ask the students to lower their hands.

At this stage your record on the board should be as follows:

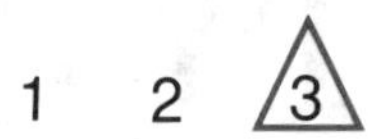

Clap. Write **4** after the **3**. Now the group of four should have their hands raised. Record this as follows, and ask them to lower their hands:

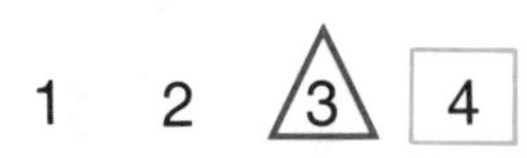

Clap. 1 2 3 4 5

Clap. 1 2 3 4 5 6

T: So far we have only had either three or four people with their hands raised. We've never had all seven with their hands raised at once. Can anyone suggest when this will happen?

S: *On 12, because we're getting a triangle on 3, 6, 9, and 12 and a square on 4, 8, and 12.*

T: Let's see.

Continue clapping and verify that both groups do indeed return to their original seats together after 12 moves.

1 2 3 4 5 6 7 8 9 10 11 12

T: If we kept on going, when would you next expect the groups to be back together again?

S: *After 24 moves, because the same pattern will go on.*

S: *And then 36, . . . , the multiples of 12.*

Distribute Worksheet L32.

T: On this worksheet are some questions about how long it will take for various-size groups to return to their original positions. See if you can work them out.

Resources Available

For class use: Worksheet L32

For out-of-class use: Any H-worksheet up through H51

ACTIVITY 36
Composition Games 2

Materials Needed

Teacher: Colored chalk, crayons or felt tip pens, Volume 2 Poster 2

Students: Colored pencils

Tape Poster 2 to the board:

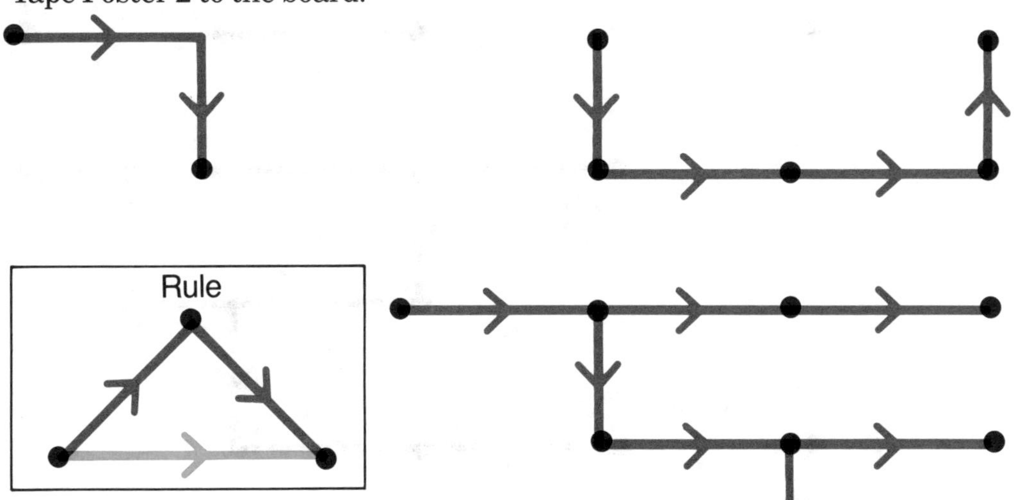

T: Here is a rule for drawing blue arrows in this arrow diagram.

As you announce the rule, carefully demonstrate with your fingers what is happening.

T: For each red arrow ...

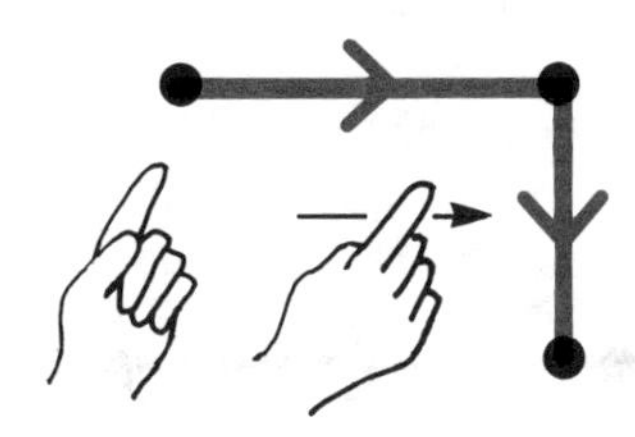

T: ... followed by another red arrow ...

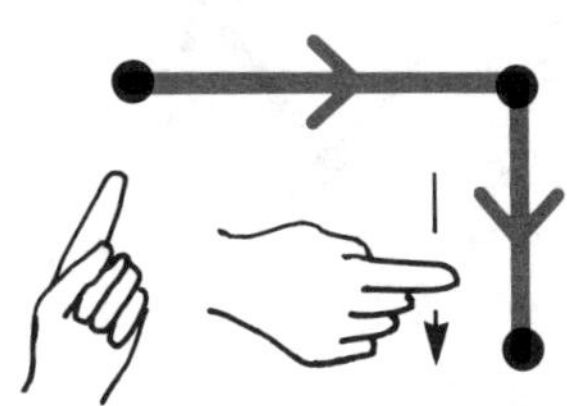

(Stop at the middle dot and then continue.)

T: ... we draw a blue arrow from the starting dot (tap it emphatically) to the ending dot (tap it emphatically and then draw the blue arrow).

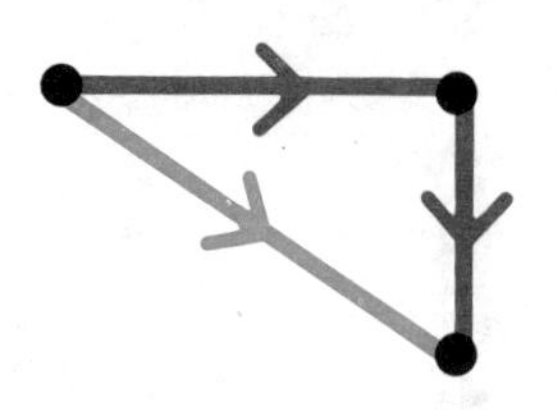

T: Now can someone show the rest of us how to find a blue arrow in the arrow diagram?

Ask a volunteer to follow the procedure you have described, including pointing at the dots and tracing along the two red arrows before drawing in the blue arrow. Continue this process slowly and carefully until all possible blue arrows are drawn.

The completed diagram is as follows:

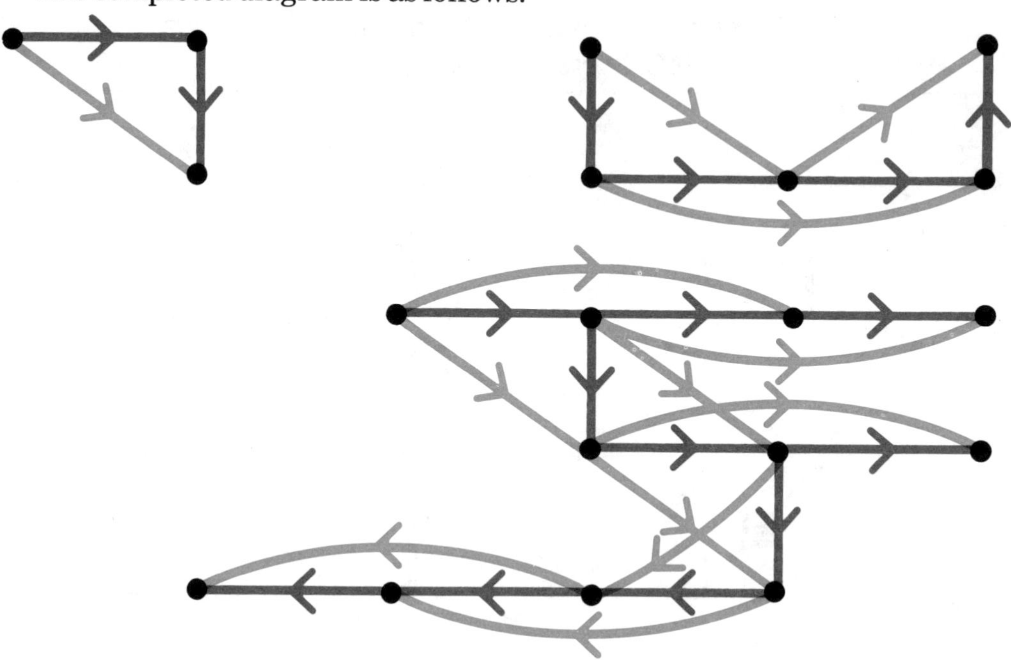

On the poster, point to the box containing the rule for drawing blue arrows.

Ask the students to add the correct blue arrows to diagrams that you then draw on the board, such as these:

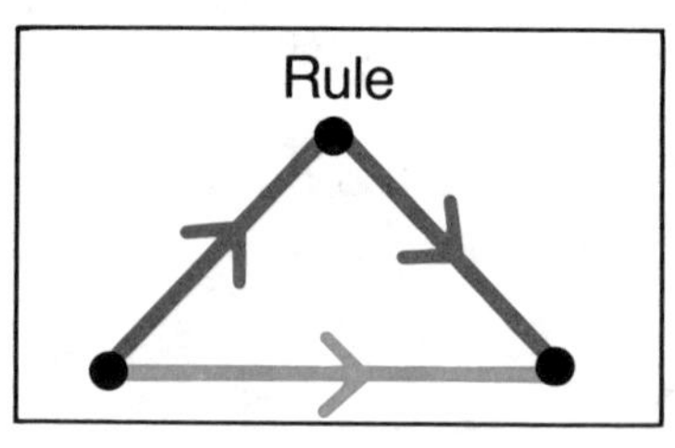

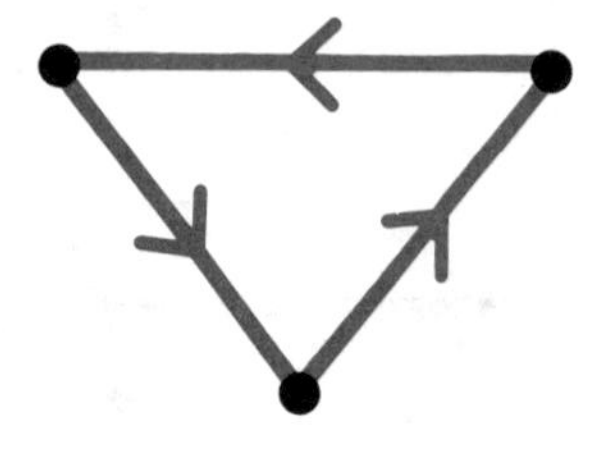

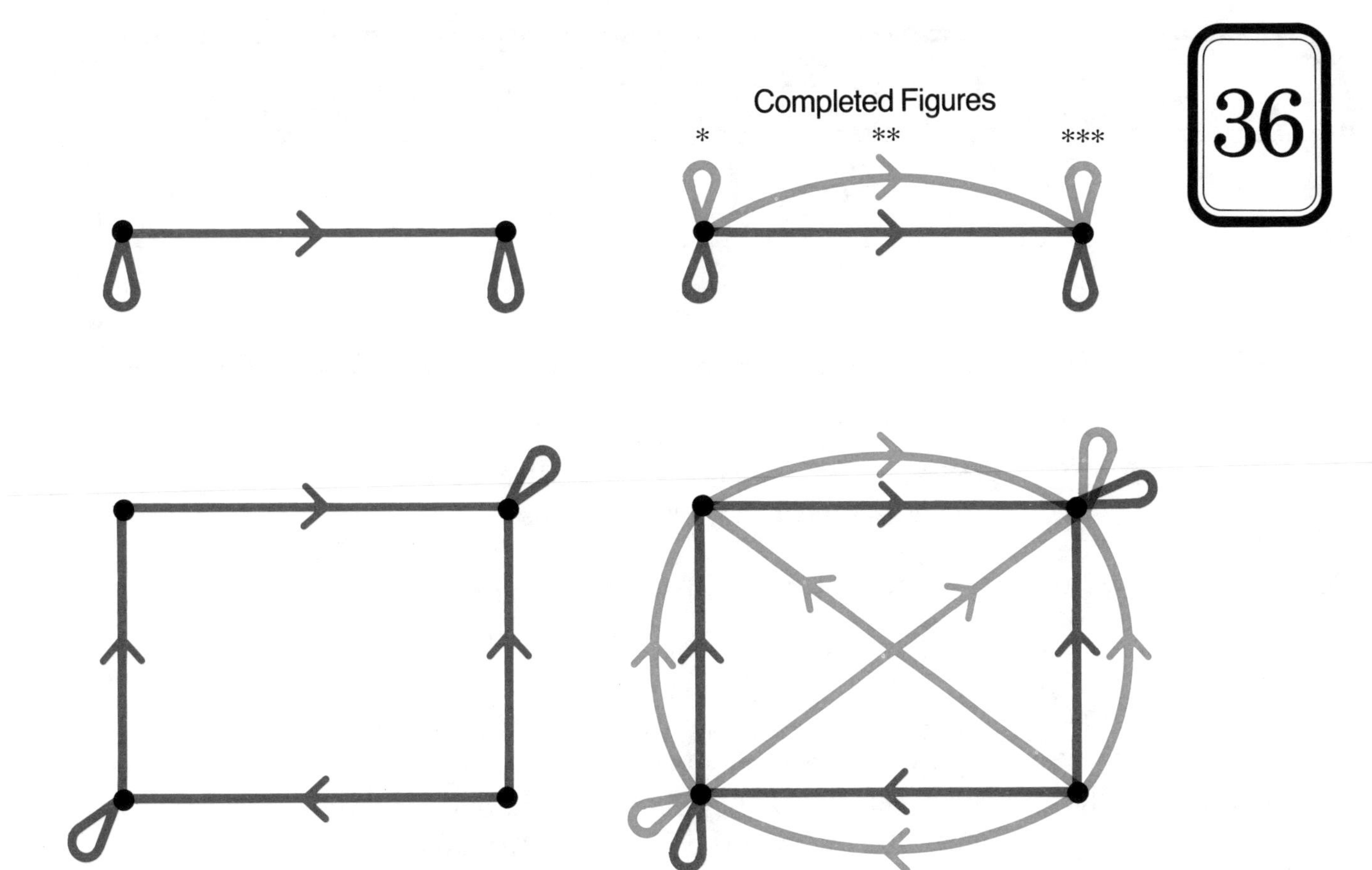

* From following the left red loop twice.
** Left loop followed by central arrow or central arrow followed by right loop.
*** Right loop twice.

Resources Available

For class use: Worksheets L33 and L34
For out-of-class use: Any H-worksheet up through H51

ACTIVITIES 37 and 38

Ten Times

1

Materials Needed
Teacher: Minicomputer kit, colored chalk
Students: Paper and colored pencils

Begin the activity with some mental arithmetic involving multiples of 10. For example:

7 × 10 (70)	10 × 10 (100)
10 × 5 (50)	6 × 10 (60)
9 × 10 (90)	10 × 12 (120)
10 × 0 (0)	10 × 20 (200)

Ask the students who answer to explain how they did the calculations. One might say that, for example, 10 × 12 is 120 because 10 × 10 is 100 and 100 + 20 is 120. Another might simply remark that all you have to do is put a **0** after the **12**.

Illustrate the "ten times" calculation with the help of 10-checkers on the Minicomputer. Place a 10-checker on the 8-square:

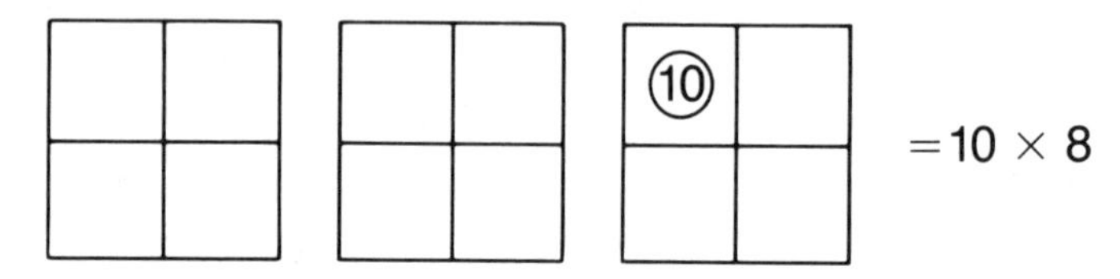

T: Instead of putting 10 regular checkers on a square, we can show this with a 10-checker. What is 10 × 8? (80)

Make the "ten times" move on the Minicomputer, and write on the board as follows:

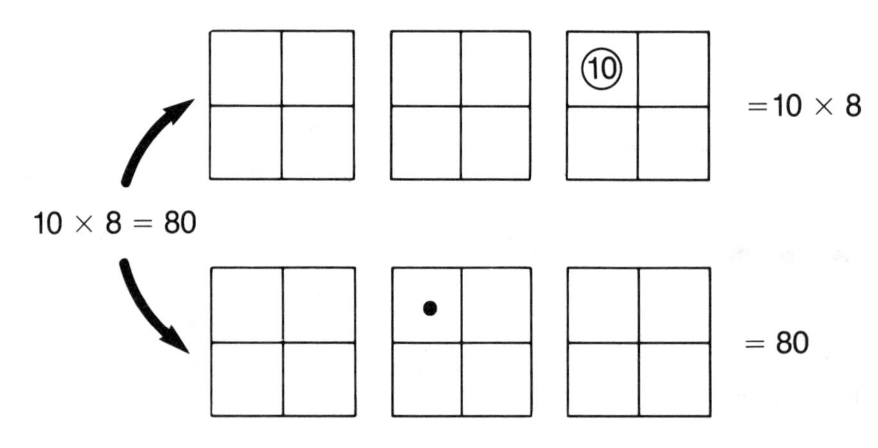

Proceed similarly for 10 × 27:

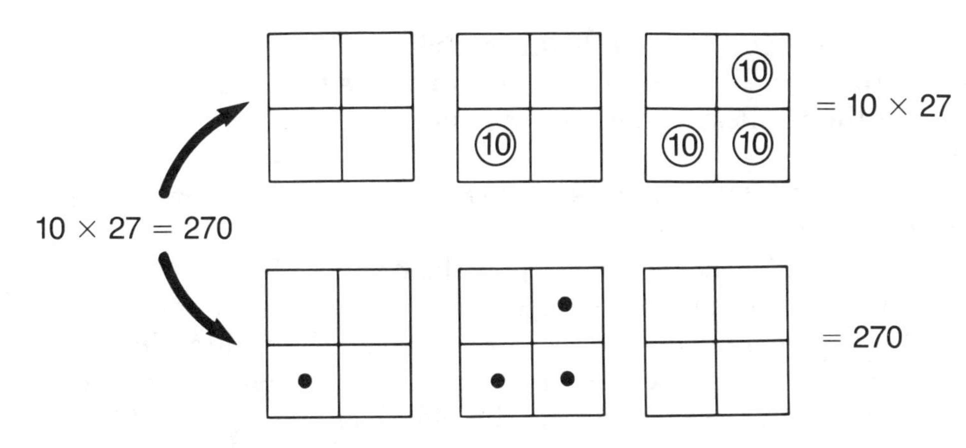

Also show that $10 \times 43 = 430$, $10 \times 100 = 1{,}000$, and so on.

At the end of this mental arithmetic session, remove the Minicomputer and erase what you have written on the board. Replace it with the following arrow road:

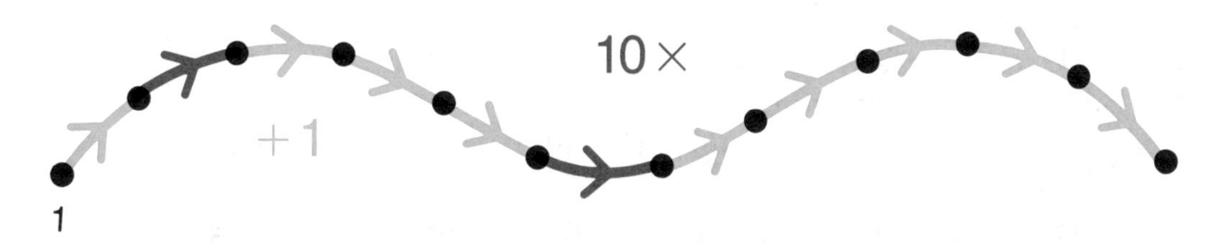

T: What number does the last dot on this road stand for?

Let students whisper the answer to you (235), and then ask a student to label all the dots in the diagram.

T: The starting number is 1 and the ending number is 235. How many 10× arrows are there? (two) How many +1 arrows are there? (nine) Do you think we could draw any different arrow roads starting at 1 and using two 10× arrows and nine +1 arrows?

Write the following on the board:

Two 10× arrows and nine +1 arrows

1 ●

Ask the students to try this individually, using the same arrows but in different orders. As you walk around the room, encourage the students to build roads that are different from their neighbors'. Check that all roads contain exactly two 10× arrows and nine +1 arrows and that they start at 1. Ask those who finish quickly to build yet another road with the same arrows and starting number, but with either a greater ending number or a smaller ending number, as appropriate.

Make a list on the board of all the ending numbers discovered by the class. There are 55 possible ending numbers, among them the following:

370	721	316	244	1,000	514
172	811	613	253	505	703

T: What is the largest possible ending number?
S: *1,000; you use all nine +1 arrows first and then the two 10 × arrows.*
T: What is the smallest possible ending number?
S: *190.*
S: *No; you can get 109, and that's smaller. Put the two 10 × arrows first and then all the +1 arrows.*

If no student provides these answers, give them yourself.

T: As we've seen, the largest ending number is 1,000. All the other possible ending numbers are less than 1,000 and have three digits. For example, 613 has the three digits: 6, 1, and 3. What is the sum of these digits? (10) Give me another three-digit ending number. (244) What is the sum of its digits? (2 + 4 + 4 = 10) Do you think that every possible three-digit ending number has digits that add up to 10? Check all the ending numbers we have found.

Give the students a few minutes to check the sum of the digits of their ending numbers.

T: Has anyone found a three-digit ending number whose digits don't add up to 10?
S: *1,000; the sum is 1.*
T: But 1,000 has four digits.

Eventually, the students will agree that all the numbers checked have 10 as the sum of their digits.

T: Tell me a three-digit number whose digits have a sum that is different from 10. (234) Can you find a road of 10 × and +1 arrows whose ending number is 234?

The attempt to answer this question will probably lead to this arrow road:

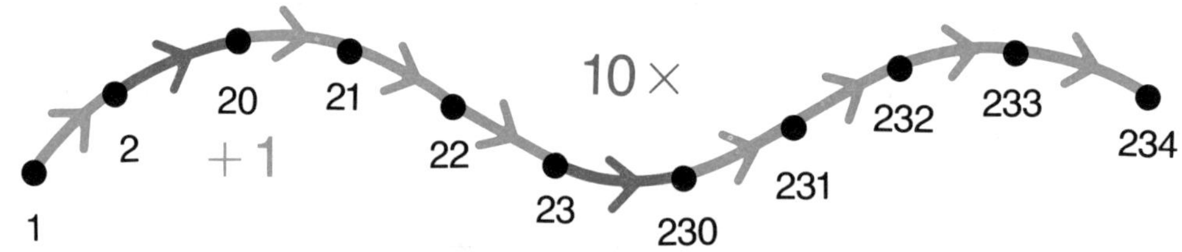

But only eight +1 arrows have been used rather than the required nine.
S: *We can't get to 234 as an ending number.*

Let the students try to reach other ending numbers whose digits have sums different from 10. In every case they will not succeed. Also let them select a three-digit number that has not been obtained so far but whose digits sum to 10. In each case they should try to find a road leading to that number. In every case they will succeed.

In the time remaining, suggest that one more 10 × arrow be added:

Three 10 × arrows and nine +1 arrows

1●

37
38

The students should again search for possible ending numbers. This time, with the exception of the largest (10,000), the numbers will all have four digits, the sum of whose digits is 10.

For example, 1,423 is a possible ending number:

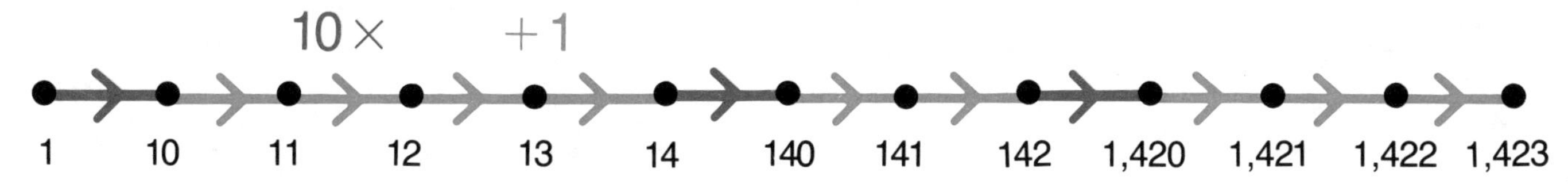

But 2,514 is not:

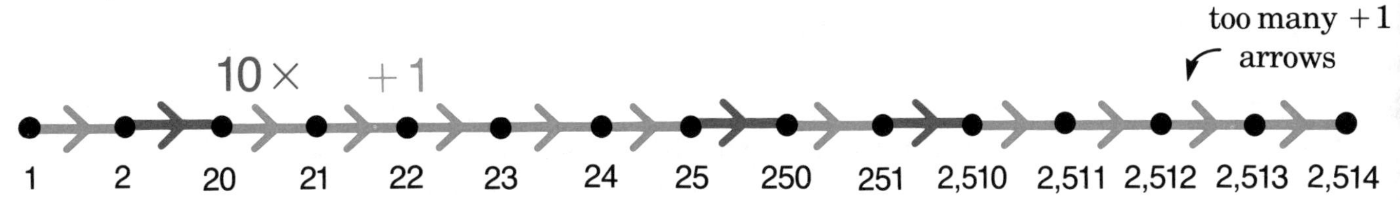

Resources Available

For out-of-class use: Any H-worksheet up through H52

ACTIVITY 39
Logical Thinking 3

Materials Needed
Teacher: Colored chalk
Students: None

Note to the Teacher

Do not linger too long on the initial stages of this activity. Proceed at such a pace that, before half the allotted time has elapsed, the basic string picture involving *S*, *B*, and *D* is drawn and the class understands why it is drawn the way it is. If, after looking through the following description of this activity, you feel that your students will have difficulty completing the work in the time available, either arrange for your class time to be extended on this occasion or set a goal about halfway through the true/false questions at the end of the activity and pace the lesson so that you reach your goal.

Draw the following string picture on the board:

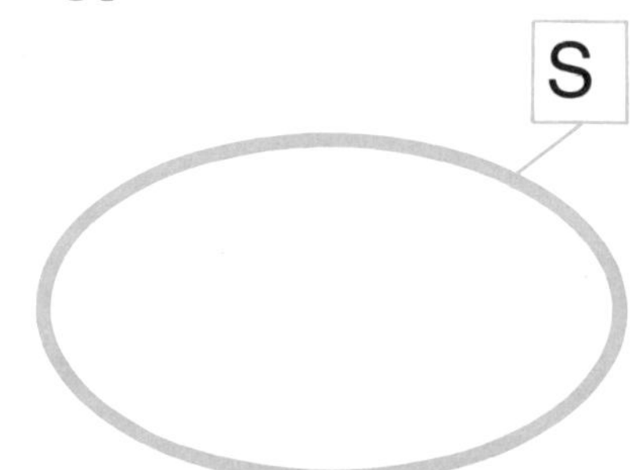

T: A third grader named Sue lives next door to me, and she has lots of friends. This blue string, *S*, is for all of Sue's friends. Some of Sue's friends are on her Pony League baseball team. Who would like to draw a red string, *B*, for all of Sue's friends who are on her baseball team?

Ask a student to come to the board and draw a suitable red string:

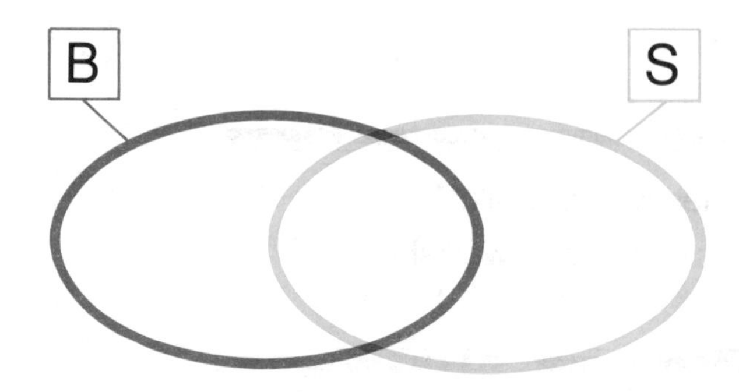

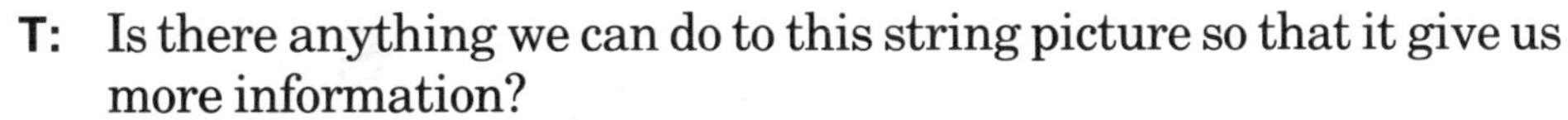

T: Is there anything we can do to this string picture so that it give us more information?

S: *We could hatch some of it.*

T: Come to the board and do it.

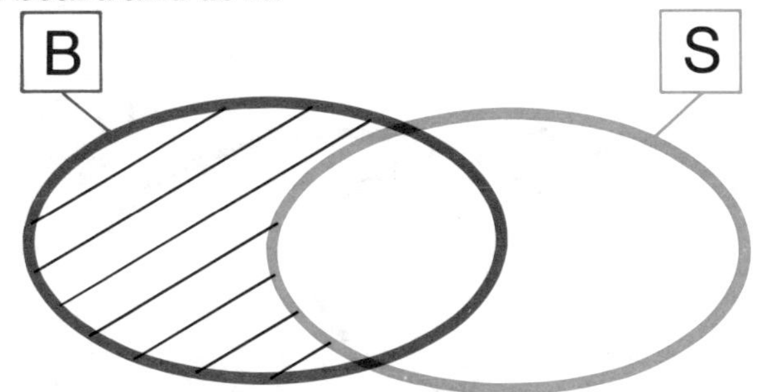

T: Explain what you've done.

S: *Nobody's in that part (pointing to the hatched region) because everyone in* B *is a friend of Sue's who also happens to be on her baseball team. If someone were in the hatched part, then that person wouldn't be a friend of Sue's, and that's impossible. So there's nobody there.*

T: That's an excellent explanation! Can anyone draw the string picture without using hatching but so that it gives the same information?

Leave the hatched string picture on the board and draw another blue string labeled *S* (on a second board, if possible). Then call on a student to draw the red string, *B*, so that no hatching is needed but the same information is conveyed.

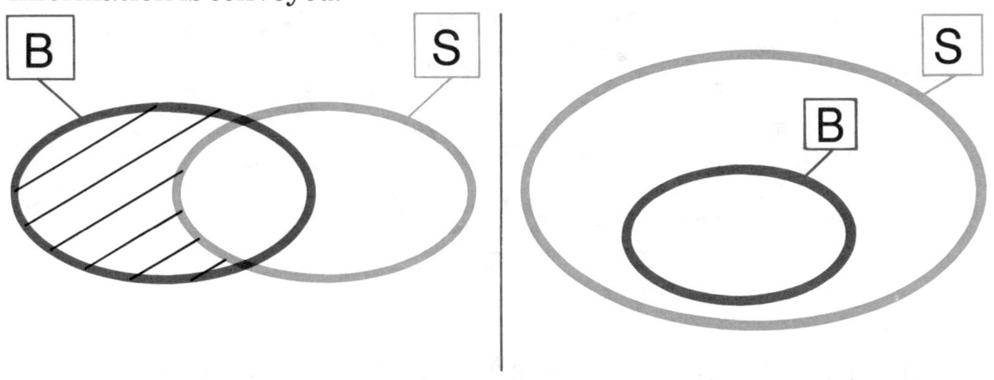

T: What do you think of this drawing?

S: *It gives the same information the hatching gives, because if a dot is in the red string,* B, *it is also in the blue string,* S.

T: Very good; so we have a choice of the two pictures. I'm going to erase the first one and keep the second for the rest of this exercise.

Do so.

T: Now I'd like a green string, *D*, for all of Sue's friends who are also in her dance class.

Ask a student to come to the board and draw a green string. Be sure that the red and green strings overlap. If they do not, ask where to put a dot for a friend of Sue's who is both on her baseball team and in her dance class. Also be sure that the green string is entirely inside the blue string. If not, remind the class that every member of *D* is a friend of Sue's, so the green string can be drawn inside the blue string in the same way as the red string can, and for the same reasons.

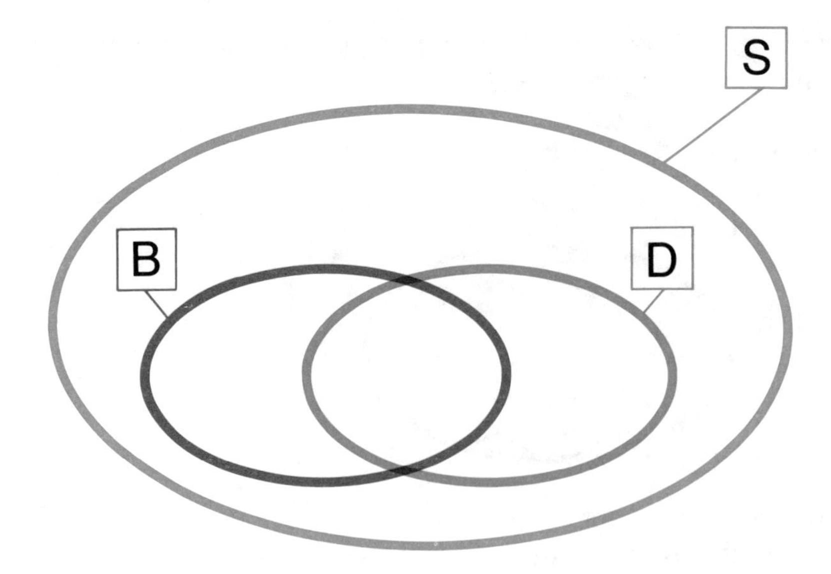

T: Very good. Now I'm going to add some information to the picture. As I do so, see if you can figure out what information I'm adding.

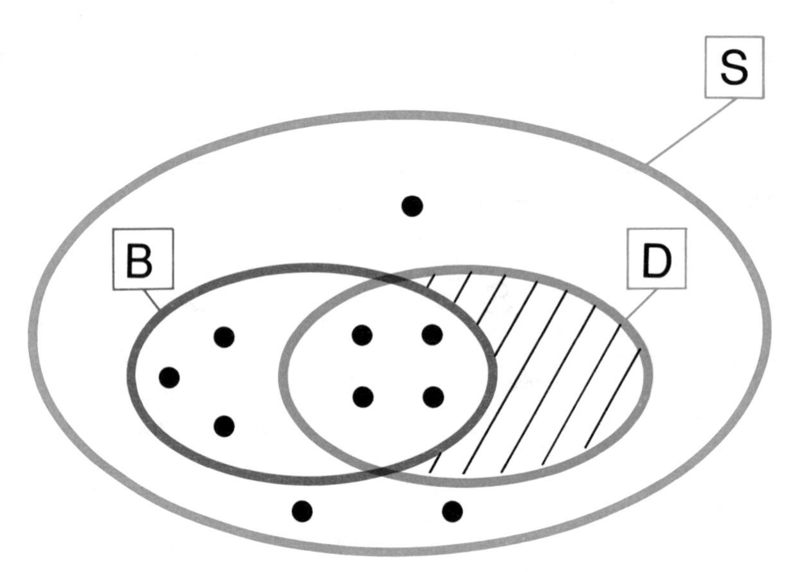

T: First, let me tell you that all the dots for Sue's friends have been drawn. She has exactly ten friends. What else can you say for sure about Sue's friends?

S(Tom): *Three of Sue's friends are on her baseball team but not in her dance class.*

S(Amy): *All we can say for sure is that* ***at least*** *three of Sue's friends are on her baseball team but not in her dance class.*

T: But I told you that all the dots have been drawn. So Tom is correct; and, of course, Amy is too.

S: *Every friend of Sue's who is in her dance class is also on her baseball team.*

S: *At least four of Sue's friends are both on her baseball team* ***and*** *in her dance class.*

T: You could also say "exactly four," because all the dots have been drawn. Is there another way to draw the picture without using hatching but so that it gives the same information?

First attempt:

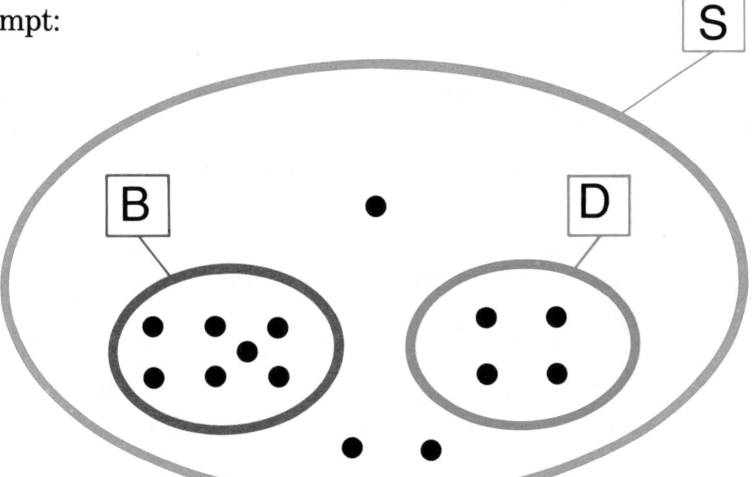

S: *That's not right. Now Sue has fourteen friends, but she's only supposed to have ten.*

S: *Also, a minute ago there were four of Sue's friends who were on her baseball team and in her dance class. Now there are none.*

Erase the first attempt.
Second attempt:

S

B

D

S: *This one's correct. Everyone in* D *is also in* B.

Leave both pictures on the board for the rest of this exercise. For some of the following questions it may be useful to ask the student who answers to come to the board and point to the appropriate dots during his or her explanation. On such occasions reference should be made to both pictures.

T: True or false? Sue has at least one friend who is on her baseball team but not in her dance class.

S: *True; Sue has three friends like that, and "at least one" means one or more than one.*

T: At most two of Sue's friends are in her dance class.

S: *False; all four of her friends in the middle are in her dance class.*

T: Every one of Sue's friends who is on her baseball team is in her dance class.

S: *False; she has three friends who are on her baseball team but not in her dance class.*

T: Every friend of Sue's who is not in her dance class is on her baseball team.

S: *False; the three friends outside both the red and the green strings are neither in her dance class nor on her baseball team.*

T: Every friend of Sue's is either on her baseball team or in her dance class.

S: *False; the same three friends as before show it's false.*

T: Sue has at least one friend in her dance class who is not on her baseball team.

S: *False, because of the hatching.*

T: At least five of Sue's friends are not in her dance class.

S: *True; exactly six of her friends are not in her dance class, and "at least five" means five or more than five.*

T: At most four of Sue's friends are not on her baseball team.

S: *True; exactly three are not, and "at most four" means four, three, two, one, or none.*

T: Everyone on Sue's baseball team is one of her friends.

S: *We can't tell the answer to that from this picture because we don't have a string for all the people on Sue's baseball team; we have only a string (*B*) for those on the team who are also her friends.*

S: *But I'm sure the answer is false because there are at least nine people on a baseball team and* B *only has seven people in it. So there are at least two more people on Sue's baseball team besides her friends. And another thing: Sue is on her own team, and I'm not sure if one of the dots in* B *is for Sue or not.*

Resources Available

For out-of-class use: Any H-worksheet up through H54

ACTIVITY 40

Logical Thinking 4

Materials Needed
Teacher: Colored chalk
Students: Pencils

Note to the Teacher

As in the case of Activity 39, be prepared to adjust your pace and the amount of the activity you set yourself to complete to the length of time you have available.

Distribute copies of Worksheet L35.

T: Everybody read the top of the page where it tells you what the three strings are.

Allow a short time for reading.

T: Do you think there are only six students in Pam's school?

S: *It looks that way because there are only six dots. It must be a very small school.*

S: *We can't be sure. Maybe you haven't drawn all the dots. Only one of the regions is hatched, so there could be more dots in the other regions.*

T: I agree. Is there anything you can say about the number of students in Pam's school?

S: *There are at least six.*

S: *There are at least five, at least four, at least three, and so on.*

T: In fact, there are more than 100 students in Pam's school. Can we say there are at most six?

S: *No, you told us there were more than 100.*

T: What's the answer to the first question on the worksheet?

S: *True, because of the hatching.*

T: What about the second question?

S: *False; there are at least three boys in the Computer Club. Here they are (pointing to the three dots in the green string and outside the red one).*

Now let the students finish the worksheet on their own. Meanwhile, draw the string diagram of Worksheet L35 on the board. After a few minutes discuss the answers.

3. True; in fact, there are at least three such boys, because there are three dots in C that are not in G.
4. False, because we have already seen in problem 3 that there are at least three such boys.

5. True; the dot in S that is outside G and C must be for a boy who is not in the Computer Club.
6. False, because of the hatching (and also by the answer to problem 1 of the worksheet).
7. True; there are four dots already in the picture that are in S but not in G. They must all be for boys.

T: Can someone draw another picture of the same situation that does not use hatching?

Let a volunteer do so at the board.

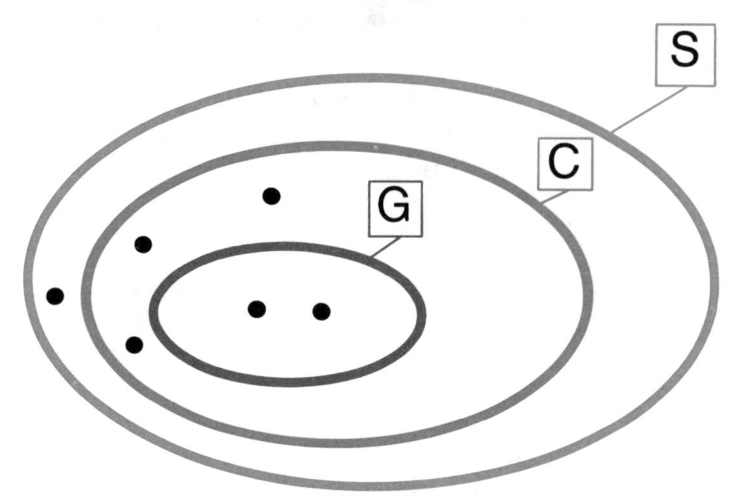

Discuss this solution if you think it worthwhile.

T: I'm going to write some more information about this school on the board, and I want you to think about how to change the picture so that it gives this new information.

Write on the board:

There are exactly seven boys in Pam's school
who are in the Computer Club.
and
There are at least ten boys in Pam's school.

Ask a student to come to the board to make the necessary alterations to one of the string pictures, and ask a second student to fix the other picture. Once again, discuss the solutions if you feel it would be useful to do so.

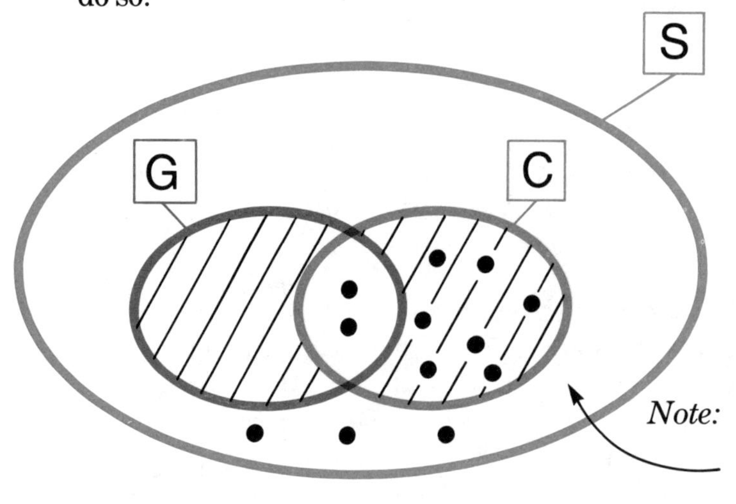

Note: There can be any number of dots (greater than or equal to 3) in this region.

40

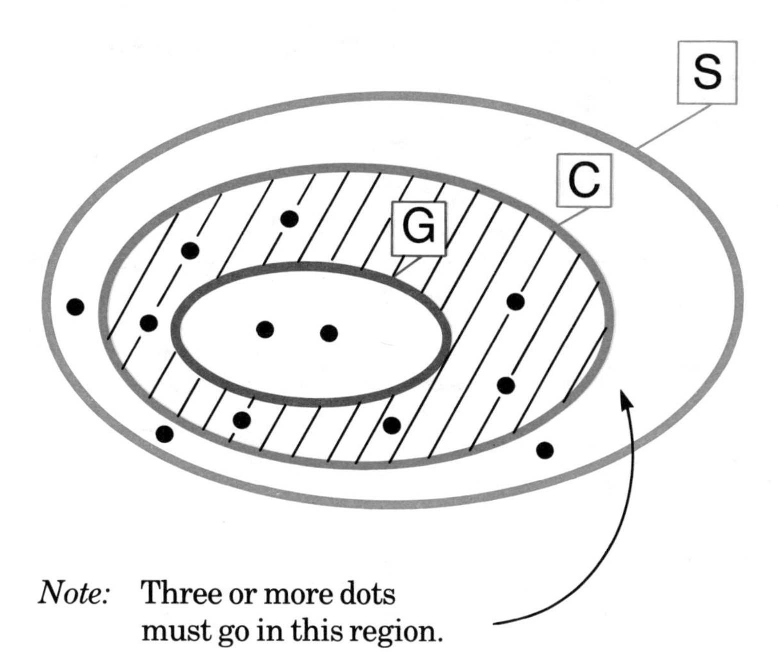

Resources Available

For class use: Worksheets L35 to L38
For out-of-class use: Any H-worksheet up through H56

ACTIVITY 41
Match the Tags 1

Materials Needed
Teacher: Colored chalk
Students: Paper and colored pencils

Draw the following arrow picture on the board:

+18	×6
÷2	÷2
−10	+45
÷3	×3
−15	×4
×4	+12

T: Today we have to try to match the red and blue tags.
Point to the +18 tag.
T: If the red arrow were for +18, what number would be here? (Point to the middle dot.)
S: *48, because 30 + 18 = 48.*
T: Then which tag would you choose for the blue arrow?
S: *+12, because 48 + 12 = 60.*
Link the +18 red tag and the +12 blue tag together with a curved line.
Point to the ×4 blue tag.
T: Suppose the blue arrow were for ×4. What number would be here? (Point to the middle dot.)
S: *15, because 15 × 4 = 60.*
T: Then which tag would you choose for the red arrow?
S: *÷2, because 30 ÷ 2 = 15.*
S: *You could also choose the −15 red tag, because 30 − 15 = 15.*
Link the ÷2 red tag and the ×4 blue tag, and the −15 red tag and the ×4 blue tag, with curved lines.

Proceed similarly for the other tags. Alternate red and blue. At the end of the exercise your picture should appear as the figure below.

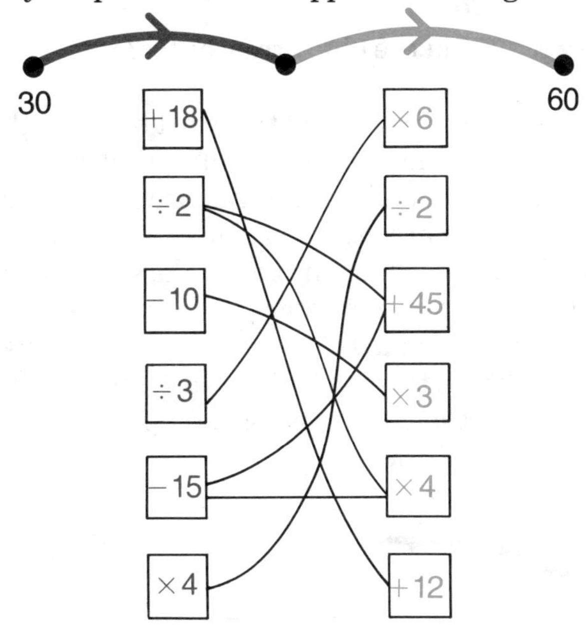

Distribute Worksheet L39 and let the students work on it individually. After a few minutes, check through the results collectively.

Erase what you have written on the board and replace it with the top figure on page 108. Ask the students to copy it onto their sheets of paper.

Point to the red arrow starting from the dot for 8.
T: You may decide what the red arrow is for. What would you like it to be?
S: *+40.*
Write **+40** in red on the first line of the chart beneath the red arrow.
Point to the middle dot.
T: If the red arrow were for +40, what number would be here?
(Adjust this last question in the light of the actual suggestion made for the red arrow.)

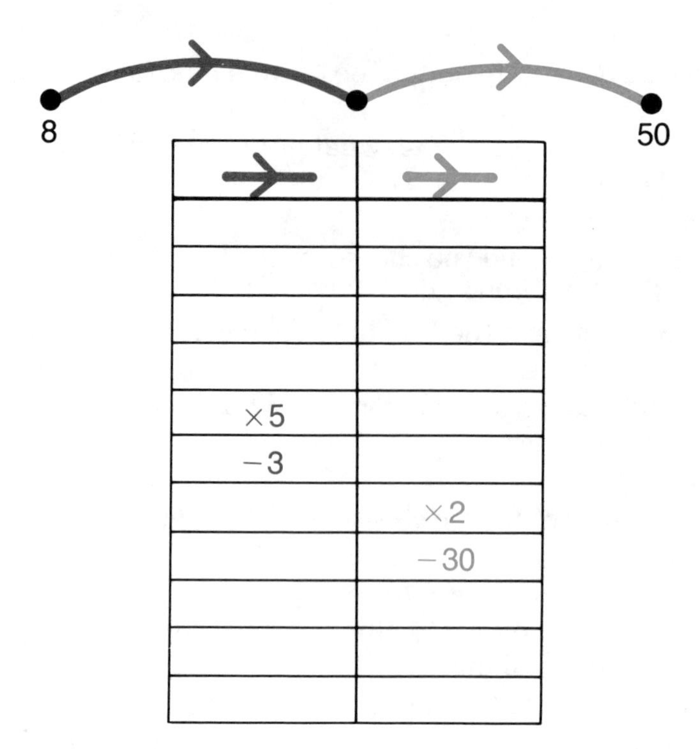

→	→
×5	
−3	
	×2
	−30

S: *48, because* $8 + 40 = 48$.
T: And then what could the blue arrow be for?
S: $+2$.
Write **+2** in blue on the first line of the chart beneath the blue arrow.

Let the students continue to work on this problem individually. Point out that for the four lines of the chart that are already partially completed, the students are expected to make use of the given choice of label for one of the arrows. Encourage the class to look for solutions that bring negative numbers or (nonintegral) decimal numbers into play (see, for example, lines 4 and 9 of the sample chart below). After a few minutes, ask volunteers to come to the board, record some of their answers, and explain them to the whole group.

Here are some possibilities:

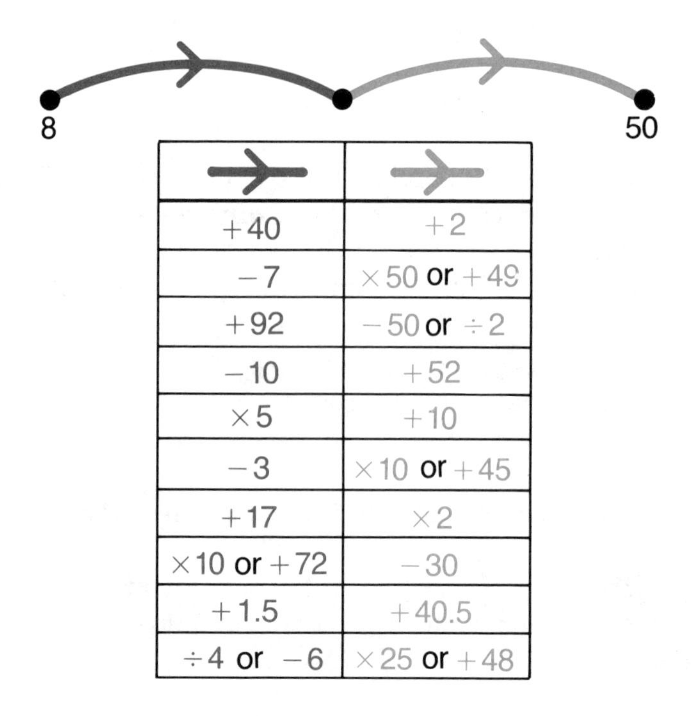

→	→
+40	+2
−7	×50 or +49
+92	−50 or ÷2
−10	+52
×5	+10
−3	×10 or +45
+17	×2
×10 or +72	−30
+1.5	+40.5
÷4 or −6	×25 or +48

If there is sufficient time remaining, distribute Worksheet L40 and let the students work on it individually. Otherwise, this worksheet may be used for homework.

Resources Available

For class use: Worksheets L39 and L40
For out-of-class use: Any H-worksheet up through H58

ACTIVITY 42
Minicomputer Golf 2

Materials Needed
Teacher: Minicomputer kit, colored chalk
Students: None

Play several games of Minicomputer Golf. Each starting configuration should include some regular and some negative checkers. You should include the following among the games you play:

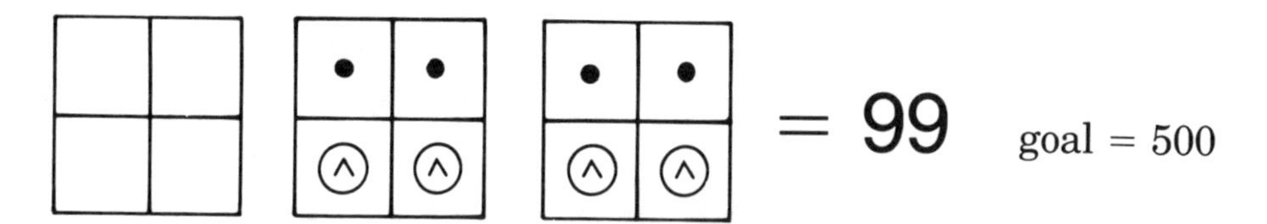

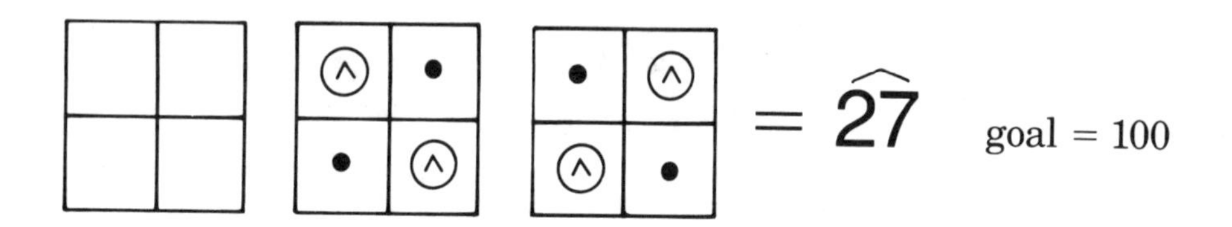

If a review is necessary, the rules for this game may be found in Activity 2 of this volume.

Resources Available

For out-of-class use: Any H-worksheet up through H60

ACTIVITY 43
Ten Times
2

Materials Needed
Teacher: Minicomputer kit, colored chalk
Students: Paper and colored pencils

Place four 10-checkers on the Minicomputer as follows:

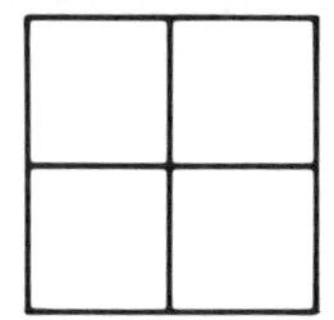
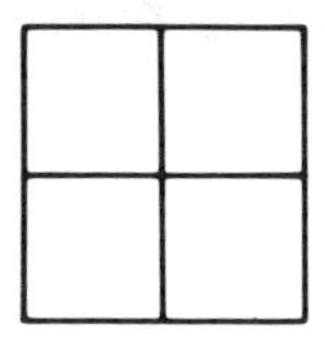

T: The checkers show ten times what number?
S: *Ten times 56.*
T: What number is 10×56?
S: *560.*
T: How do you know that?
S: *I just put a **0** on the end of **56**.*
S: *Or you could make a "ten times" move on the Minicomputer.*

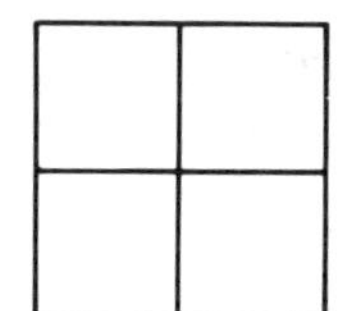
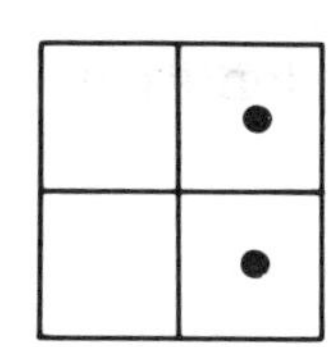
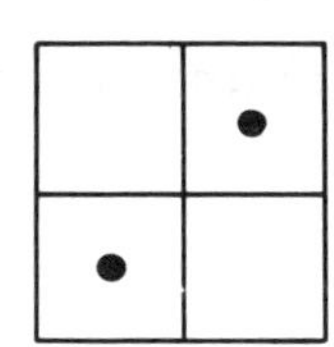
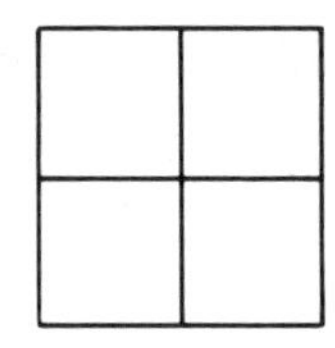
= 560

T: Remember that when there are no checkers on the ones' board, the last digit of the number is 0.

Repeat this for several similar calculations:

$10 \times 87 = 870$ $\quad$ $10 \times 102 = 1{,}020$
$10 \times 121 = 1{,}210$ $\quad$ $10 \times 120 = 1{,}200$

As an exercise, write ten calculations of the following type on the board:

10×36 $\quad$ $10 \times 3{,}006$
10×306 $\quad$ $10 \times 3{,}060$
10×360 $\quad$ $10 \times 3{,}600$

When some students have completed all the calculations, let them begin writing their results on the board.

Then erase what is written on the board and replace it with this diagram:

6 ● $\qquad$ ● 42 $\qquad$ 10× $\;$ +1 $\;$ −1

T: Build a $10\times$, $+1$, -1 arrow road between 6 and 42, but try to use fewer than eight arrows.

Circulate among the students, giving assistance as required. Those who finish quickly should begin work on Worksheets L41 and L42. Those who took more than seven arrows should be encouraged to try to find a shorter road.

After several minutes, ask everyone to stop working, and direct attention to the board.

T: Which multiple of 10 is nearest to 42? (40)

Draw a dot for 40 near the dot for 42.

T: How can we fill in the part of the arrow road between 40 and 42?

S: *Draw two +1 arrows from 40 to 42.*

T: How can we build a road between 6 and 40?

S: *Go from 6 to 4, and then from 4 to 40.*

T: How do we do that?

S: *Two −1 arrows from 6 to 4; then a 10 × arrow from 4 to 40.*

Invite a student to draw the suggested road on the board:

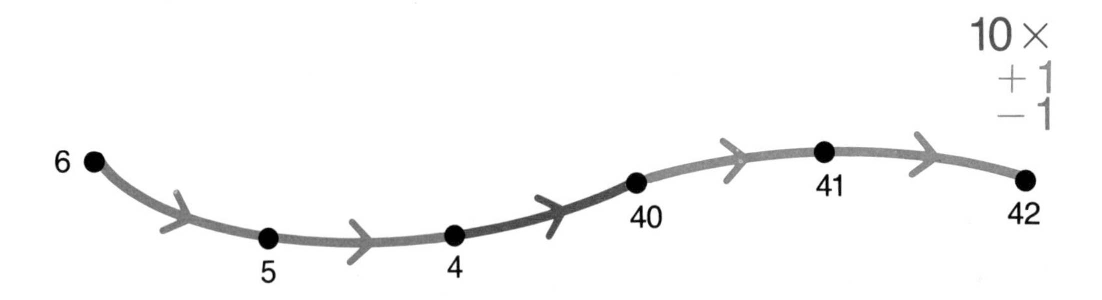

If any time remains, the students can work on Worksheets L41 and L42.

Resources Available

For class use: Worksheets L41 and L42

For out-of-class use: Any H-worksheet up through H61

ACTIVITY 44
Number Line Tug-of-War

Materials Needed
Teacher: Colored chalk
Students: None

Before the start of the class period, draw on the board this portion of the number line using a very large scale (say, 20 cm or 10 in. between neighboring marks):

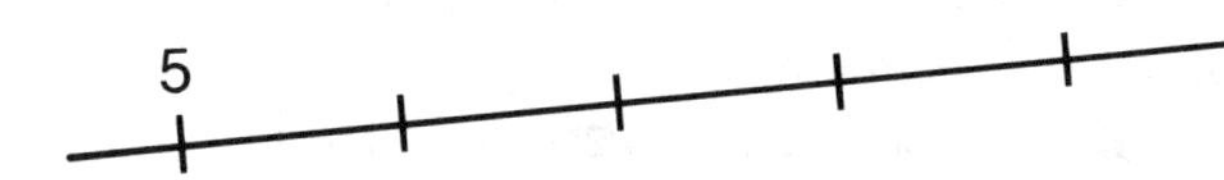

T: I am thinking of two numbers that are on this part of the number line. They are 6.3 and 13.6.

Write these numbers on the board to the side of the number line.

T: Will someone please mark where these numbers are located on the line?

Let the class discuss the various attempts at placement of 6.3 until it is decided that 6.3 is between 6 and 7 and between 6.2 and 6.4. If no one suggests marking out ten equal spaces between 6 and 7, do so yourself. Carry out this procedure with the help of a meterstick or yardstick. (If you are using a scale of 20 cm/unit, then the marks for 0.1 units will be 2 cm apart; if your scale is 10 in./unit, then the marks for 0.1 units will be 1 in. apart.)

After 6.3 and 13.6 have been located to everyone's satisfaction, let other students mark the locations of 11.2, 9.8, 11.1, 9.7, 11.15, 9.75 (and other numbers if you feel that further experience is needed).

The board should now look something like this:

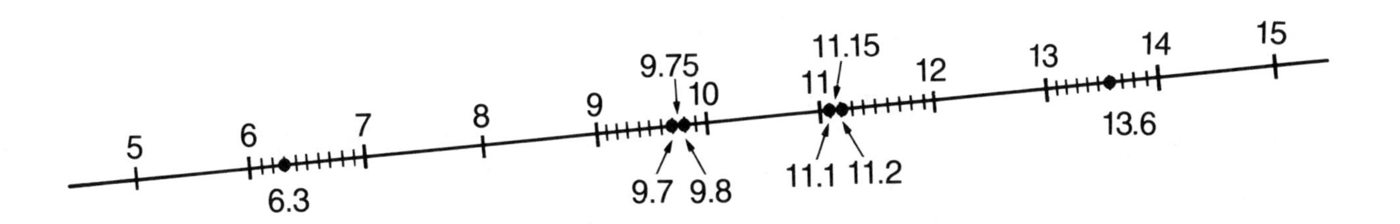

Next, erase all the labels on the line except those for 5, 6.3, 13.6, and 15, leaving the following:

44

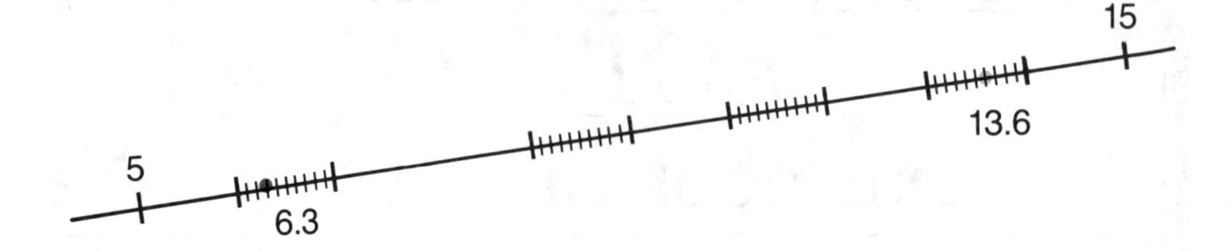

T: Today we are going to play the game of Number Line Tug-of-War.
Separate the class into two teams, the Red team and the Blue team.

T: The Red team will start at 6.3 and move to the right. The Blue team will start at 13.6 and move to the left. The teams will take turns, starting with the Red team. The rules are the following:

(As you announce the rules, write them on the board.)

> Red may add any positive number to the Red number.
> Blue may subtract any positive number from the Blue number.
> Each team must try not to equal or pass the other team's number.
> The first team to do so loses.

T: For example, suppose Red moves $+1.4$. Is this a legal move?

S: *Yes; adding 1.4 is adding some positive number.*

T: What is $6.3 + 1.4$? (7.7) So Red moves to 7.7. Then suppose Blue moves -4.6. Is that a legal move for Blue? (yes) What is $13.6 - 4.6$? (9) So Blue moves to 9.

As you discuss these examples of moves, ask members of the teams to mark red and blue dots, one at 7.7 in red and one at 9 in blue.

T: Has either number passed the other? (no) So let's continue the game.

Let volunteers from the Red and Blue teams alternate in making moves. On each move the player should announce the positive number that is to be added to or subtracted from the playing team's number. The player then calculates the team's new number and draws a red or blue dot for the new number.

In order that the students do not get lost in the calculations, it is suggested that you give a calculator to one of your more careful students and let him or her check each calculation as it is announced by the player making the move.

A possible sequence of moves might be the following:

	Red		Blue
$+1.4$:	$6.3 + 1.4 = 7.7$		
		-4.6:	$13.6 - 4.6 = 9$
$+1$:	$7.7 + 1 = 8.7$		
		-0.2:	$9 - 0.2 = 8.8$
$+0.05$:	$8.7 + 0.05 = 8.75$		
		-0.2:	$8.8 - 0.2 = 8.6$

44

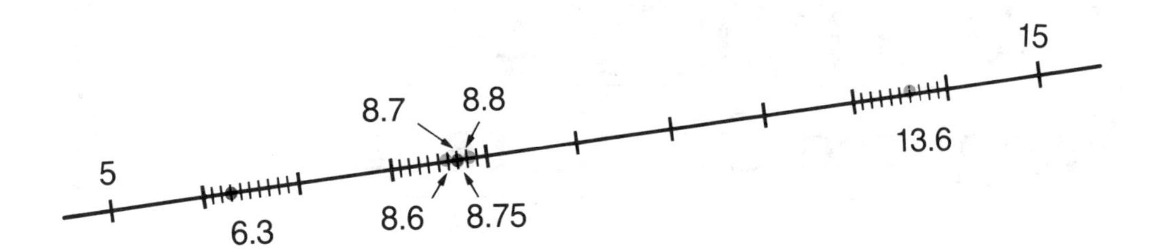

At this point both teams should realize that the Blue team has passed the Red number, and consequently loses.

Many other sequences of moves are possible, and classes that are not so adept at adding and subtracting decimals may well blunder before the sixth move. Other classes may quickly realize that it is possible to continue forever with neither team losing. (For example, if on the sixth move the Blue player had chosen -0.02 rather than -0.2, the game would have continued, with the next Red player perhaps choosing $+0.02$, and so on.)

If there is sufficient time, play the game again, using the same starting numbers. This time switch the membership of the two teams so that each student will have had the experience of both adding and subtracting. Do not hint at strategies for prolonging the game.

Resources Available

For out-of-class use: Any H-worksheet up through H61

ACTIVITY 45
Weighted Checkers 1

Materials Needed
Teacher: Minicomputer kit, colored chalk
Students: None

Set up two Minicomputer boards and display one set of weighted checkers on the board, keeping the other sets available when needed:

② ③ ④ ⑤ ⑥ ⑦ ⑧ ⑨ ⑩

T: Here are some new kinds of checkers. They are called *weighted checkers*. I'll put a 4-checker on the Minicomputer. What is this number?

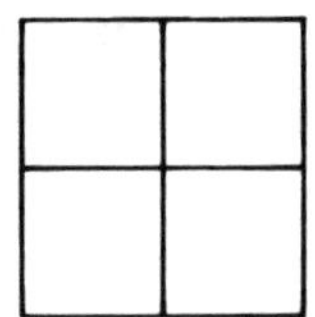
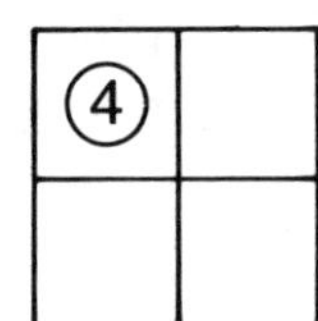

S: *4 times 8.*
S: *32.*
T: And this number?

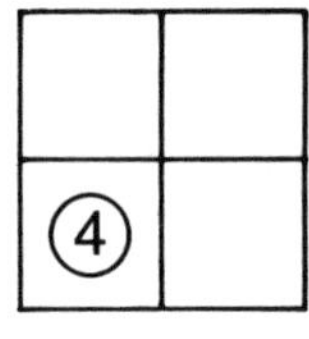
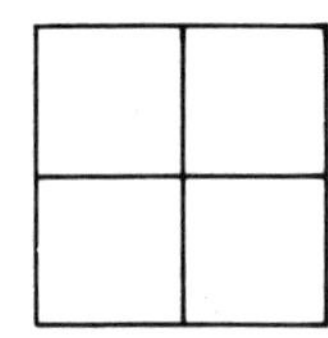

S: *4 times 20.*
S: *80.*
Continue with the following:

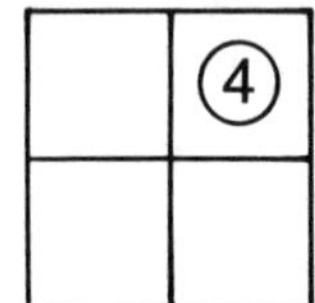
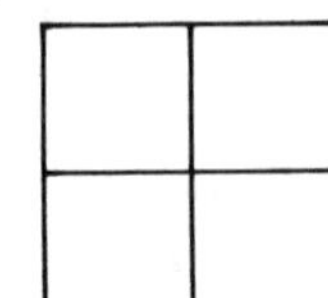

$= 4 \times 40 = 160$

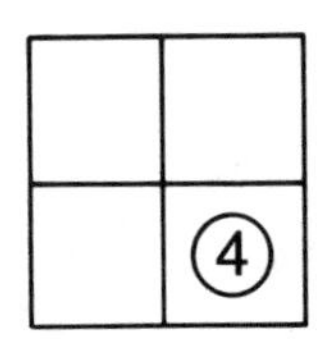
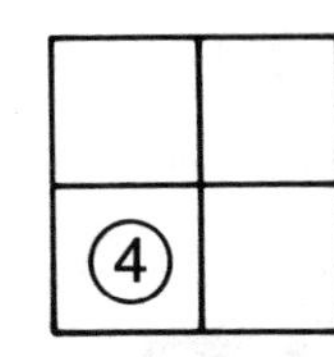

$= 4 \times 12 = 48$

Also, present similar examples with 5-checkers and 7-checkers. Then display a single Minicomputer board.

T: Can anyone show the number 18 using exactly one weighted checker?

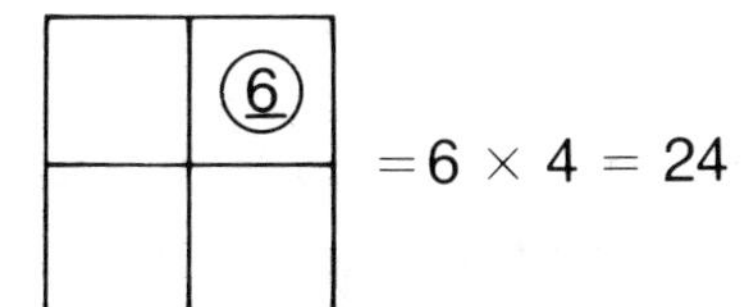

T: 24, using exactly one weighted checker?

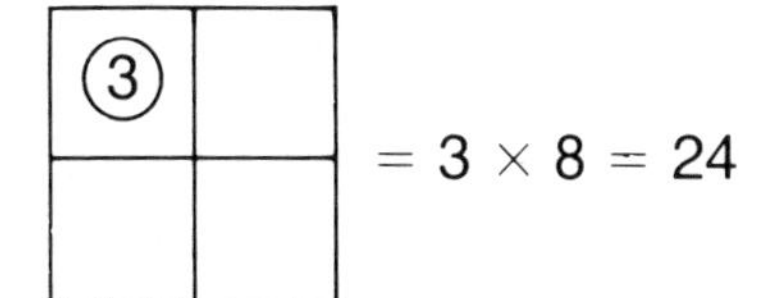

T: 12, using exactly one weighted checker?

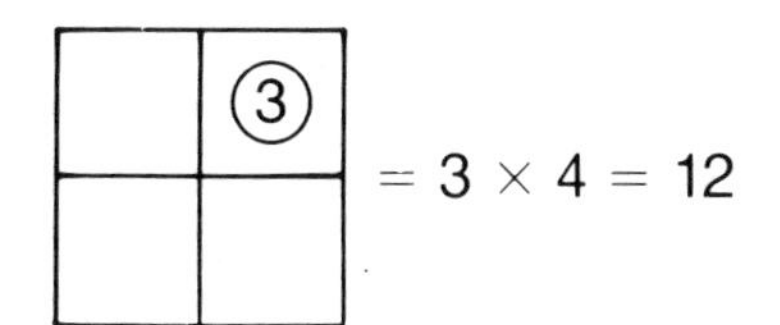

T: 30, using exactly one weighted checker?

Of course this is not possible, but give the students the time to discover that it cannot be done.

T: Can anyone show 30 on one Minicomputer board using exactly two weighted checkers? You may use two of the same kind if needed.

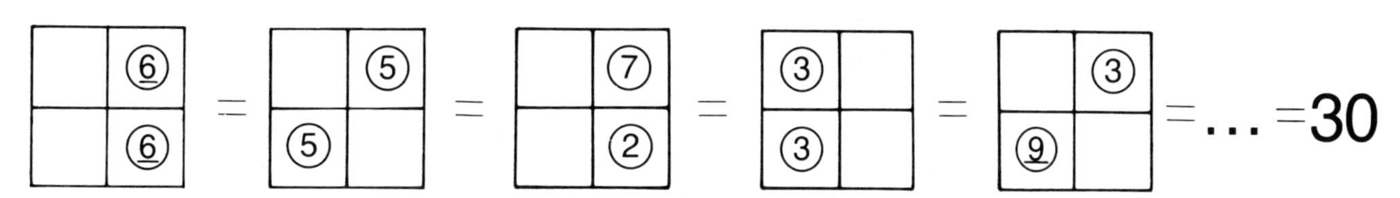

Let the class try to find as many of these and other possibilities as they can.

T: 42 on one Minicomputer board, using exactly two weighted checkers?

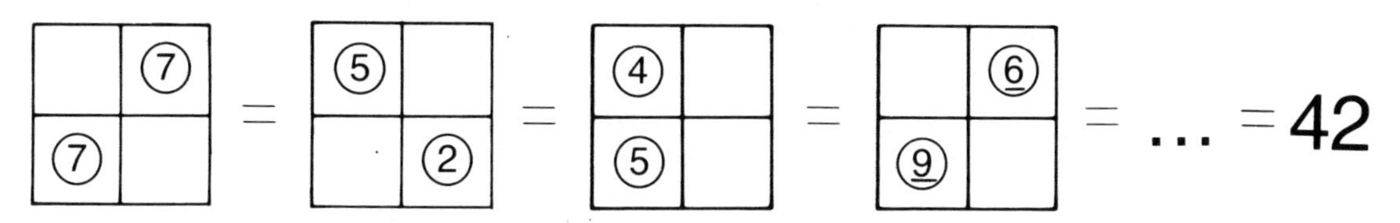

Now place a tens' board next to the ones' board.

T: Can anyone show 160 on two Minicomputer boards using exactly one weighted checker?

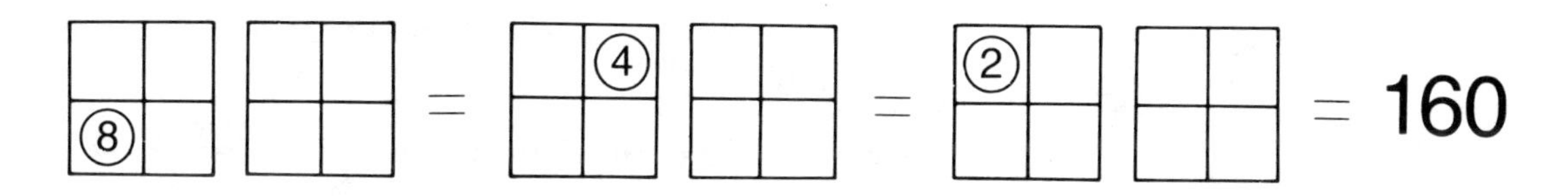

T: 60, with exactly one weighted checker?

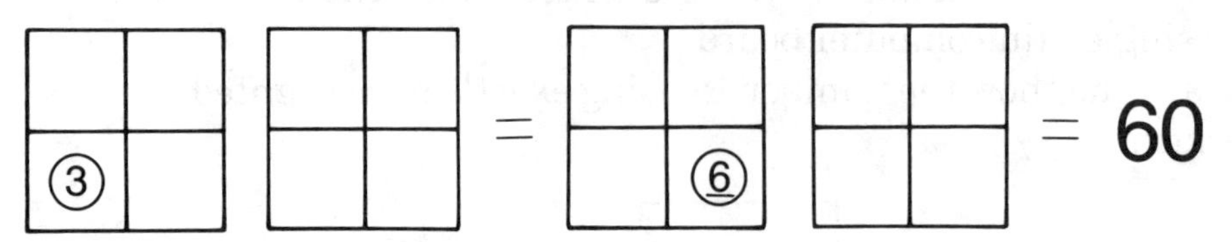

T: 360, with exactly one checker?

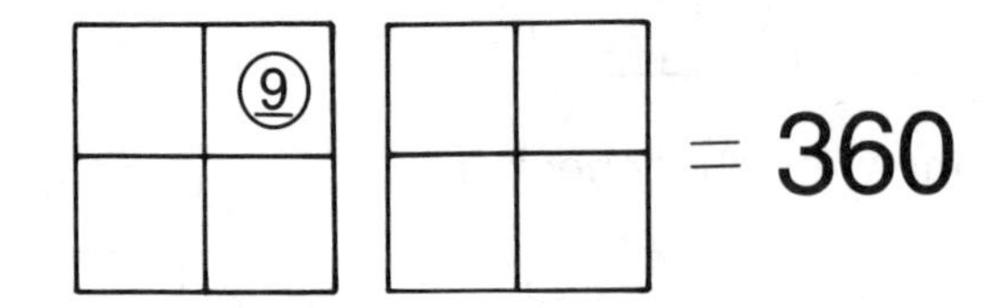

Continue this type of activity, varying the number of Minicomputer boards and the number of weighted checkers that are to be used.

Resources Available

For out-of-class use: Any H-worksheet up through H65

ACTIVITY 46

Weighted Checkers 2

Materials Needed
Teacher: Minicomputer kit, chalk
Students: Pencils

Note to the Teacher

If you are able to teach this activity immediately following Activity 45, then omit the first part of this activity and start instead at ■.

Set up two Minicomputer boards and display one set of weighted checkers on the board:

② ③ ④ ⑤ ⑥ ⑦ ⑧ ⑨ ⑩

T: Can someone show 84 on two Minicomputer boards using exactly two weighted checkers? You may use two of the same kind.

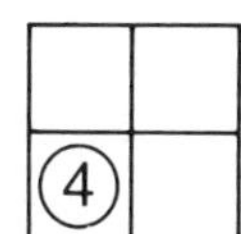 = 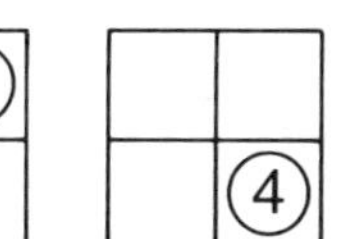 =

= ... = 84

T: 200 on two boards, using exactly two weighted checkers?

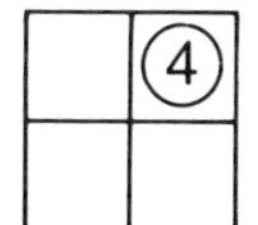 = 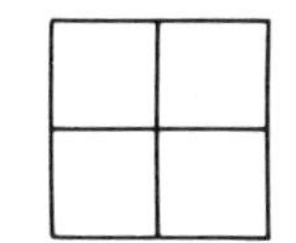 = ... = 200

■ Set up three Minicomputer boards.

T: Can someone show 4 times 284 on the Minicomputer using weighted checkers?

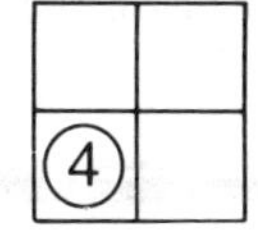 = 4 × 284

T: What is this number?
S: *I know how to do it.*
Invite the volunteer to do the calculation using a method of his or her choice.

$$\begin{array}{r} 284 \\ \times \quad 4 \\ \hline 1{,}136 \\ \hline \end{array}$$

T: How can we check that result? What numbers are on the boards?
S: *$4 \times 4 = 16$ (on the ones' board)*
$4 \times 80 = 320$ (on the tens' board)
$4 \times 200 = 800$ (on the hundreds' board)
S: *They add up to 1,136. It checks.*
Repeat this exercise for 8×485.

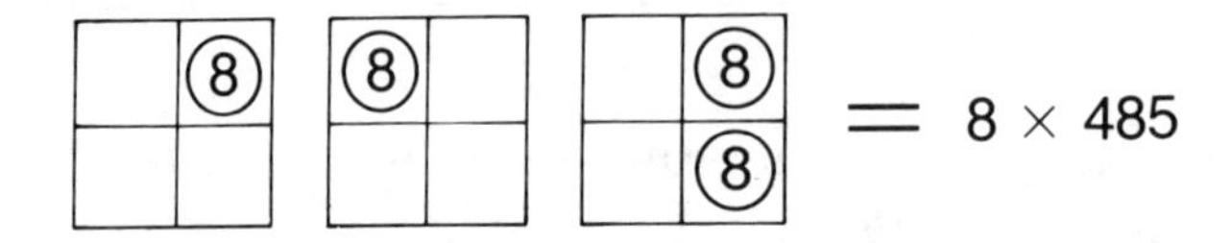

For the rest of the time available, let the students work on Worksheets L43 and L44.

Resources Available
For class use: Worksheets L43 and L44
For out-of-class use: Any H-worksheet up through H69

ACTIVITY 47
Subtracting Integers

Materials Needed
Teacher: Chalk
Students: Paper and pencils

Write on the board: **3 − 5 =**

T: Copy this problem onto your papers, and try to solve it.

Circulate around the room and let the students know whether they have found the correct answer.

T: Quite a few of you have written **2** or **2**, but neither of these is correct. How can we find out the correct answer?

S: *We have to take 5 away from 3, and that's not possible.*

T: I'm not so sure it's impossible. What we need is some sort of trick.

Draw this picture on the board:

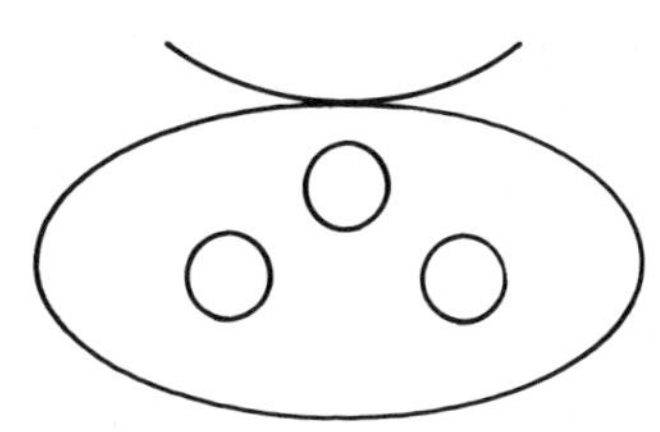

T: Do you remember the story of Meg the monkey and her magic peanuts? Here's Meg's bag with three regular peanuts in it. The problem says that we have to take five magic peanuts out of the bag. How could we do that?

Let the students make suggestions, and discuss those with merit. If no one suggests the following method, do so yourself.

S: *There are no magic peanuts in the bag, so the only way we could take five out of the bag is if we first put five in.*

T: But we can't just put five magic peanuts into the bag; that would alter the number of peanuts in the bag. So let's imagine that we add five magic peanuts and five regular peanuts to the bag.

S: *But don't put them too close together or all the new ones added will disappear before you can take away the five magic ones.*

Modify the picture on the board:

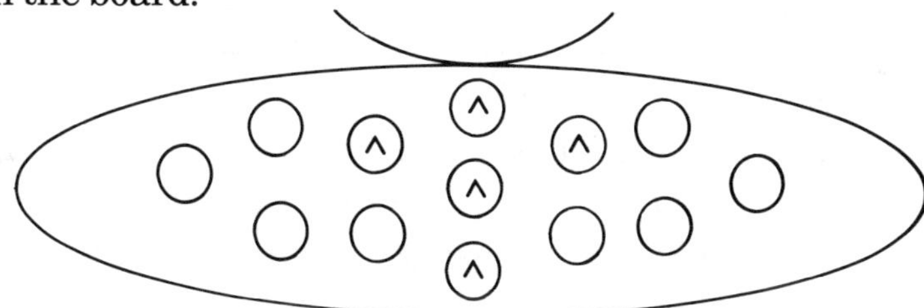

T: Now we can take away the five magic peanuts. What will be left?
S: *Eight regular peanuts.*
Complete the calculation on the board: $\mathbf{3 - \widehat{5} = 8}$
T: Let's try another one.
Write on the board: $\mathbf{\widehat{6} - \widehat{4} =}$
S: *That's easy. It means that Meg has six magic peanuts in her bag, and we have to take away four of them. That will leave two magic peanuts.*
Complete the calculation on the board: $\mathbf{\widehat{6} - \widehat{4} = \widehat{2}}$
T: Here's another problem: $\mathbf{\widehat{4} - 2 =}$
S: *That's just like the first one, except that this time we have to take regular peanuts away from magic peanuts. That means we'll have to put two regular peanuts into Meg's bag, and of course, two magic peanuts as well.*
T: Come to the board and draw a picture showing how to do the calculation.

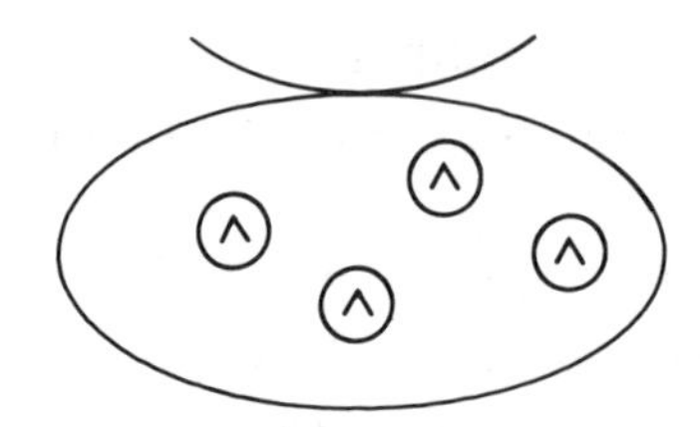

S: *Here are the four magic peanuts. Now I'll put in two regular peanuts and two magic peanuts.*

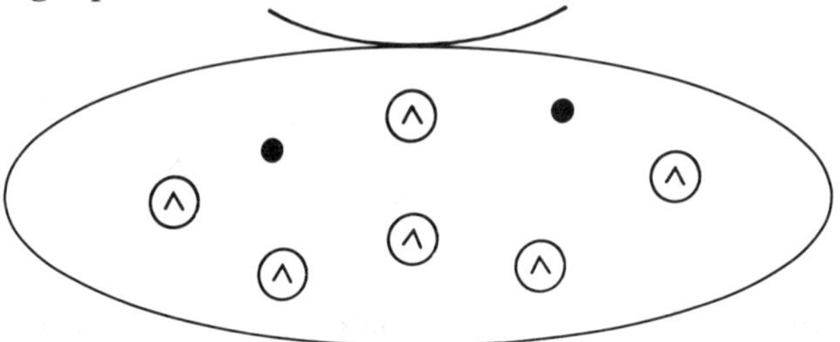

S: *Now I can take away the two regular peanuts, and there will be six magic ones left.*
Complete the calculation on the board: $\mathbf{\widehat{4} - 2 = \widehat{6}}$

Note to the Teacher

At this stage you want to get across to the class an arithmetical procedure for subtracting integers that does not depend on drawing pictures. You may be fortunate and have such a procedure suggested by one of your students. We indicate how the lesson might proceed in this case in scenario 1 below. On the other hand, you may have to plant the basic idea yourself. We indicate how the lesson might proceed in this case in scenario 2.

Scenario 1:
S(Laura): *I think I know how to do these problems without drawing pictures. You just change the second number to its opposite (from positive to negative, or from negative to positive) and then add.*

T: Explain how that works for our last calculation.

S: *Change 2 to its opposite, $\widehat{2}$, and add it to $\widehat{4}$: $\widehat{4} + \widehat{2} = \widehat{6}$.*

T: Very good. How about for our other two calculations?

Write on the board: $\mathbf{3 - \widehat{5} = 3 + 5 = 8}$ and $\mathbf{\widehat{6} - \widehat{4} = \widehat{6} + 4 = \widehat{2}}$

Continue from ■ below.

Scenario 2:

T: I'd like for us to find a quicker way of doing these problems without having to draw all these pictures. Look at the last calculation. To begin with, we had four magic peanuts, and at the end we had six magic peanuts. So what had we ended up doing when we were solving the problem?

S: *Adding two magic peanuts.*

Write on the board: $\mathbf{\widehat{4} - 2 = \widehat{4} + \widehat{2} = \widehat{6}}$

T: Let's look at the second calculation. There we started with six magic peanuts and we ended with two magic peanuts. How could we have gotten that result by adding?

S: *Add four regular peanuts.*

Write on the board: $\mathbf{\widehat{6} - \widehat{4} = \widehat{6} + 4 = \widehat{2}}$

T: Can anyone see how to change these subtraction problems into addition problems?

S(Laura): *Yes; you have to change the number you're taking away to the other kind, and then add.*

T: What do you mean "the other kind"?

S: *You change regular peanuts to magic ones, and magic ones to regular ones.*

T: Let's check that with the first calculation.

Write on the board: $\mathbf{3 - \widehat{5} = 3 + 5 = 8}$

T: Well, it seems to work in all three cases. Let's just try one more.

■ Write on the board: $\mathbf{\widehat{6} - \widehat{9} =}$

T: First we'll solve it by the picture method.

Let a volunteer come to the board, draw the relevant pictures, and explain how the solution is arrived at.

S: *Here are the six magic peanuts we start with:*

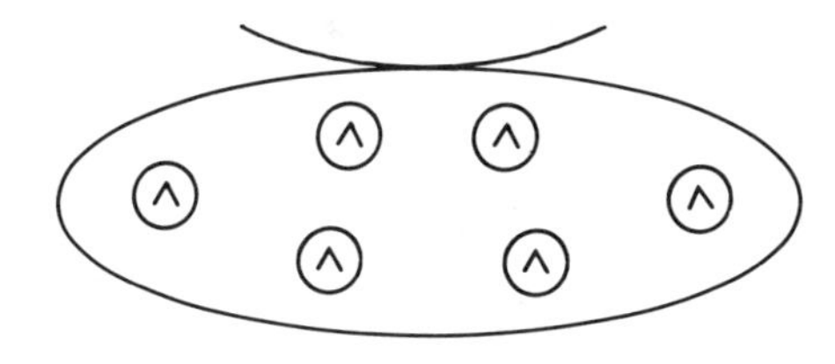

I've got to put three more magic peanuts in the bag so that there will be nine magic peanuts in there for me to take away. That means I've got to put in three magic peanuts and three regular peanuts.

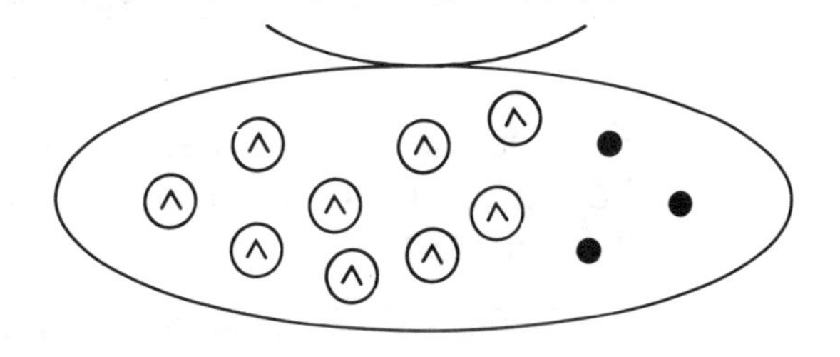

Now I can take away the nine magic peanuts and there are three regular ones left. So $\widehat{6} - \widehat{9} = 3$

T: Let's do it by Laura's method and see if we get the same result.

Write on the board: $\mathbf{\widehat{6} - \widehat{9} = \widehat{6} + 9 = 3}$

As you are doing so, ask for prompts from the class about when to change the minus sign to a plus sign and what the opposite of $\widehat{9}$ is.

T: So we get the same answer whichever way we do it.

S: *But Laura's method is quicker!*

Resources Available

For class use: Worksheets L45 and L46

For out-of-class use: Any H-worksheet up through H69

ACTIVITY 48

Guess My Rule 5

Materials Needed
Teacher: Chalk
Students: Paper and pencils

Note to the Teacher

The secret rule $*$ in this lesson is given by:

$$a * b = \frac{1}{2}\,(a + b)$$

That is, take one-half of the sum of the two numbers. This is for your information only. Do not divulge the rule to your students until they guess it.

Tell the class that you are going to play another game of Guess My Rule. As in Activities 15, 16, 25, and 26, begin by giving four completed calculations as clues. Then let the students try to complete five or six more calculations on their own.

Clues:

$$8 * 2 = 5$$
$$9 * 15 = 12$$
$$15 * 9 = 12$$
$$3 * 2 = 2.5$$

For the students to try (answers are given in parentheses):

$$10 * 4 = (7)$$
$$20 * 40 = (30)$$
$$2 * 6 = (4)$$
$$5 * 10 = (7.5)$$
$$3 * 9 = (3)$$

If you think that by now someone knows the rule, let him or her explain it to the class. Otherwise, let the class work on a few more calculations first and then ask for the rule.

Write on the board: **☐ $*$ 3 = 9**

S: ***15*** *goes in the box, because 15 + 3 = 18 and $\frac{1}{2}$ of 18 = 9.*
Ask the students to copy the following problems onto their papers and then complete them. Answers are given in parentheses.

$\square * 5 = 7$	(9)	
$12 * \square = 11$	(10)	
$\square * 3 = 3.5$	(4)	
$4 * \square = \widehat{3}$	$(\widehat{10})$	
$\square * \square = 30$	(30)	*Remember:* Same number in each box.
$\square * \square = 41$	(41)	

Go over the solutions with the class, and discuss those that most students had difficulty with.

Resources Available

For class use: Worksheets L47 and L48
For out-of-class use: Any H-worksheet up through H69

ACTIVITY 49

Match the Tags 2

Materials Needed
Teacher: Colored chalk
Students: Colored pencils

Draw the following arrow diagram on the board, omitting the letters.

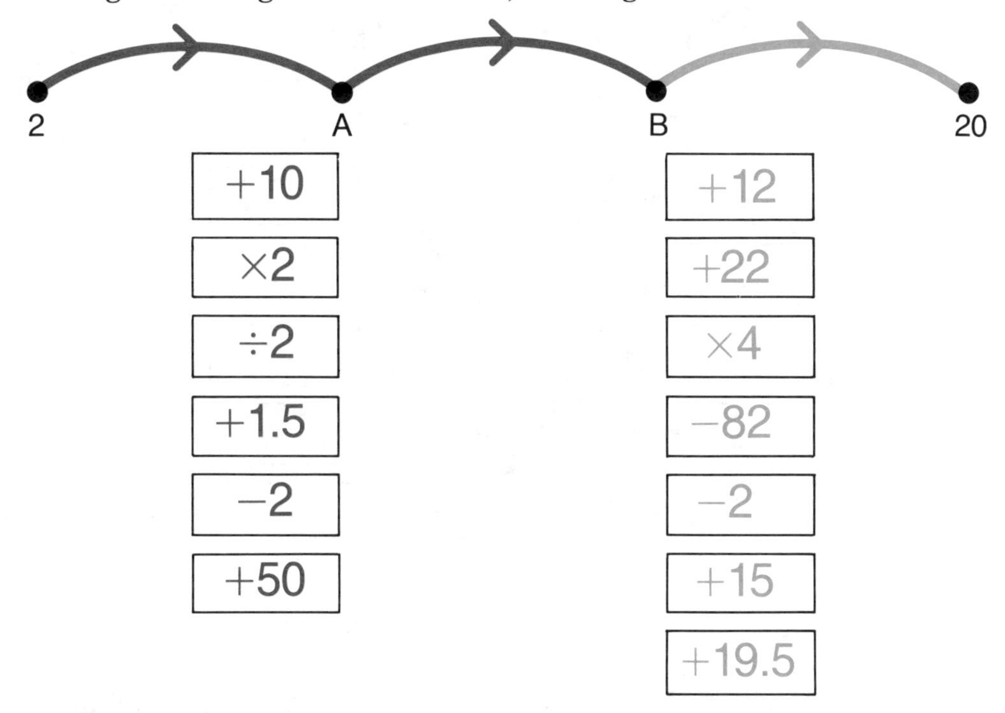

T: Here we have to match the red and blue tags.

Point to the +10 red tag.

T: If the red arrows were for +10, what numbers would be here (point to dot A) and here (point to dot B)?

S: *12 for the first one, and 22 for the next.*

Label the appropriate dots **12** and **22**.

T: Now which tag do you choose for the blue arrow?

S: *−2.*

Connect the +10 red tag and the −2 blue tag with a curved line. Erase the **12** and **22** labels. Point to the +1.5 tag.

T: If the red arrows were for +1.5, what numbers would be here (point to dot A) and here (point to dot B)?

S: *3.5 for the first one, and 5 for the next.*

Label the appropriate dots **3.5** and **5**.

T: And which tag would you choose for the blue arrow?

S: $\times 4$.

S: $+15$.

With curved lines, connect the $+1.5$ red tag and the $\times 4$ blue tag, and the 1.5 red tag and the $+15$ blue tag. Erase the **3.5** and **5** labels. Point to the blue $+12$ tag.

T: If the blue arrow were for $+12$, what number would be here (point to dot B)?

S: *8.*

Label dot B **8.**

T: Now which tag would you choose for the red arrows?

S: $\times 2$.

Connect the $\times 2$ red tag and the $+12$ blue tag with a curved line. Erase the **8** label, and proceed similarly for the remaining tags. Take turns starting with a red tag and then a blue tag. At the end of this exercise your diagram should look like the following one.

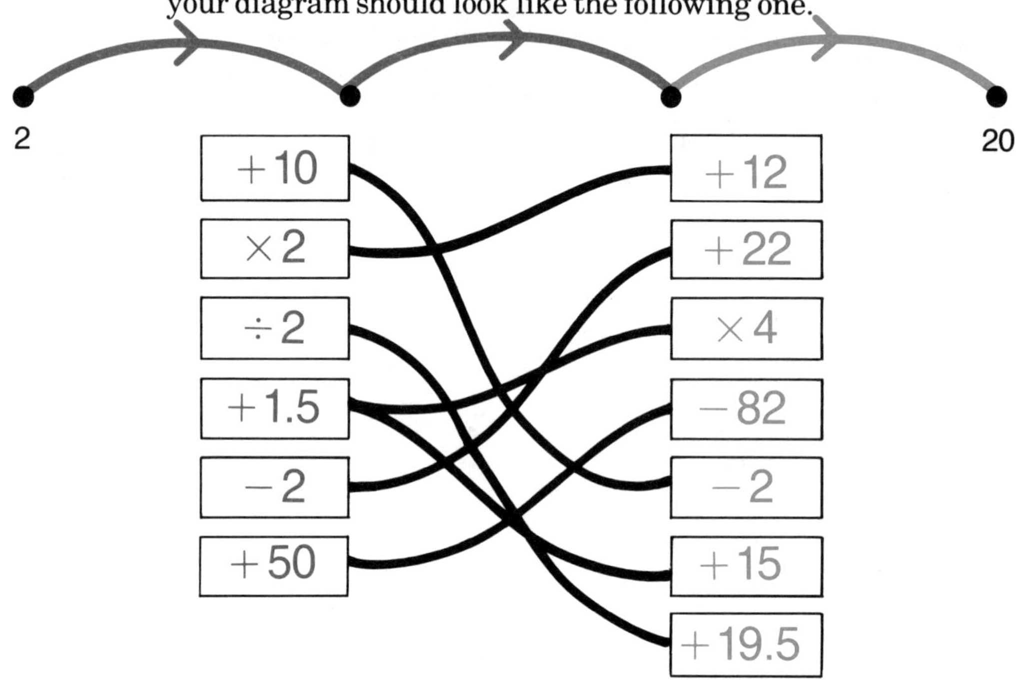

Distribute Worksheet L49 and tell the students that they are to complete the chart. On some lines they are free to choose whichever color arrow they wish and then determine the other. On lines where one arrow is already specified, students should find the other. Encourage them to find solutions that introduce negative or noninteger decimals as labels for the middle two dots. After a while, draw a copy of the worksheet on the board and ask volunteers to record their answers on it, explaining what they have done, if necessary.

Resources Available

For class use: Worksheets L49 to L51

For out-of-class use: Any H-worksheet up through H71

ACTIVITY 50
Calculator Golf 2

Materials Needed
Teacher: Colored chalk
Students: One calculator each

Play several games of Calculator Golf (See Activity 31, Calculator Golf 1). Use the following starting numbers and goals.

Starting Numbers	Goals
911	206
57	2,131
1,111	9,808
$\widehat{141}$	816
$\widehat{232}$	$\widehat{46}$
27.2	45.1
104.8	39
15.21	92.14

Resources Available

For out-of-class use: Any H-worksheet up through H71

ACTIVITY 51

Return Arrows 1

Materials Needed
Teacher: Colored chalk
Students: Paper and colored pencils

Give a calculator to one of your students, who shall be referred to in the following description as "Tracy".

T: Tracy, please choose a whole number between 0 and 100 and write it on a piece of paper. Don't let anyone see your secret number. Now enter the number into your calculator. Then add 16 to the number.

While Tracy is doing this, draw on the board:

T: Ready to go on, Tracy? Now multiply the new number by 3.

While Tracy is doing this, extend the arrow diagram on the board:

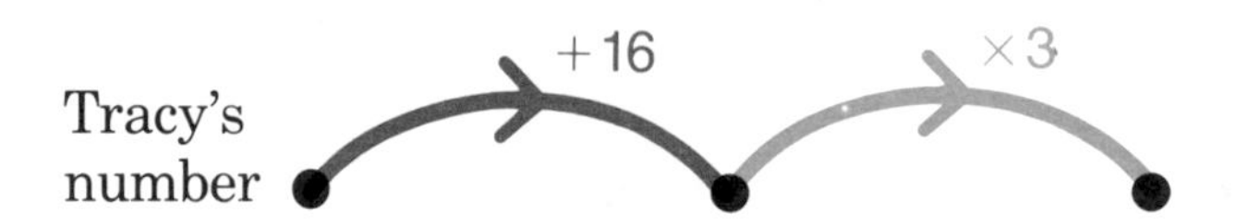

T: Now subtract 21.

T: Now add 43.

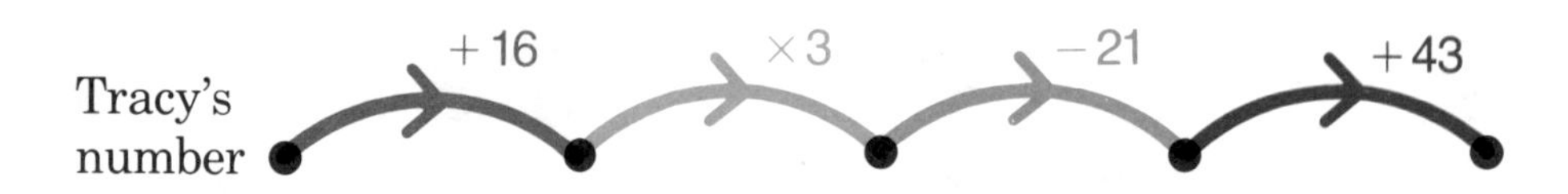

T: Tracy, tell us what number is now on your calculator.

Label the ending dot with the number Tracy names. Suppose it is 91.

T: How can we find out what number Tracy wrote on her paper?

S: *We can draw the arrows back from 91 to her number.*

T: We call those arrows *return arrows*.

As you say this, draw the return arrows. Then, with the help of the students label the arrows and the dots. Finally, check that the starting number discovered as a result of this process agrees with the number written on Tracy's paper.

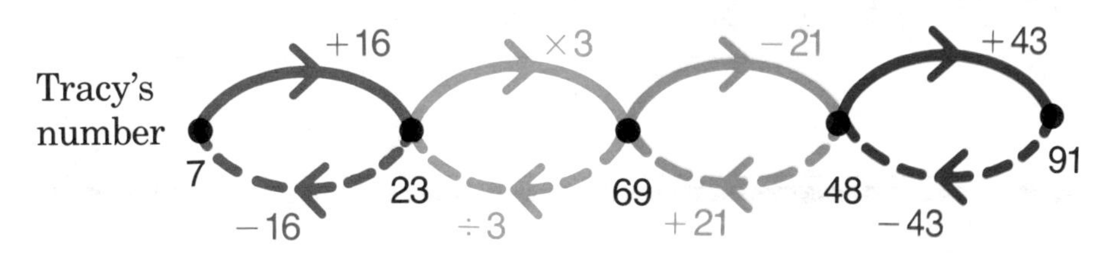

Repeat this activity several times, each time with a different student selecting a secret number and announcing the ending number after following a different sequence of instructions. For example:

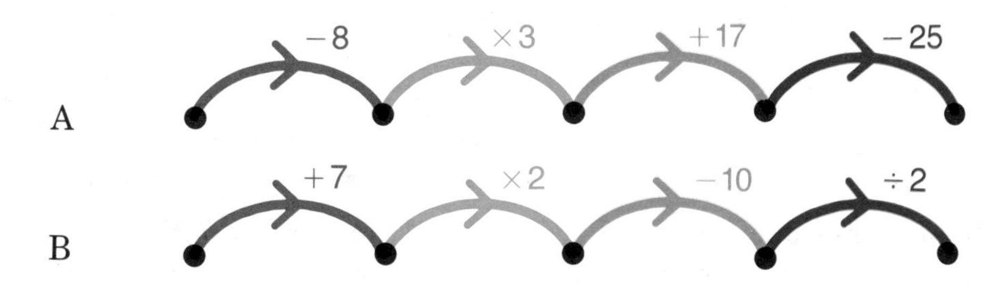

(In this sequence, as you draw the return arrows make sure that both ×2 arrows are drawn in the same color and both ÷2 arrows are drawn in the same color.)
Ask the students to copy the following arrow diagram onto their papers. Then ask them to draw the return arrows, label the arrows and dots, and whisper the secret number to you. After most students have had time to solve the problem individually, complete the arrow diagram on the board together as a class.

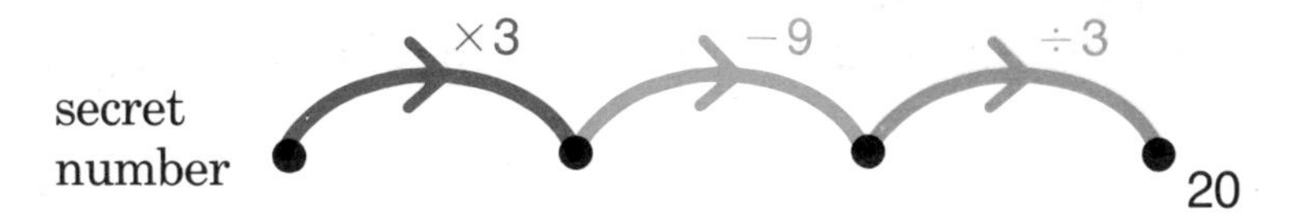

(The secret number is 23.)

Resources Available

For out-of-class use: Any H-worksheet up through H73

ACTIVITY 52
Return Arrows 2

Materials Needed
Teacher: Colored chalk
Students: Paper and colored pencils

Draw this arrow diagram on the board:

T: If the ending dot were for 30, what would the starting dot be for?
Let the students do the necessary calculations with paper and pencil, and then ask them to whisper the starting number to you. They will find that the starting number is the same as the ending number.

T: If the ending dot were for 40, what would the starting dot be for?
Again, the class will find that the starting number is the same as the ending number.

T: Do you think that on this arrow road the ending and the starting numbers are always the same? (yes) Why do you think so?

S: *Because we subtract 21 and then later we subtract 19. That's the same as subtracting 40. But we also add 26 and then later we add 14. That's the same as adding 40.*

T: How should we draw this road if the start and the end are the same dot?

S: *In a circle.*

Draw the diagram according to the student's directions:

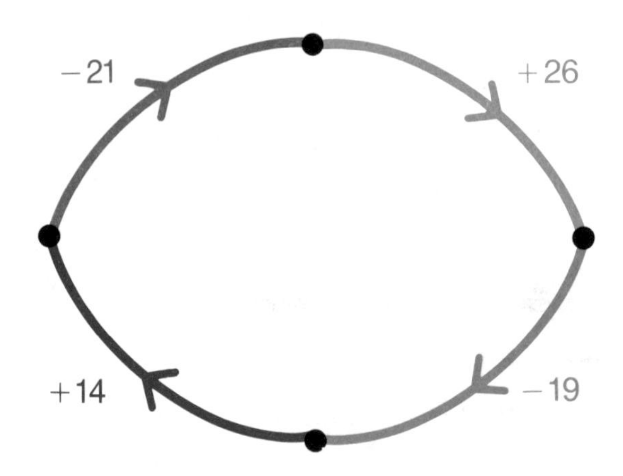

Erase what is drawn on the board and replace it with the following diagram:

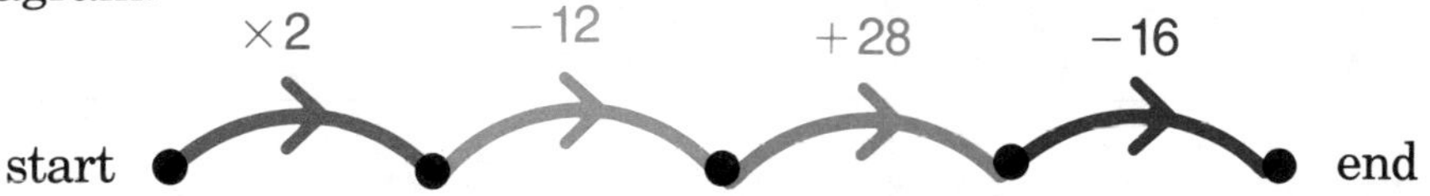

T: I want each of you to think of a secret number for the starting number. Write your number on a piece of paper but don't let me see it. Then calculate your ending number.

Wait until most of the class has done this.

T: Now, one at a time, I want you to tell me your ending number and I will say what your secret starting number is.

The given sequence of operations is equivalent to the single operation ×2. So you can immediately tell what each student's secret starting number is by taking one-half of his or her ending number. Once all the students have had their starting numbers revealed, ask the class to explain how you were able to respond so quickly. The discussion should establish the following:

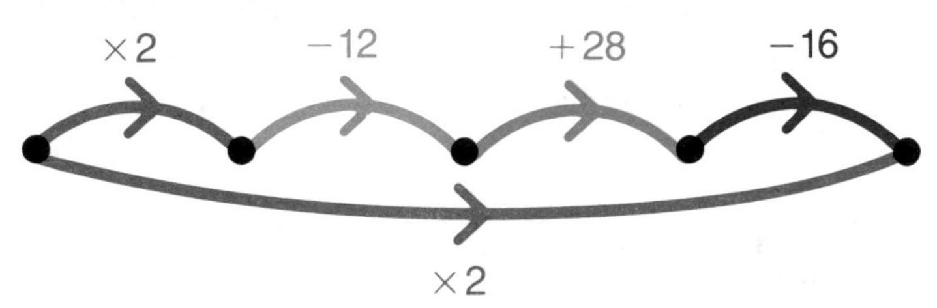

As individual or collective class exercises for the remaining class time, let students develop quick ways to find starting numbers, given ending numbers for these sequences of operations.

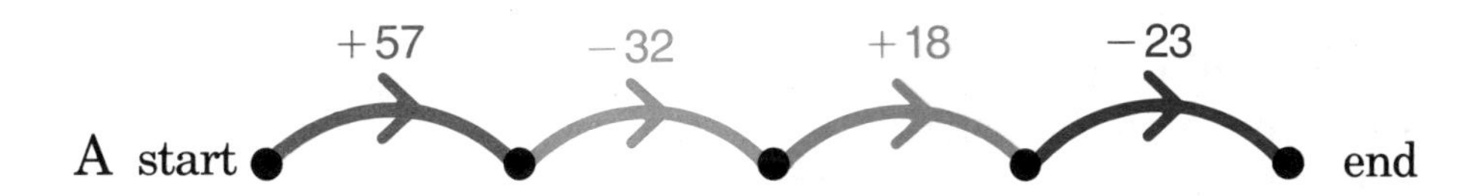

(Equivalent to +20; to find starting number, subtract 20 from ending number.)

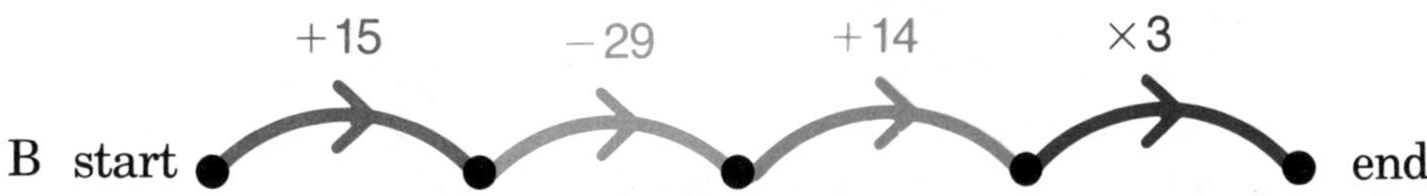

(Equivalent to ×3; to find starting number, take one-third of ending number.)

Resources Available

For out-of-class use: Any H-worksheet up through H73

ACTIVITY 53
Comparing Prices 3

Materials Needed
Teacher: Colored chalk
Students: Paper and colored pencils

Tell a story similar to the following:

T: Mark's father decided to join a health club so that he and his friend could play his favorite sport, racquetball. He can't decide between club A and club B. He likes club A because it allows non-members as well as members to use its courts. These are club A's rates.

Write them on the board as you say them.

Club A
Membership fee: $50 per year
Rates for using the courts:
for members: $7 per hour
for non-members: $10 per hour

T: But Mark's father also likes club B because it seems to charge lower rates. These are club B's rates.

Club B
Membership fee: $80 per year
Rates for using the courts:
for members: $6 per hour
(only members allowed)

T: If Mark's father wants to spend as little as possible to play his sport, at which club should he play?

S: *That's easy. Club B only charges 6 dollars an hour.*

S: *But it costs more to join club B.*

S: *First we must find out how many hours he wants to play.*

T: That's right. I didn't finish my story. Mark's father likes to play three hours each week during the 12 winter weeks of the year. Now we must find out how much this would cost at each club.

Divide the class into two groups. Give one group the task of working out Mark's father's cost at club A and the other group the task of working out the cost at club B. Let them work collectively or individually. Give hints, such as the suggestion that we must first decide how many hours Mark's father plans to use the court in a year (36), and help the group to present their findings on the board in an organized manner.

The results might be presented as follows:

Club A

Membership fee:	\$ 50
36 hours of play: $\$7 \times 36 =$	\$252
Total cost for member:	\$302

- -

Total cost for non-member:
36 hours of play: $\$10 \times 36 =$ \$360

Club B

Membership fee:	\$ 80
36 hours of play: $\$6 \times 36 =$	\$216
Total cost for member:	\$296

T: What should Mark's father decide? Remember that he has three choices: he can become a member of club A and play 36 hours, he can play 36 hours at club A as a non-member, or he can become a member of club B and play 36 hours.

S: *It's cheapest to become a member of club B and play 36 hours.*

For the remainder of the class time let the students work individually or in groups to solve the following problems.

1. Mark's father heard about a third club, club C, which requires a membership fee of only 10 dollars per year and charges 8 dollars per hour of play. If he expects to play 36 hours per year, should he play at club C rather than at club A or B?
   Answer: Club C is more expensive for members than club B but less expensive than club A: 36 hours of play cost
   $\$10 + (\$8 \times 36) = \$298$.

2. If Mark's father decides instead to play only a total of four hours per year, at which club should he play?
   Answer: Four hours of play cost:

\$40 as a non-member at club A	$\$10 \times 4 = \$40$
\$78 as a member of club A	$\$50 + (\$7 \times 4) = \$78$
\$104 at club B	$\$80 + (\$6 \times 4) = \$104$
\$42 at club C	$\$10 + (\$8 \times 4) = \$42$

   It is cheapest as a non-member at club A.

3. If Mark's father decides to play a total of 40 hours per year, at which club should he play?
   Answer: Forty hours of play cost:

\$400 as a non-member at club A	$\$10 \times 40 = \$400$
\$330 as a member at club A	$\$50 + (\$7 \times 40) = \$330$
\$320 at club B	$\$80 + (\$6 \times 40) = \$320$
\$330 at club C	$\$10 + (\$8 \times 40) = \$330$

   It is cheapest as a member of club B.

4. If Mark's father plays 30 hours per year, at which club should he play?
   Answer: Thirty hours of play cost:

\$300 as a non-member at club A	$\$10 \times 30 = \$300$
\$260 as a member at club A	$\$50 + (\$7 \times 30) = \$260$
\$260 as a member at club B	$\$80 + (\$6 \times 30) = \$260$
\$250 as a member at club C	$\$10 + (\$8 \times 30) = \$250$

   It is cheapest as a member of club C.

Resources Available

For out-of-class use: Any H-worksheet up through H75

ACTIVITY 54
Calculator Tug-of-War 2

Materials Needed
Teacher: Colored chalk
Students: One calculator each

Play several games of Calculator Tug-of-War as in Activity 19. In the third game, before declaring the winner, tell the class that instead of adding or subtracting just whole numbers they can now also add or subtract decimal numbers. Suppose the Red number is 147 and the Blue number is 148 and it is the Red team's turn.
S(Red team): *+0.1.*
Now the Red number is 147.1.
S(Blue team): *−0.5.*
Now the Blue number is 147.5.

Continue until the students cannot make any more moves. Theoretically this game should never end, but more than likely third-grade students will not be aware of this. If some are, play for a while and then call the game a draw.

For the rest of the time remaining, use the new rule and pick some noninteger starting numbers. For example:

Red	Blue
32.6	215.4
406.8	93.2
7.08	29.13

Resources Available

For out-of-class use: Any H-worksheet up through H77

ACTIVITY 55

Detective Story 2

Materials Needed

Teacher: Colored chalk, Minicomputer kit
Students: None

T: Today we have another detective story. But one of the clues deals with square numbers, so I want to begin by making sure that you all know what a square number is.

Draw the following picture on the board:

$$\square \times \square = \triangle$$

T: When we put the same whole number in each of the square boxes, the answer in the triangle will be a square number. Let's try it with the number 7.

$$\boxed{7} \times \boxed{7} = \triangle$$

T: Marilyn, would you come up here and write in the triangle the square number this gives?

$$\boxed{7} \times \boxed{7} = \triangle_{49}$$

T: Good. So 49 is a square number.

Erase the numbers from the boxes.

$$\square \times \square = \triangle$$

T: Tell me some more square numbers.

S: *100, because 100 = 10 × 10.*

S: *16, because 16 = 4 × 4.*

T: Let's record some square numbers on the board.

Draw the following string picture:

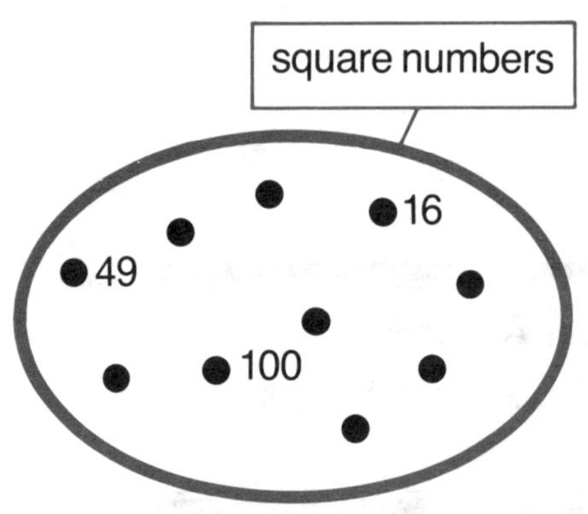

Allow the volunteers to label the additional dots.

T: Is the number 1 a square number?

S: *Yes, because* $1 = 1 \times 1$.

T: What about 0?

S: *Yes, because* $0 = 0 \times 0$.

T: Can anyone give me a square number between 60 and 90?

S: *81.*

S: *64.*

T: Greater than 150.

S: $225 = 15 \times 15$.

S: $10{,}000 = 100 \times 100$.

T: Now here's a tougher question. Can you tell me a prime number that is one more than a square number?

Write on the board: **A prime number that is one more than a square number.**

S: *The number 2 is a prime that is one more than the square number 1.*

S: *The number 5 is a prime that is one more than the square number 4.*

Others include 17, 37, and 101.

T: Now tell me a prime number that is one less than a square number.

Alter the statement on the board by replacing "more" with "less."

S: *The number 3 is one less than 4.*

S: *The number 99 is one less than 100.*

S: *Yes, but 99 isn't prime;* $99 = 3 \times 33$, *so 99 has at least four divisors (1, 3, 33, and 99) rather than exactly two.*

In fact, 3 is the only prime number that is one less than a square number.

T: Now, let's see how this information is going to help us in our detective story. There are two secret numbers called Hansel and Gretel.

Clue 1: Hansel may be shown on this Minicomputer by adding exactly one regular checker.

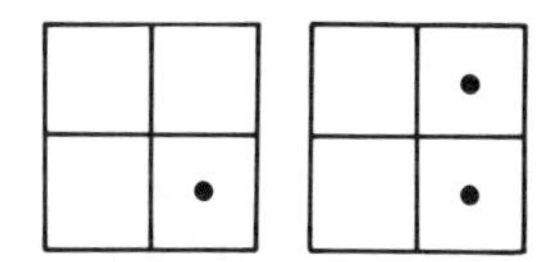

T: Tell me all the numbers Hansel could be.

S: *16, 17, 19, 23, 25, 35, 55, and 95.*

Clue 2: Gretel is a square number, and Hansel is somewhere in this arrow diagram.

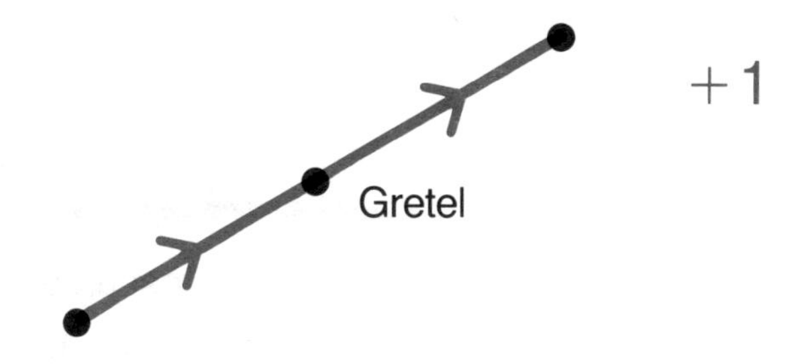

T: What numbers are left for Hansel?

S: *17 and 35.*

55

T: The third clue will help us decide. Here it is.
Clue 3:

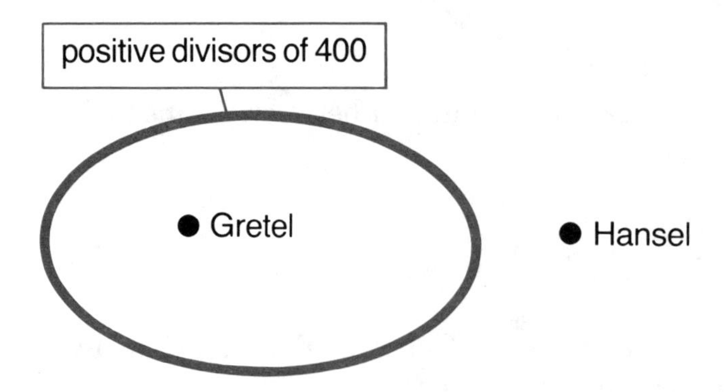

T: Who can tell me which numbers Hansel and Gretel are?
S: *Hansel is 17, and Gretel is 16.*

Resources Available

For out-of-class use: Any H-worksheet up through H78

ACTIVITY 56
Numerical String Game 2

Materials Needed
Teacher: Colored chalk, Numerical String Game kit
Students: None

Play the Numerical String Game twice using the following starting clues:

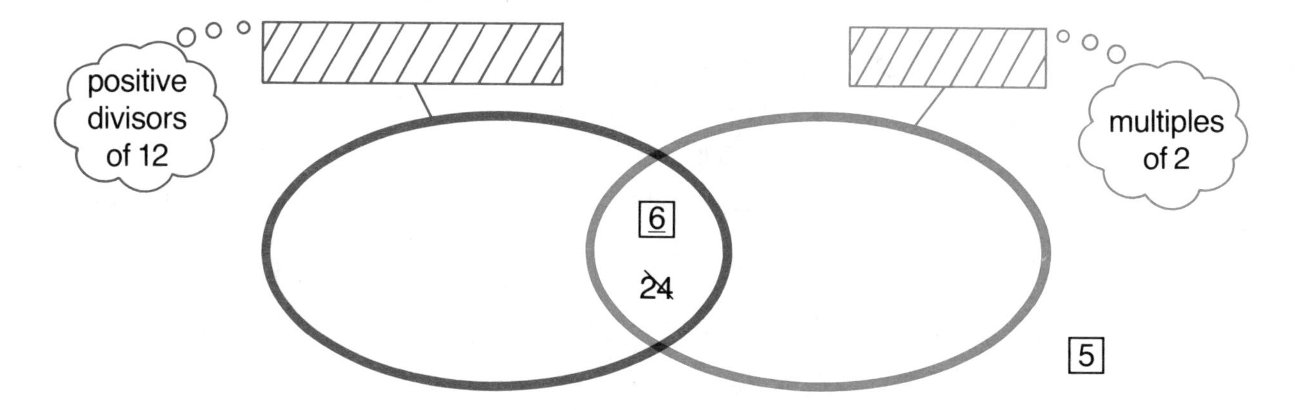

Crib sheet:

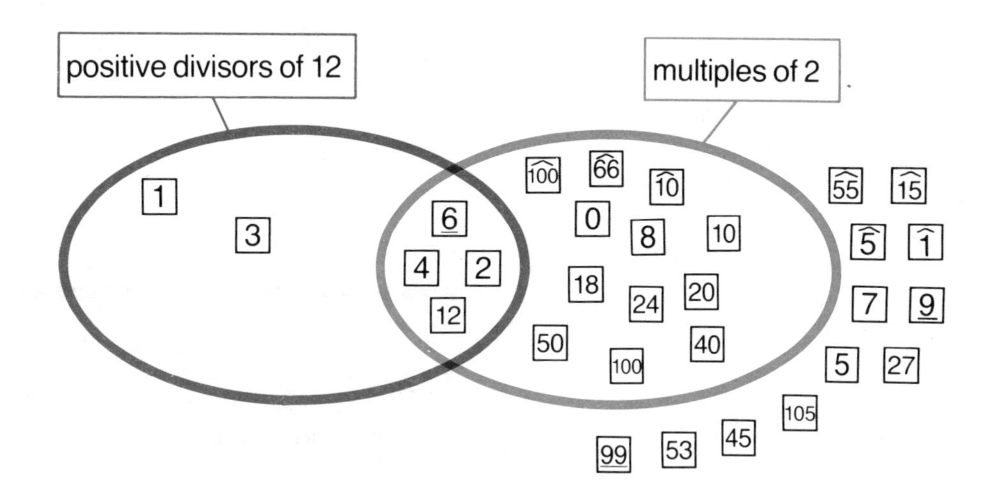

56

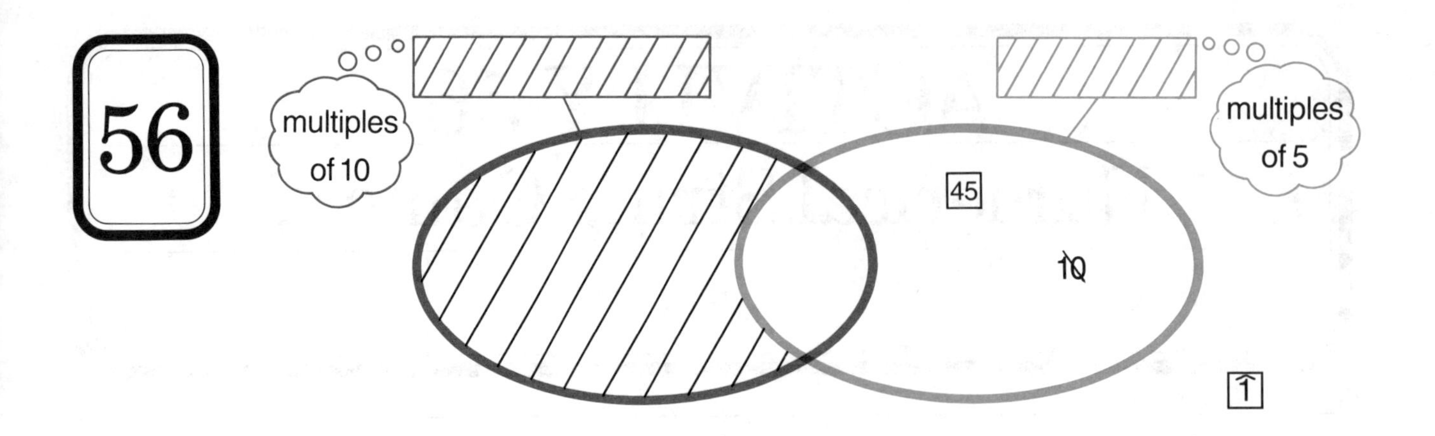

Crib sheet:

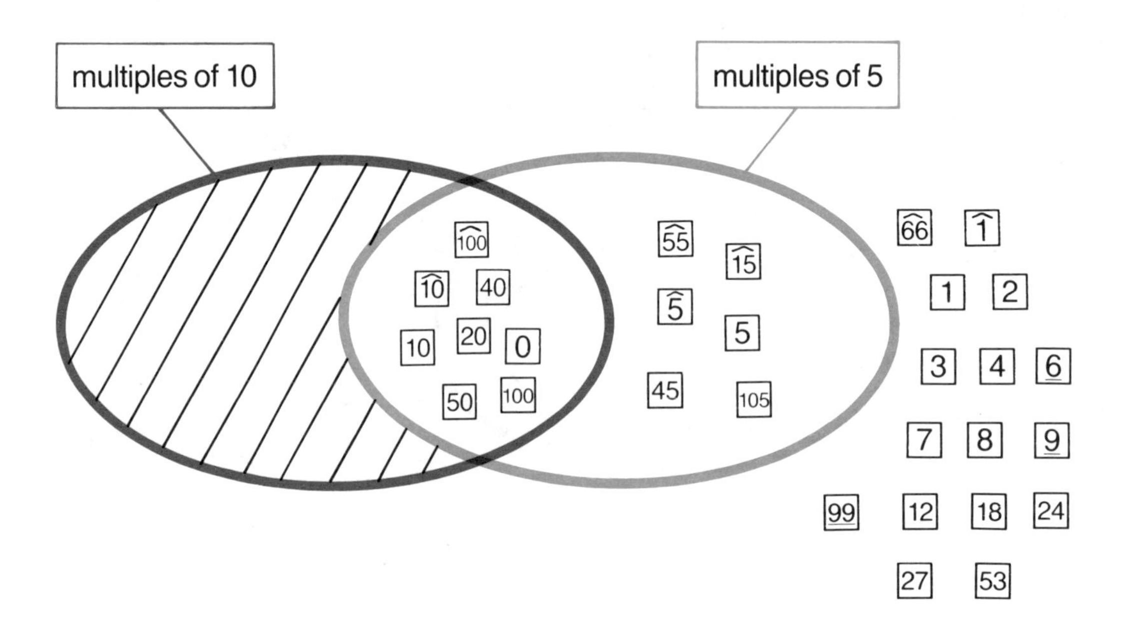

Resources Available

For class use: Worksheets L52 and L53
For out-of-class use: Any H-worksheet up through H79

ACTIVITY 57
Calculator 2

Materials Needed
Teacher: Colored chalk
Students: One calculator each, paper and colored pencils

Note to the Teacher

See Activity 24 for a note concerning our assumptions about the way your calculators work and what to do if your calculators behave differently.

Distribute calculators to your students. Draw the following diagram on the board, omitting the letters.

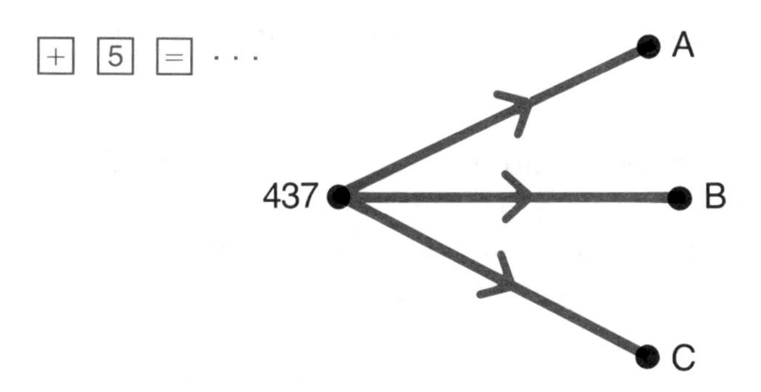

T: The arrows are for [+] [5] [=] [=] [=] ··· as many times as you like. The three dots just mean "keep on pressing [=] as many times as you like".

Point to the dot for 437 and trace along the arrow from there to dot A.

T: We start with 437 on the display and press [+] [5] [=] [=] [=] [=] and so on. What numbers could go here? You may use your calculator to help you. (Any whole number that ends in 7 or 2 and is more than 437.)

Label dot A with any correct response.

T: Press [=] a few more times and watch the numbers that appear on the display.

Point to dot B.

T: What numbers could go here?

Let several students respond. Label dot B with one of the correct responses.

Point to dot C.

T: I want a number here that is greater than 1,000.

Label dot C with any correct response.

T: What patterns did you notice in the numbers that appeared on the display?
S: *The ones' digit is always 2 or 7.*
Add another red arrow as follows:

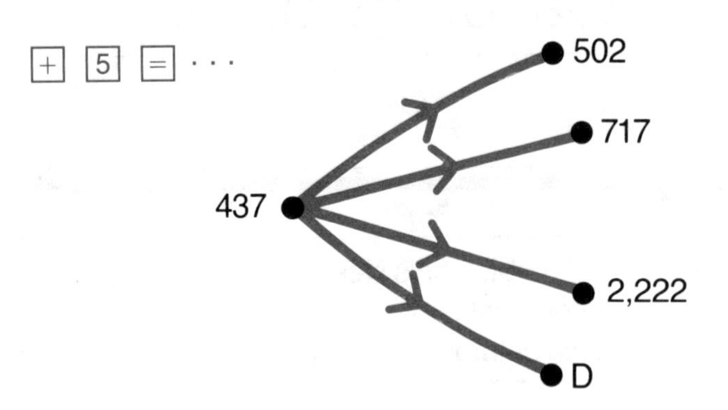

(The first three dots will almost certainly be labeled differently in your diagram.)

Challenge the students to find as close a neighbor of 1,000 as they can for dot D; that is, either the largest number less than 1,000 (997) or the smallest number greater than 1,000 (1,002).

Label dot D with one of these numbers. Then erase the labels of dots A, B, and C. Point to dot A.

T: Here I want the largest number that would appear that is less than 5,000. (4,997)

Label dot A **4,997**. Point to dot B.

T: Here I want the smallest number that is greater than 6,518. (6,522)

Label dot B **6,522**. Point to dot C.

T: And here I want the largest number that is less than 10,000. (9,997)

Label dot C **9,997**. Add the following arrows to your picture:

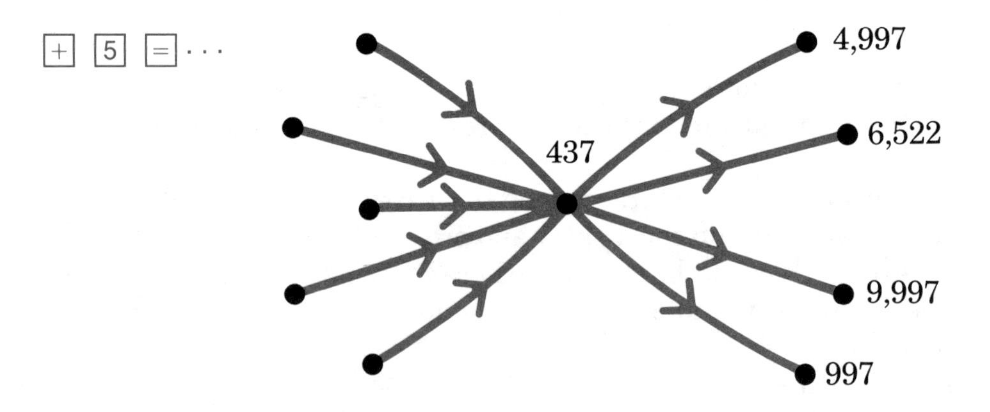

T: What are some numbers that these dots could be for?
(Any whole number less than 437 with a ones' digit of 2 or 7, or any negative number with a ones' digit of 3 or 8.)
Let the students make suggestions. As correct answers are given, choose two of them and label the first two dots. Then ask for the smallest number greater than 0 that could be in the picture (2), and label the third dot **2**. Finally, ask for some negative numbers and label the last two dots.

In the time remaining, ask the students to draw their own [+] [5] [=] · · · pictures. Have them each draw a dot on their paper, label it with whatever number they like, draw several arrows beginning at the dot and several more ending at the dot, and then label all the dots they have drawn. Encourage them to be creative with their designs and to be sure to include some negative numbers. The most interesting pictures could be put on display in your classroom.

Resources Available

For out-of-class use: Any H-worksheet up through H80

ACTIVITY 58
Calculator 3

Materials Needed
Teacher: Colored chalk
Students: One calculator each, paper and colored pencils

Distribute calculators to the students. Draw the following picture on the board (omitting the letters), and ask the students to copy it onto their papers.

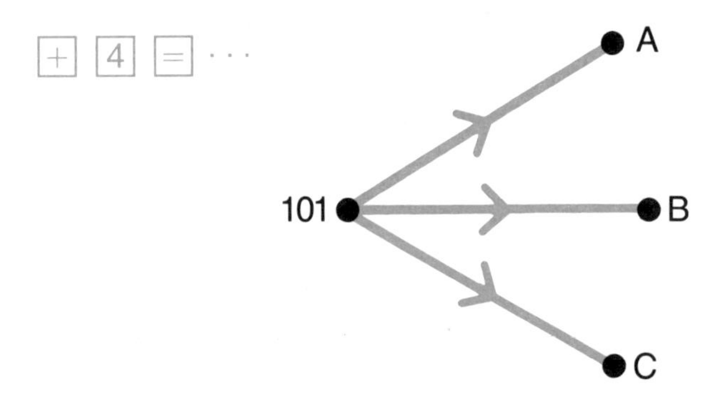

T: The arrows are for [+] [4] [=] [=] [=] . . .
Point to the arrow from the dot for 101 to dot A.
T: This means put 101 on your display, press [+] [4] [=], and then the three dots tell us to go on pressing [=] as often as we like.
Point to dot A.
T: This dot is for the closest neighbor to 200 that we can get with these arrows. What is this number? (201)
Label dot A **201**.
T: How many times did you have to press [=] to reach 201?
S: *Twenty-five times.*
T: Could 301 be in this arrow picture?
S: *Yes; just press [=] 25 more times.*
Point to dot B.
T: This dot is for the largest possible number that is less than 1,000.
S: *That means it's for 997.*
Label dot B **997**. Point to dot C.
T: This dot is for the smallest number that could appear on the display and be greater than 1,000,000. What number is it?
S: *1,000,001.*
Label dot C **1,000,001**. Extend the arrow picture on the board as follows:

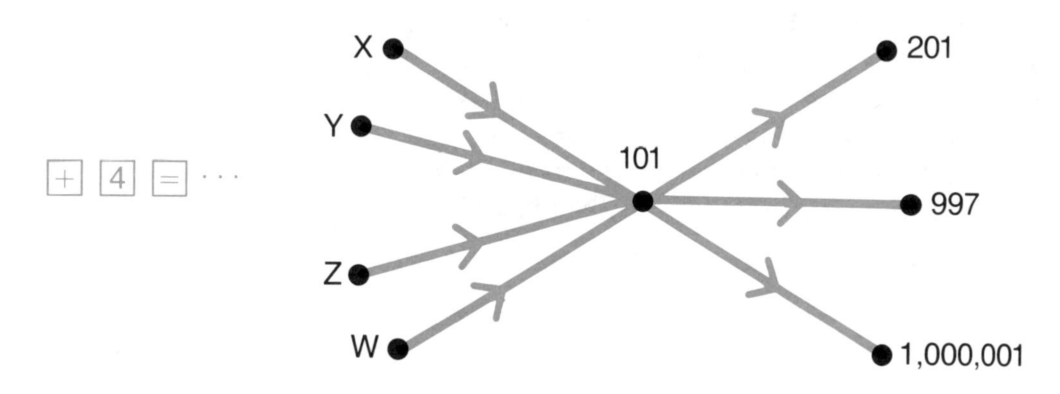

Point to dot X.

T: What number could be here?

Let several students answer, then label dots X and Y with two of the correct answers. Point to dot Z.

T: Label this dot with the smallest possible whole number. Try to do it without using your calculator.

Let a student label dot Z **1** and explain how he or she obtained the answer without using a calculator. Point to dot W.

T: Here I want the largest number that is smaller than 12.

Let a student who gives the correct answer (9) label the dot appropriately. Erase what is drawn on the board and replace it with the first clue below as you explain:

T: Now I think we just have time for a detective story. Here's the first clue.

Clue 1:

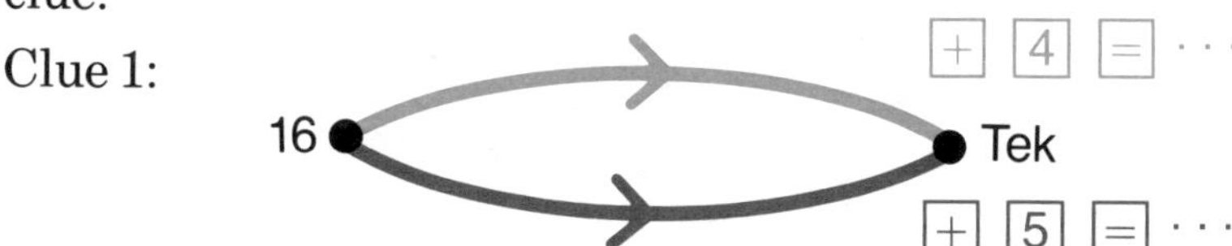

T: This arrow picture tells us that if we put **16** on the display and press [+] [4] [=] · · · and keep on pressing [=] as often as we wish, then Tek will be one of the numbers that will appear. Also, if we put **16** on the display and press [+] [5] [=] · · · , then Tek is one of the numbers that will appear. What are some of the number Tek could be?

Have the students work in pairs. Each student should put **16** on the display, and then while one presses [+] [4] [=] · · · the other presses [+] [5] [=] · · · .

Encourage them to record the possibilities for Tek. (36, 56, 76, 96, 116, . . .) They should observe that the numbers go up in twenties from 16.

Clue 2:

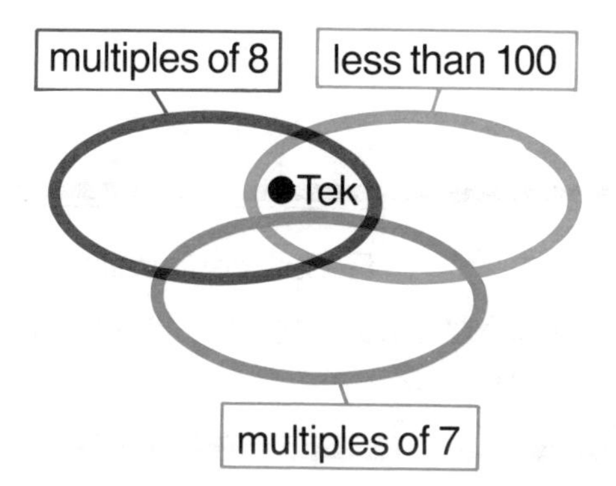

T: What does the blue string tell us about Tek?
S: *Tek is less than 100. So Tek is 36, 56, 76, or 96.*
T: What does the red string tell us about Tek?
S: *Tek is a multiple of 8. So Tek is 56 or 96.*
T: What does the green string tell us about Tek?
S: *Tek is not a multiple of 7. So Tek must be 96.*

Resources Available

For out-of-class use: Any H-worksheet up through H82

ACTIVITY 59

Comparing Prices 4

Materials Needed
Teacher: Colored chalk
Students: Paper and colored pencils

Tell a story similar to the following:

T: A certain movie theater sells passes to its shows. You can buy a three-movie pass for $8.00 and a seven-movie pass for $17.50. Each time you go to a movie at this theater your pass card is punched so that they'll know how many more times you can use it.

Write the following information on the board:

3 movies for $8.00
7 movies for $17.50

T: Which pass would you buy?

Let the students discuss this question. From their experience in earlier lessons on comparing prices, they might suggest finding the cost of the same number of movies at the two prices. If not, suggest it yourself. Any common multiple of 3 and 7 will be acceptable in the class discussion. Suppose that a student suggests finding the cost of 21 movies at each price.

T: How many three-movie passes would we have to buy in order to see 21 movies?

S: *Seven, because* $7 \times 3 = 21$.

Draw this diagram on the board:

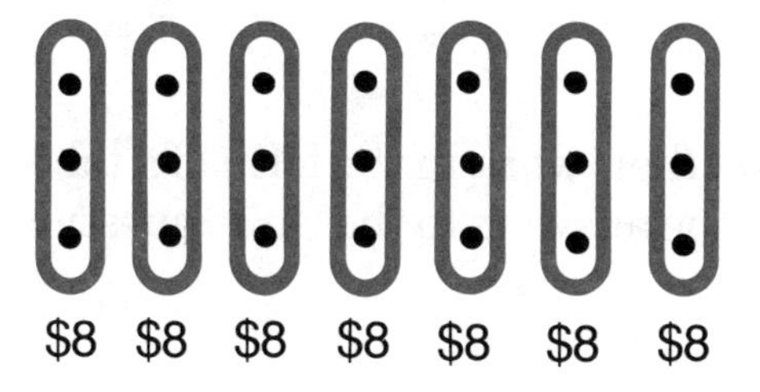

T: Each three-movie pass costs 8 dollars. How much would it cost to buy enough three-movie passes to see 21 movies?

S: *56 dollars, because* $7 \times 8 = 56$.

Add this result to the information written on the board:

3 movies for $8.00   21 movies for $56.00
7 movies for $17.50

T: How many seven-movie passes would we have to buy in order to see 21 movies?

S: *Three, because* $3 \times 7 = 21$.

59

Modify your diagram on the board as follows:

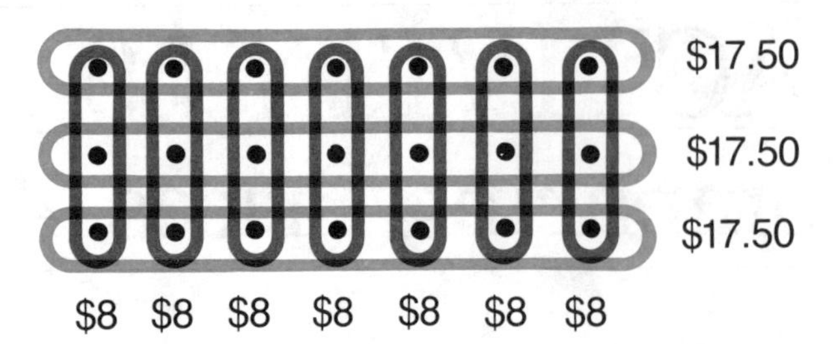

T: How much would it cost to buy enough seven-movie passes to see 21 movies?

Give students sufficient time to carry out the necessary calculation. Some may need help with it.

S: *I've got it. It would cost $52.50, because $3 \times 17.50 = (3 \times 17) + (3 \times 50¢) = 51 + 1.50$.*

Add this result to the information written on the board:

3 movies for $8.00	21 movies for $56.00
7 movies for $17.50	21 movies for $52.50

S: *We would save $3.50 by buying seven-movie passes.*

T: So which kind of passes should we buy?

S: *The seven-movie passes.*

S: If *we wanted to see 21 movies.*

T: Would we ever buy three-movie passes?

S: *Yes, if we wanted to see only three movies.*

T: What would be the lowest cost to see 13 movies?

S: *Buy two three-movie passes and one seven-movie pass.*

T: Are you sure that's cheaper than two seven-movie passes?

S: *Yes, because two seven-movie passes cost $35.00, but two three-movie passes and a seven-movie pass cost $16.00 + $17.50 = $33.50.*

For the remainder of the time available, let the students work individually or in groups on determining the lowest costs of buying passes in order to see:

1. 17 movies
2. 30 movies
3. 48 movies

Encourage the students to organize their work in the form of a table such as the one that follows, displaying the answers to the three questions.

Number of Movies	Number of Three-movie Passes	Number of Seven-movie Passes	Cost	Calculations
17	1	2	\$43.00	$8 + (2 \times 17.50) = 43$
30	3	3	\$76.50	$(3 \times 8) + (3 \times 17.50)$ $= 76.50$
	10	0	\$80.00	$10 \times 8 = 80$
48	2	6	\$121.00	$(2 \times 8) + (6 \times 17.50)$ $= 121.00$
	9	3	\$124.50	$(9 \times 8) + (3 \times 17.50)$ $= 124.50$
	16	0	\$128.00	$16 \times 8 = 128$

Resources Available

For out-of-class use: Any H-worksheet up through H84

ACTIVITY 60
Calculator 4

Materials Needed
Teacher: Colored chalk
Students: Colored pencils, one calculator each

Distribute the calculators to the students. Draw the following on the board:

T: Who can tell me some one-digit numbers?
S: *0, 1, 2, 3, 4, 5, 6, 7, 8, and 9.*
T: We're going to build a one-digit road from 7 to 100. Each arrow in a one-digit road must be plus, minus, multiplied by, or divided by some one-digit number. We'll try to make the road as short as we can. Who would like to start?
S: *+8.*
Draw a +8 arrow and ask the student to label the dot. Explain that these calculations should be carried out mentally whenever possible. The calculators have been provided so that the overall goal of building the arrow road need not be held up while the more difficult calculations are done with pencil and paper.

S: *Now do +7.*
Continue the road on the board. Use the same color for the arrow. Label it and ask the student to label the dot.

S: *+50.*
T: But 50 is not a one-digit number.
S: *+3.*

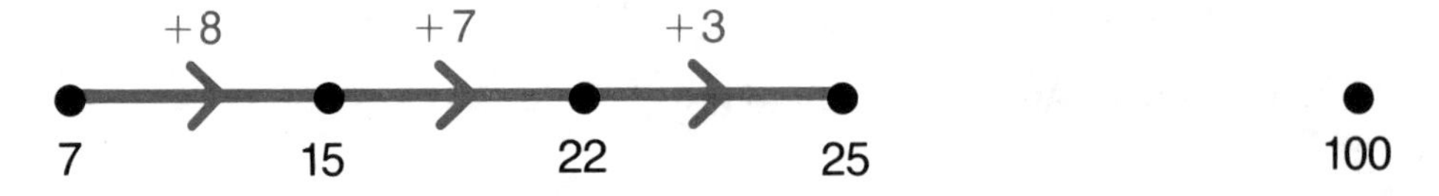

S: *×4, and we've gotten to 100.*

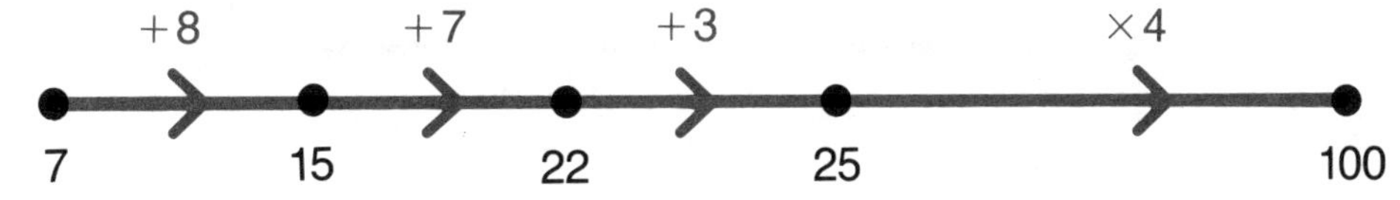

T: This road has four arrows. Can anyone make a one-digit road from 7 to 100 that has fewer than four arrows?

Have the students work individually on this problem. Let a few of those who solve it draw their solutions on the board. The smallest possible number of arrows is three, although there are several one-digit roads from 7 to 100 with three arrows. Here is one of them:

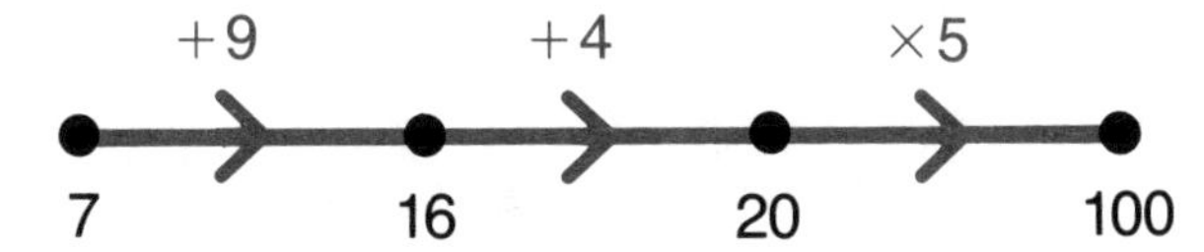

Now ask the students to work individually on the following roads. Challenge them to find roads that are as short as possible. You could organize it as a contest: As soon as a student has found a road, let the class know how many arrows it contains and ask whether anyone has found a shorter one. Those who find shortest roads are winners. Ask one or two students with shortest roads to draw them on the board.

(In each case below we include a shortest road for your information. In some instances other shortest roads—of the same length as the one shown—are also possible.)

1. From 1 to 250.

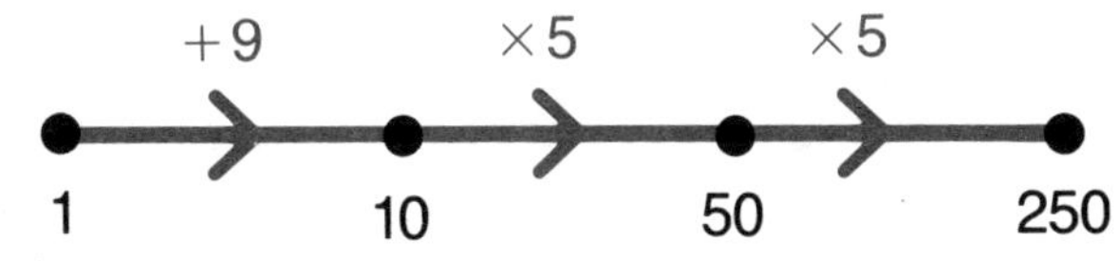

2. From 250 to 1.

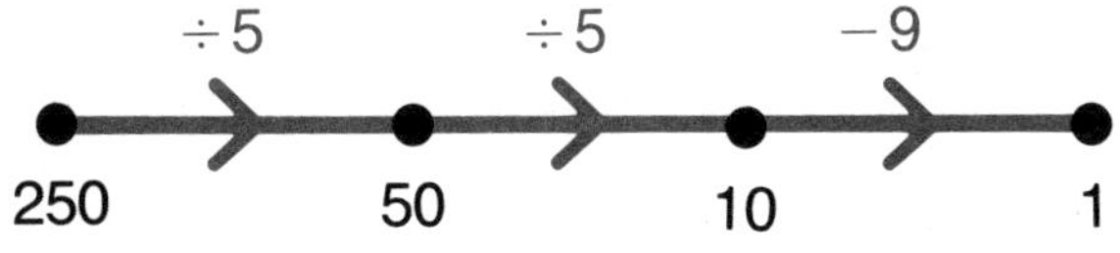

3. From 17 to 400.

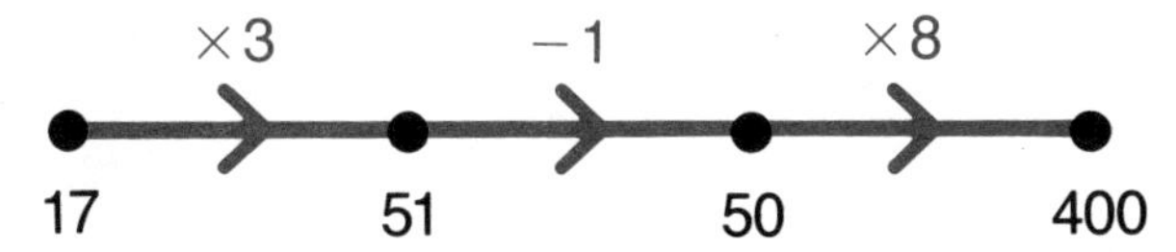

4. From $\widehat{4}$ to 18.

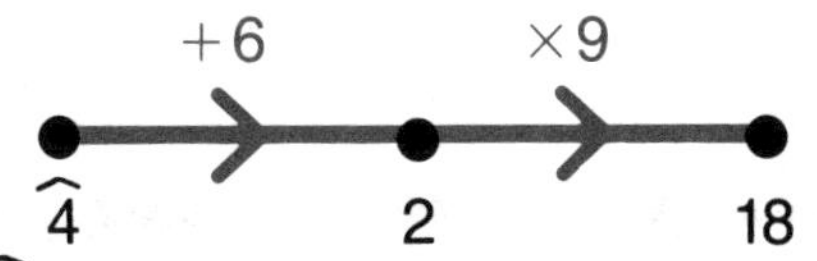

5. From 37 to $\widehat{6}$.

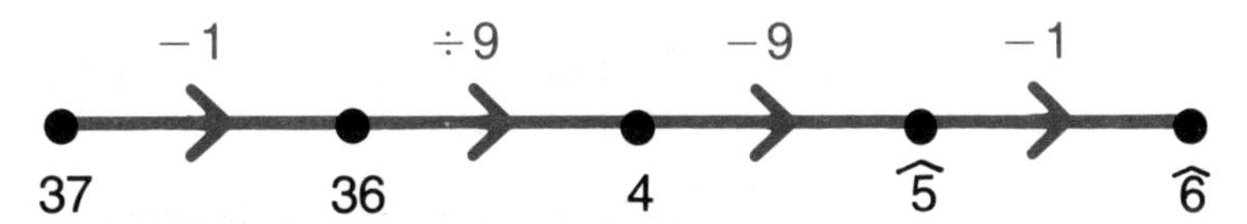

60

6. From 1.5 to 80.

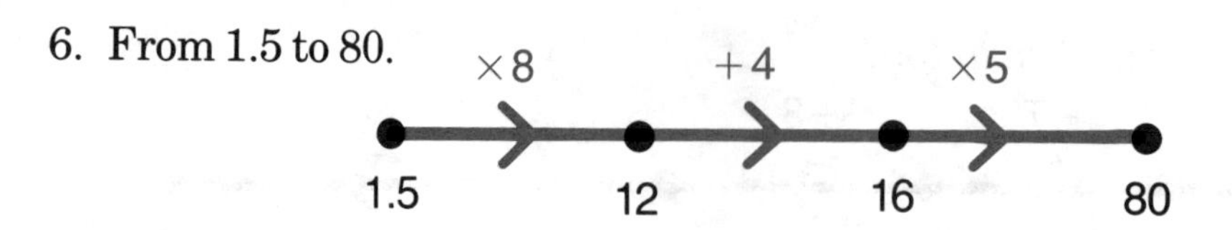

Resources Available

For out-of-class use: Any H-worksheet up through H84

ACTIVITY 61

String Game Analysis 1

Materials Needed

Teacher: Colored chalk, Numerical String Game kit

Students: Numerical String Game Analysis Sheets (a supply of these is at the back of the workbook), colored pencils

Before the lesson begins, set up your board for the String Game as shown below. The bubbles show what is written on the face-down string cards. Tape Numerical String Game Poster 2 on the board. Head the first two columns "Red" and "Blue," as shown below.

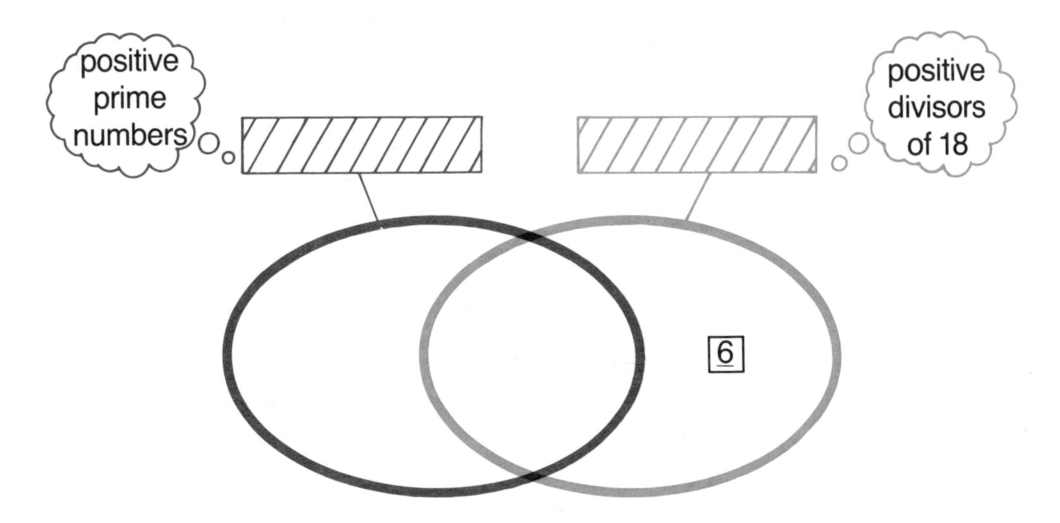

	Red	Blue	
MULTIPLES OF 2			
MULTIPLES OF 3			
MULTIPLES OF 4			
MULTIPLES OF 5			
MULTIPLES OF 10			
ODD NUMBERS			
POSITIVE PRIME NUMBERS			
GREATER THAN 50			
LESS THAN 50			
GREATER THAN $\widehat{10}$			
LESS THAN $\widehat{10}$			
POSITIVE DIVISORS OF 12			
POSITIVE DIVISORS OF 18			
POSITIVE DIVISORS OF 20			
POSITIVE DIVISORS OF 24			
POSITIVE DIVISORS OF 27			

T: Today we're going to learn how to become better at the String Game. Playing the String Game is a bit like solving a detective story. The aim of the game is to find out what the tags of the red and blue strings are, and each piece that is played is a clue. Let's see if we can learn how to analyze the clues to help us find the tags after just a few pieces have been correctly placed.

Direct the attention of the class to the board. In particular, point to the list of possible string labels on the left of Poster 2.

T: Here is a list of all the possible string labels. In this column (point to the column headed "Red") we're going to keep track of what the red tag could be, and in this column (point to the one headed "Blue") we're going to keep track of what the blue tag could be.

Our first clue is that 6 belongs here (point to the 6-card), inside the blue string but outside the red string. What does this clue tell us about the strings?

S*: *The blue string could be for the multiples of 2 or the multiples of 3.*

T: That's correct. But it would be more helpful to say what the blue string *cannot* be for, because 6 is here.

S: *The blue string cannot be for the multiples of 4.*

T: Why not?

S: *Because 6 is in the blue string and 6 is not a multiple of 4.*

Mark a blue cross in the Blue column of Poster 2.

	Red	Blue	
MULTIPLES OF 2			
MULTIPLES OF 3			
MULTIPLES OF 4		X	
MULTIPLES OF 5			
MULTIPLES OF 10			
ODD NUMBERS			
POSITIVE PRIME NUMBERS			
GREATER THAN 50			
LESS THAN 50			
GREATER THAN 10			
LESS THAN 10			
POSITIVE DIVISORS OF 12			
POSITIVE DIVISORS OF 18			
POSITIVE DIVISORS OF 20			
POSITIVE DIVISORS OF 24			
POSITIVE DIVISORS OF 27			

Let the students eliminate as many possibilities for the blue string as they can. Do not mark a blue cross in the Blue column next to a possible label until an adequate explanation has been given. For example:

S: *The blue string cannot be for the positive divisors of 20, because 6 is not a positive divisor of 20.*

Here is what your poster should look like after all possible information about the blue string has been drawn from this clue.

61

	Red	Blue	
MULTIPLES OF 2			
MULTIPLES OF 3			
MULTIPLES OF 4		X	
MULTIPLES OF 5		X	
MULTIPLES OF 10		X	
ODD NUMBERS		X	
POSITIVE PRIME NUMBERS		X	
GREATER THAN 50		X	
LESS THAN 50			
GREATER THAN 10			
LESS THAN 10		X	
POSITIVE DIVISORS OF 12			
POSITIVE DIVISORS OF 18			
POSITIVE DIVISORS OF 20		X	
POSITIVE DIVISORS OF 24			
POSITIVE DIVISORS OF 27		X	

Distribute Analysis Sheets to the students, and ask them to copy the results obtained so far onto their own sheets. Also ask them to keep track on their analysis sheets as the analysis develops during the rest of the activity.

T: Now let's think about the red string. Is there any number that the red string cannot be for because 6 is here? (point to the 6-card)

S: *No; 6 is in the blue string only, so it doesn't tell us anything about the red string.*

S: *But the red string cannot be for the multiples of 2, so it's not true that we can't say anything about the red string.*

T: Why can't the red string be for the multiples of 2?

S: *Because if it were, 6 would have to be in the red string, because 6 is a multiple of 2. But 6 isn't in the red string, so the red string can't be for the multiples of 2.*

T: That's very good thinking.

Repeat the explanation slowly so that everyone has a chance to follow it. This is a higher level of reasoning and is very important for the proper analysis of String Game clues, so the more time you take now to emphasize this type of argument the easier it will be for your students to make their own correct analyses in the future.

T: What other possibilities can we cross off the Red list? Be sure to explain your answers.

S: *The red string cannot be for the multiples of 3, because 6 is a multiple of 3 and it's not in the red string.*

As each correct suggestion is made and verified, mark a red cross in the appropriate part of the Red column on Poster 2.

S: *The red string cannot be for the positive divisors of 12, because 6 is a positive divisor of 12 and it's not in the red string.*

S: *I think I see a pattern. Everything that's not crossed off the Blue list can be crossed off the Red list. The reason is that every number that's a possibility for the blue string because 6 is in it is not a possibility for the red string, because 6 is not in it.*

T: That's excellent reasoning!

Once again, take the time to make sure that this argument is understood

by everyone. To avoid students' making use of this generalization incorrectly at a later stage, make sure the class appreciates the fact that it may be applied only in the case of a clue that is in one string but not in the other.

Cross off all the other possibilities from the Red list that result from this observation. Your poster should now look like the one below.

T: Are there any more labels we can cross off either list?
S: *No.*
T: I think you're right. How many labels were there altogether at the beginning?
S: *There were 32: 16 possibilities for each string.*

	Red	Blue	
MULTIPLES OF 2	X		
MULTIPLES OF 3	X		
MULTIPLES OF 4		X	
MULTIPLES OF 5		X	
MULTIPLES OF 10		X	
ODD NUMBERS		X	
POSITIVE PRIME NUMBERS		X	
GREATER THAN 50		X	
LESS THAN 50	X		
GREATER THAN 10	X		
LESS THAN 10		X	
POSITIVE DIVISORS OF 12	X		
POSITIVE DIVISORS OF 18	X		
POSITIVE DIVISORS OF 20		X	
POSITIVE DIVISORS OF 24	X		
POSITIVE DIVISORS OF 27		X	

T: And how many have we crossed off?
S: *16.*
T: So this one clue allowed us to get rid of half the possibilities. Not bad! Now I'll give you a second clue and you can tell me about some more crossing-off we can do. Use your analysis sheets and cross off what you can as a result of this clue.

Place the 10-card as follows on the board:

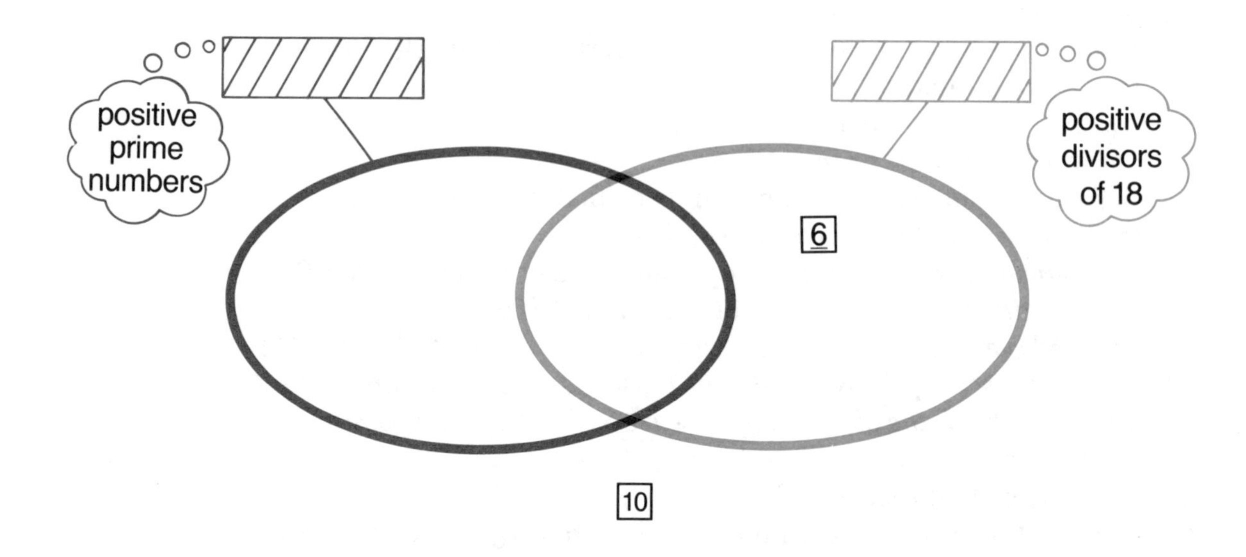

Walk around the room and check several students' analysis sheets before calling on a student with correct answers to announce what can be deduced from this clue.

Point to the 10-card.

T: What can we cross off the Red list because 10 is here?

S: *"Multiples of 10," because, if the red string were for the multiples of 10, 10 would have to be in the red string, and it's not.*

S: *"Positive divisors of 20," for the same reason.*

S: *That's all we can cross off the Red list. But we can cross "Greater than $\widehat{10}$" off the Blue list, because 10 is greater than $\widehat{10}$ and 10 is not in the blue string.*

S: *Cross "Less than 50" off the Blue list, for the same reason.*

S: *Now we've got them all. We need another clue.*

Your poster should now look like this:

	Red	Blue	
MULTIPLES OF 2	X		
MULTIPLES OF 3	X		
MULTIPLES OF 4		X	
MULTIPLES OF 5		X	
MULTIPLES OF 10	X	X	
ODD NUMBERS		X	
POSITIVE PRIME NUMBERS		X	
GREATER THAN 50		X	
LESS THAN 50	X	X	
GREATER THAN $\widehat{10}$	X	X	
LESS THAN $\widehat{10}$		X	
POSITIVE DIVISORS OF 12	X		
POSITIVE DIVISORS OF 18	X		
POSITIVE DIVISORS OF 20	X	X	
POSITIVE DIVISORS OF 24	X		
POSITIVE DIVISORS OF 27		X	

T: Here's the next clue. What new information do we get from it? Use your analysis sheets.

Place the 9-card as follows on the board:

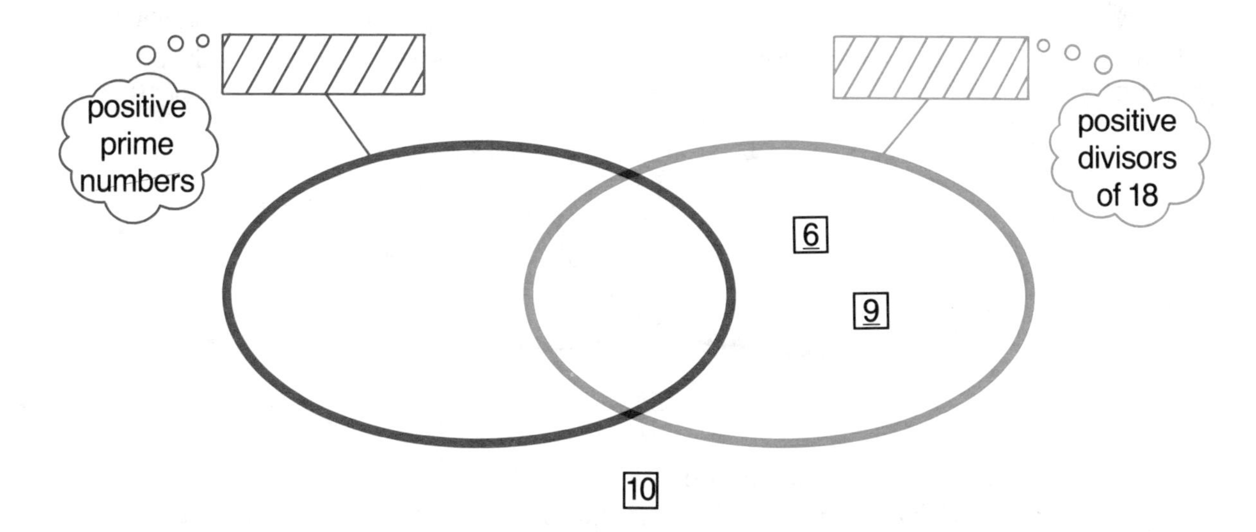

S: *Now we can cross "Multiples of 2," "Positive divisors of 12," and "Positive divisors of 24" off the Blue list, because 9 is none of these things and 9 is in the blue string.*
S: *Cross "Positive divisors of 27" and "Odd numbers" off the Red list, because 9 is both of these but 9 is not in the red string.*
S: *That's all that can be crossed off. We need at least one more clue.*
Your poster should now look like this:

	Red	Blue	
MULTIPLES OF 2	X	X	
MULTIPLES OF 3	X		
MULTIPLES OF 4		X	
MULTIPLES OF 5		X	
MULTIPLES OF 10	X	X	
ODD NUMBERS	X	X	
POSITIVE PRIME NUMBERS		X	
GREATER THAN 50		X	
LESS THAN 50	X	X	
GREATER THAN 10	X	X	
LESS THAN 10		X	
POSITIVE DIVISORS OF 12	X	X	
POSITIVE DIVISORS OF 18	X		
POSITIVE DIVISORS OF 20	X	X	
POSITIVE DIVISORS OF 24	X	X	
POSITIVE DIVISORS OF 27	X	X	

T: This will be the fourth clue. Do you think we'll know both strings after we analyze it?
S: *Probably not the red string, but most likely the blue string.*
T: Use your analysis sheets and cross off what you can. If you know what either string is for, draw a big check mark in the correct place of that string's column on your analysis sheet.
Place the 2-card as shown here:

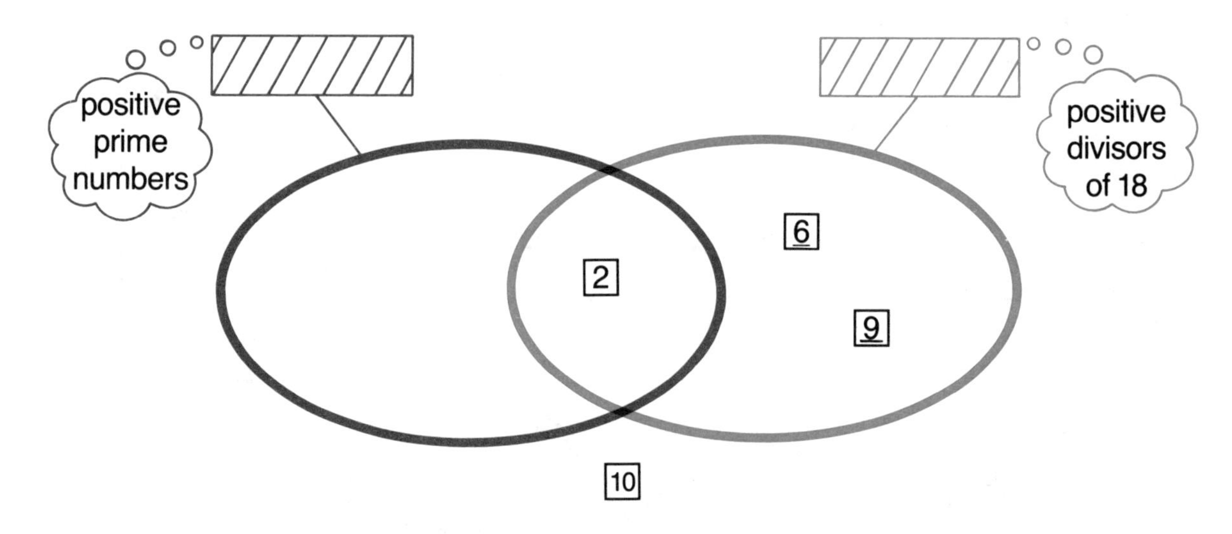

T: What can we cross off now?
S: *"Multiples of 3" from the Blue list. The blue string must be for the positive divisors of 18.*

Reveal the string card for the blue string, and verify that it does indeed read "Positive divisors of 18."

S: *But 2 is also in the red string, so the red string has to be for the positive prime numbers.*

T: How can you be so sure?

S: *Well, 2 is not a multiple of 4 or 5, and 2 is not greater than 50, and it's not less than 10. So because the red string contains 2, the only thing left for the red string is for it to be for the positive prime numbers.*

Reveal the string card for the red string.

T: So we were able to find out what both strings are with the help of this last clue. Notice that we needed only four clues this time before we could work out both strings. Very often in the String Game it's possible to work out what the strings are for after only a small number of pieces have been placed correctly. It all depends on whether you can concentrate hard enough and analyze the clues. If you can, then you'll become a very good player!

Resources Available

For out-of-class use: Any H-worksheet up through H84

ACTIVITY 62

Numerical String Game 5

Materials Needed

Teacher: Colored chalk, Numerical String Game kit

Students: Numerical String Game Analysis Sheets, colored pencils

Play the Numerical String Game twice, using the starting clues given below. Encourage the students to use their analysis sheets to analyze the game as they play. In the early stages of each game be sure to provide sufficient time between plays for this analysis to be carried out.

When a number is placed incorrectly, remember to write that number in the region where it was placed and then draw a cross through it.

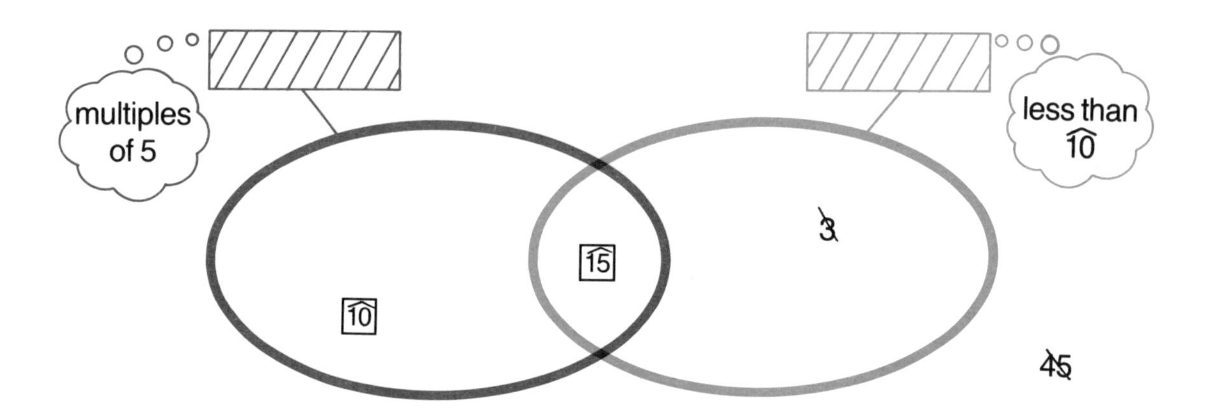

Crib sheet:

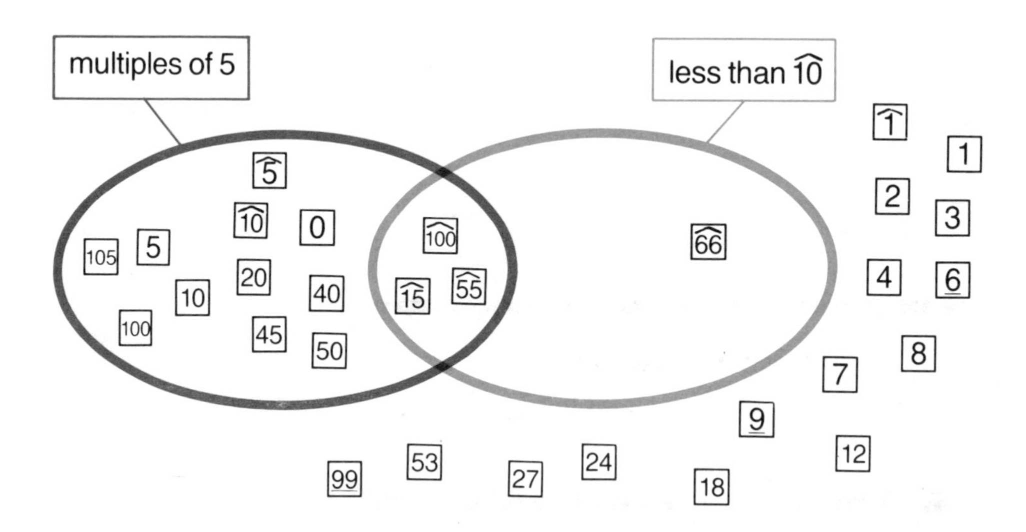

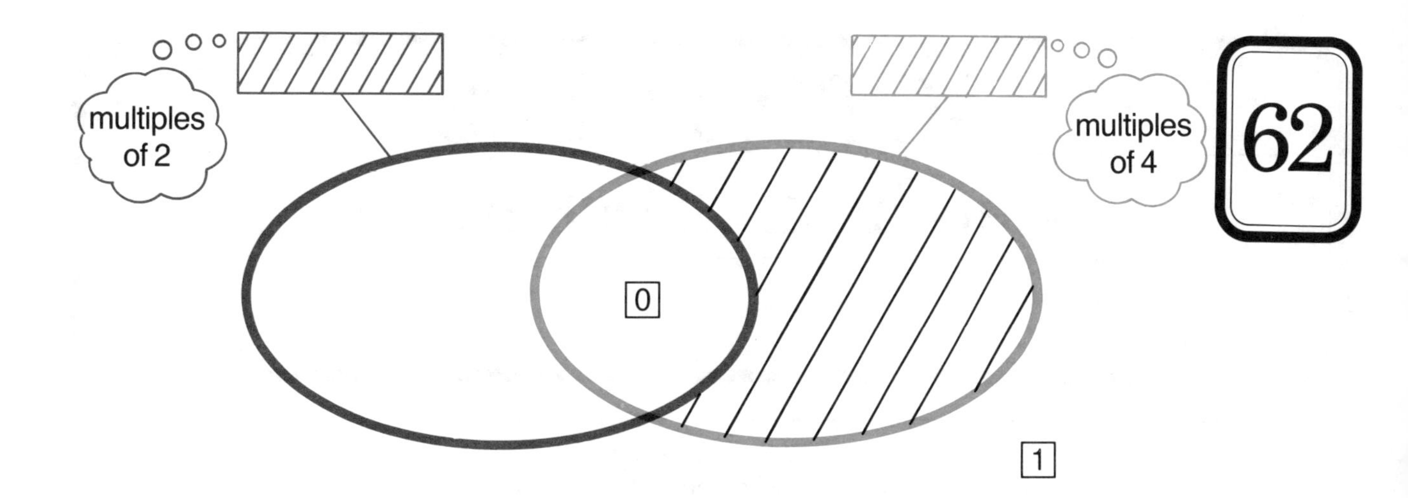

Crib sheet:

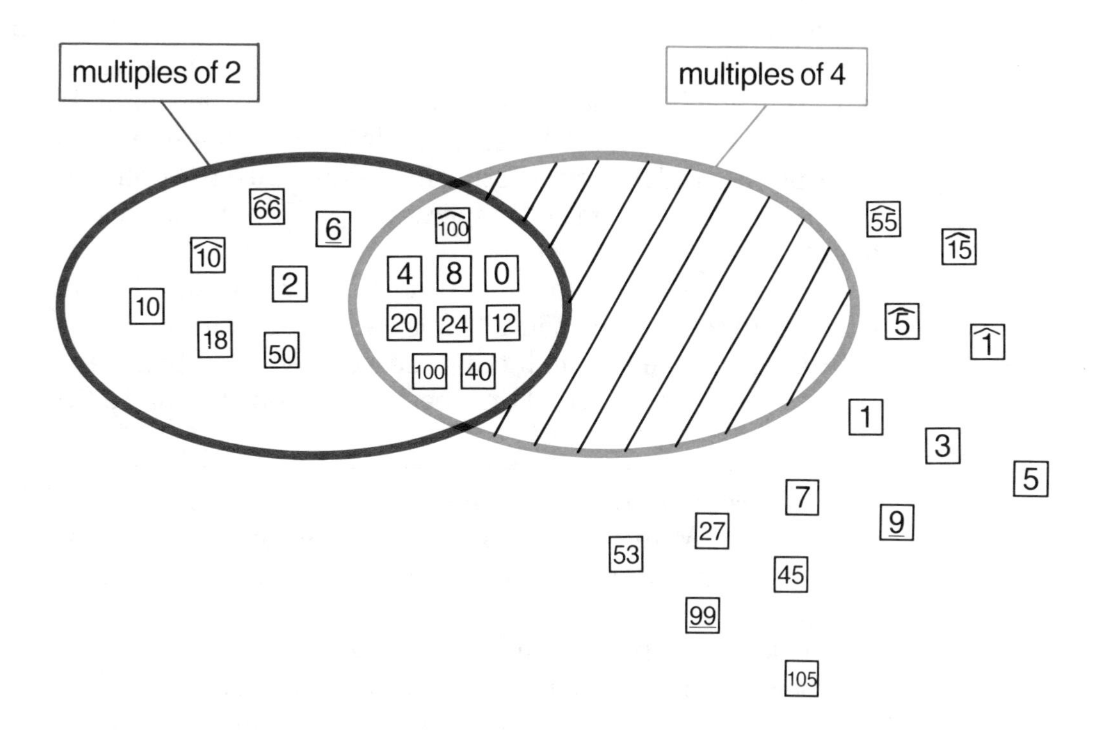

Resources Available

For out-of-class use: Any H-worksheet up through H86

ACTIVITY 63

Weighted Checkers 3

Materials Needed
Teacher: Minicomputer kit, chalk
Students: Paper and pencils

Note to the Teacher

You may wish to conduct this exercise as a game between two teams. If so, begin by dividing the class into two teams. Alternate between the teams in calling on students to come to the board and solve the problem. If the solution is correct, award the player's team one point. If the solution is incorrect, call on someone from the other team to solve the same problem. Continue alternating teams until the problem is solved. The player who is eventually successful earns one point for his or her team.

If you choose not to play the exercise as a game, simply call on students to come to the board to answer the questions.

In either method of conducting the exercise, you should avoid calling on a student for the second time before everyone has had a first opportunity.

Display a complete set of weighted checkers on the board, and also display three Minicomputer boards. After each problem is solved in the following exercise, change the configuration of checkers ready for the next problem.

T: Look at the Minicomputer. The checkers that are there don't make the number written beside the Minicomputer. That's because a joker has taken away exactly one weighted checker. Your job is to put it back.

(1) $= 100$

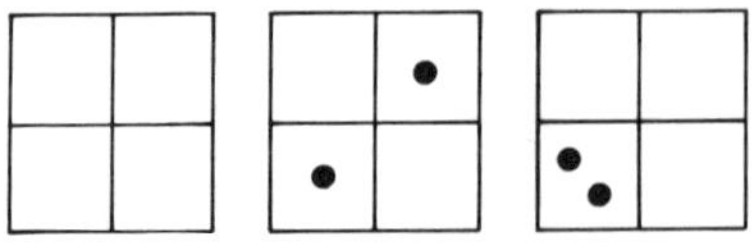

(Put ⑨ on the 4-square.)

(2) $= 200$

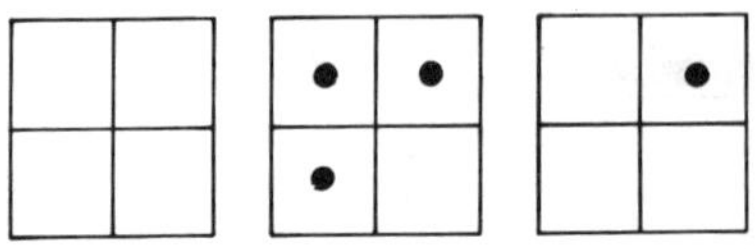

(Put ⑦ on the 8-square.)

63

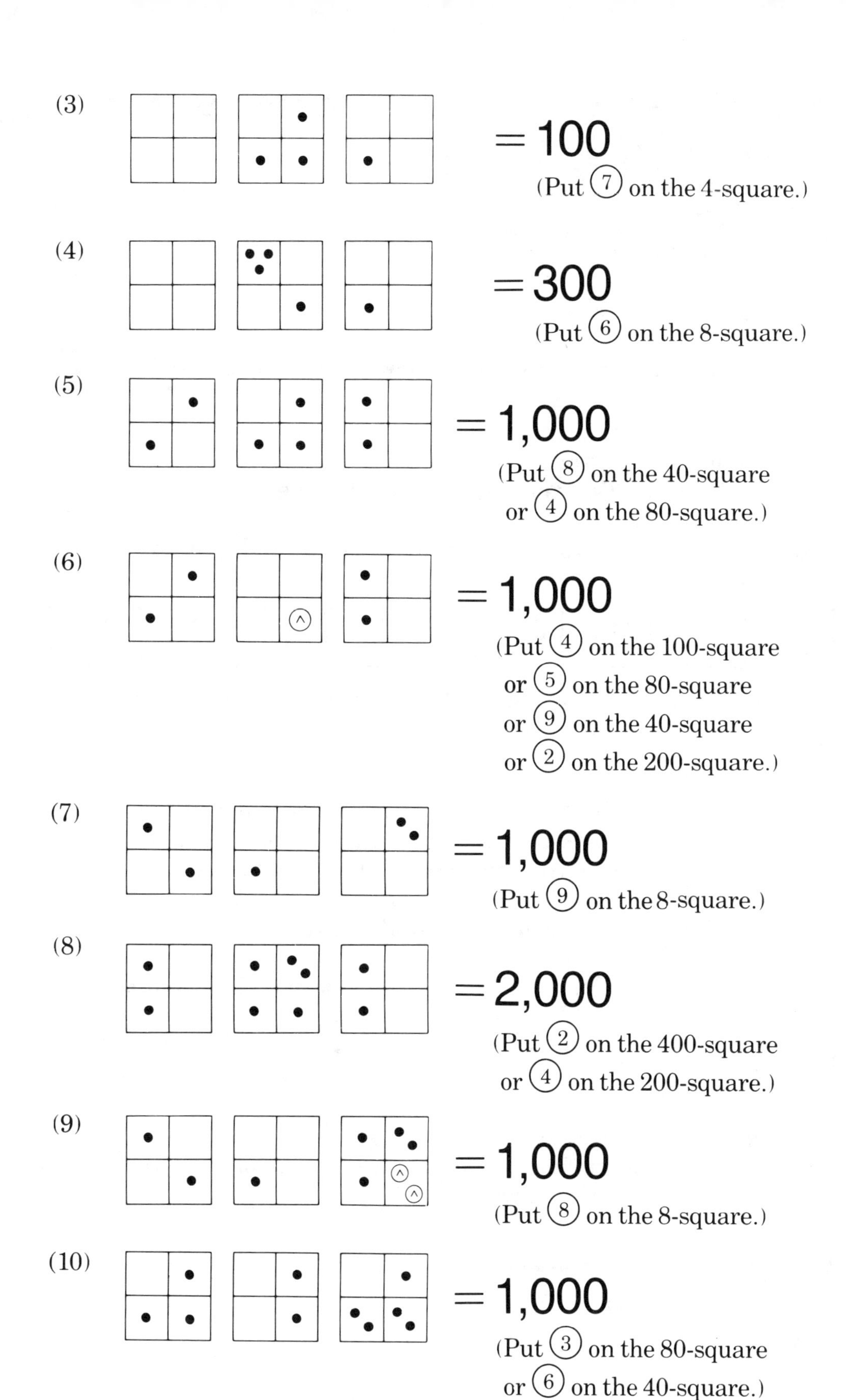

(3) = 100
(Put ⑦ on the 4-square.)

(4) = 300
(Put ⑥ on the 8-square.)

(5) = 1,000
(Put ⑧ on the 40-square
or ④ on the 80-square.)

(6) = 1,000
(Put ④ on the 100-square
or ⑤ on the 80-square
or ⑨ on the 40-square
or ② on the 200-square.)

(7) = 1,000
(Put ⑨ on the 8-square.)

(8) = 2,000
(Put ② on the 400-square
or ④ on the 200-square.)

(9) = 1,000
(Put ⑧ on the 8-square.)

(10) = 1,000
(Put ③ on the 80-square
or ⑥ on the 40-square.)

Resources Available
For class use: Worksheets L54 and L55
For out-of-class use: Any H-worksheet up through H86

ACTIVITY 64
Calculator 5

Materials Needed
Teacher: Colored chalk
Students: Colored pencils, one calculator each

Distribute the calculators to the students. Draw the following symbols on the board:

In addition, draw these two labeled dots on the board, some distance apart:

7 ● 

T: Today we are going to build roads using our calculators. But you have to make believe that the calculators are broken. You can use only the keys I've listed on the board. Who would like to suggest the first arrow in our road?

Adjust the following dialog to fit your students' responses.

S: *+8.*

Draw a +8 arrow from 7 and ask the student for the ending number.

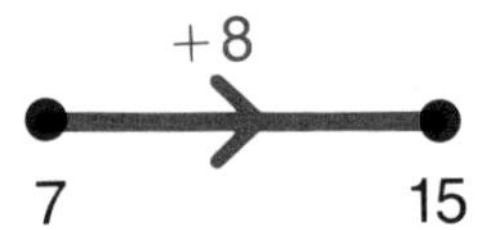

S: *+5.*

Continue extending your diagram, using the same color for all the arrows. Label each arrow individually.

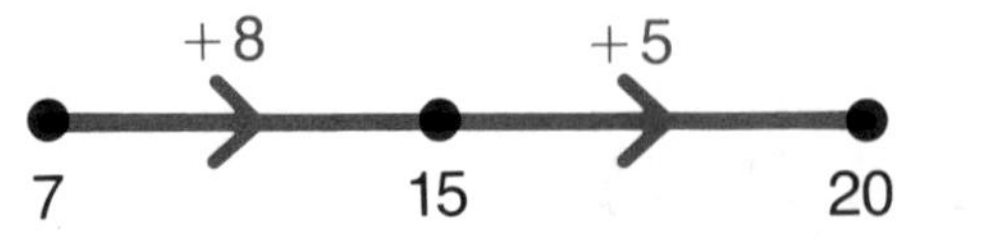

S: *−9.*

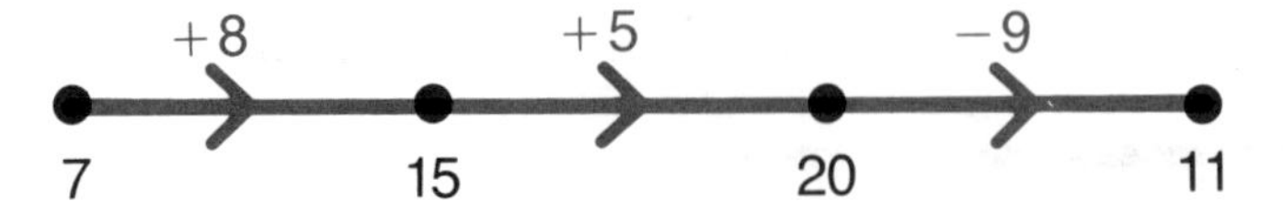

T: Now I want each of you to try to find a road from 7 to 11 that is different from the one we have just found. You should also try to make your road shorter than this one, which has three arrows.

64

If anyone finds a two-arrow road, ask him or her to copy it onto the board. Here are two possible two-arrow roads. There are others.

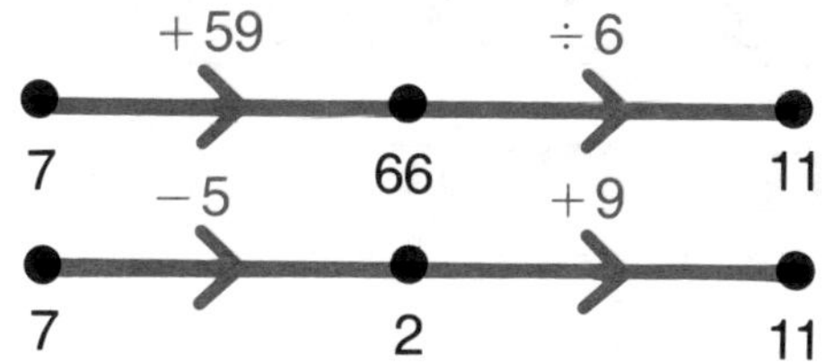

Let the students work independently on the following roads.

Challenge the class to find roads that are as short as possible. You could have a contest to find shortest roads. As soon as a student has a road, announce to the class how many arrows long it is, and ask if anyone has found a shorter one. Those finding shortest roads are the winners. Have students draw on the board one or two of the shortest roads found for each problem.

In each case below a shortest road is shown for your information.

1. From 21 to 8.

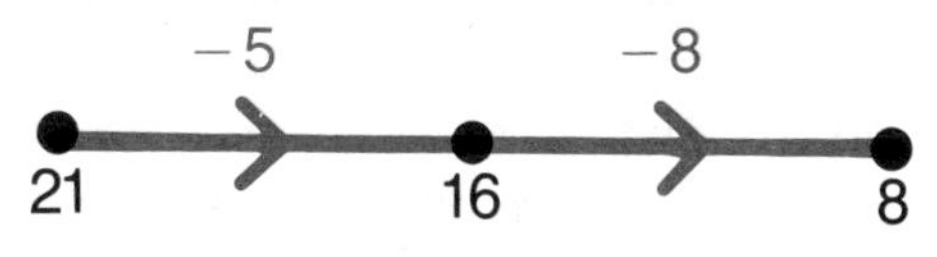

2. From 43 to 132.

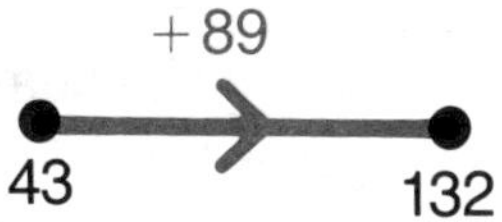

3. From 555 to 107.

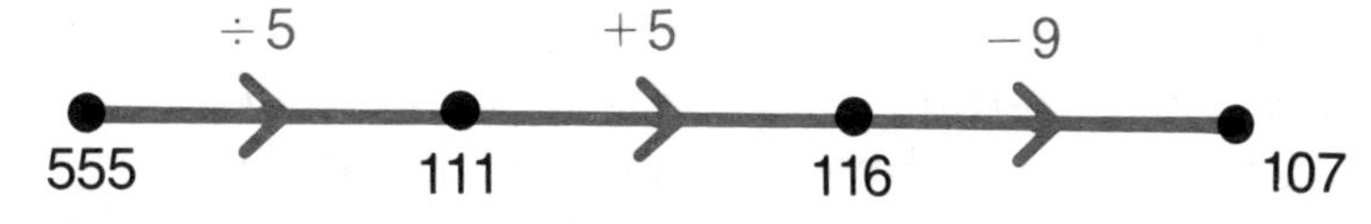

4. From 5 to 0.5.

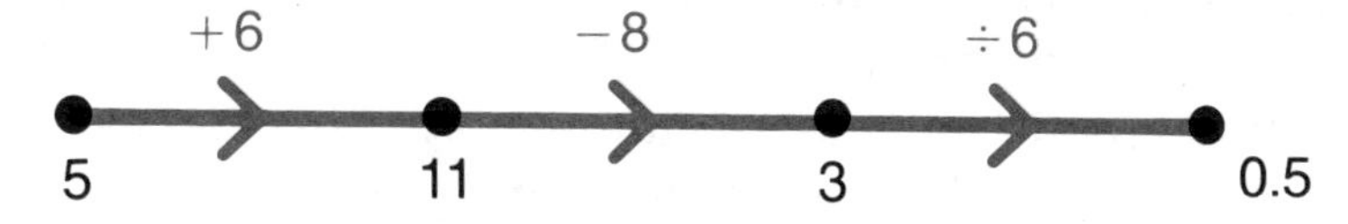

5. From 97 to $\widehat{3}$.

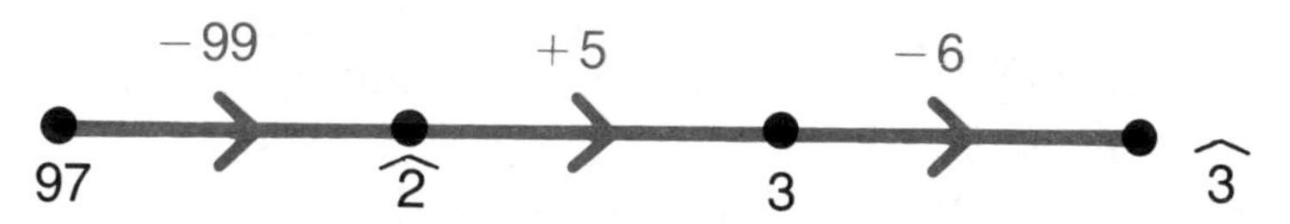

Resources Available

For out-of-class use: Any H-worksheet up through H86

ACTIVITIES 65 and 66

Return Arrows 3

Materials Needed
Teacher: Colored chalk
Students: Paper and colored pencils, two calculators

Give the calculators to two students (called "Tom" and "Lisa" in the following dialog) and ask them to enter the number 20 onto their calculator displays.

T: What number is on the display? (20) Now do exactly what I say. Put your hand over the display and press these keys:

[×] [4] [−] [6] [=]

As you mention each key, draw its symbol on the board. Pause between keys so that Lisa and Tom have time to press them.

T(to the rest of the class): What number should now be on the displays? (74)

After several students have given their answers, ask Tom and Lisa to uncover their displays and announce what number is there. If either calculator shows some number other than 74, tell the student to clear the calculator and enter 74.

T(to Lisa and Tom): What number is on the display? (74) Now put your hand over the display again and press:

[+] [1] [6] [÷] [3] [=]

List the key symbols on the board, reading them as "plus sixteen divided by three equals."

T(to the class): What number should now be on the displays? (30)

Once again, allow several students to give their answers before asking Tom and Lisa to uncover their displays as a check.

Continue this activity with the following sequences of operations:

[+] [8] [×] [2] [=] (76)

[−] [2] [6] [÷] [1] [0] [=] (5)

[×] [7] [−] [5] [=] (30)

[+] [2] [÷] [4] [=] (8)

Ask Tom and Lisa each to pick a secret number between 50 and 100 and write it on a piece of paper so that no one can see it.

T: We don't know what Tom's and Lisa's secret numbers are. (To Tom and Lisa:) Whatever they are, enter them onto your calculator displays, but be sure that no one can see. Then press these keys:

[×] [2] [+] [2] [0] [÷] [2] [−] [1] [5] [=]

As you announce the keys, draw the corresponding arrow diagram on the board:

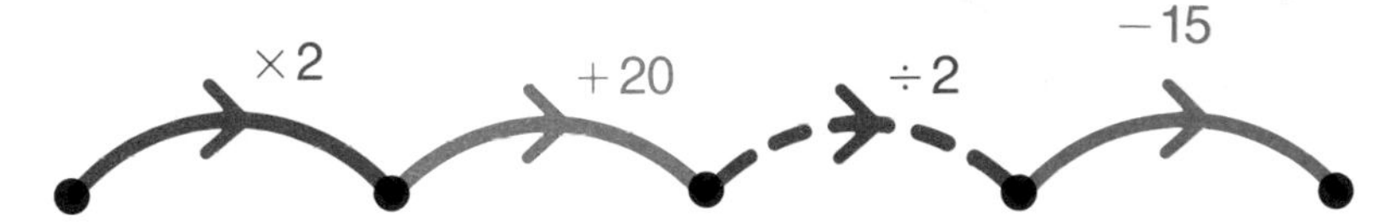

T(to Tom and Lisa): What is on your display, Tom? (Suppose he says "83.") And what is on your display, Lisa? (Suppose she says "66.") (to the rest of the class): You (motion to half the class) try to find Tom's secret number, and you (motion to the other half of the class) try to find Lisa's secret number. How can we do this?

S: *By drawing return arrows.*

Allow a few minutes for everyone to work on these problems. After several students have whispered the correct solutions to you, let them draw the return arrows and label the dots in the diagrams on the board:

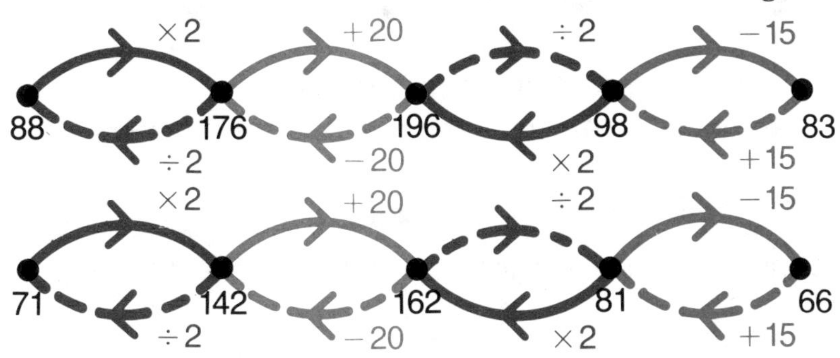

Notice that with this sequence of operations the starting number is always five greater than the ending number.

Check with Tom and Lisa that their secret numbers are indeed as discovered by the rest of the class. Give the calculators to two other students. Ask them to pick a secret number each (between 50 and 100 as in the first case), record it on a piece of paper, and operate on their number with the following sequence of operations:

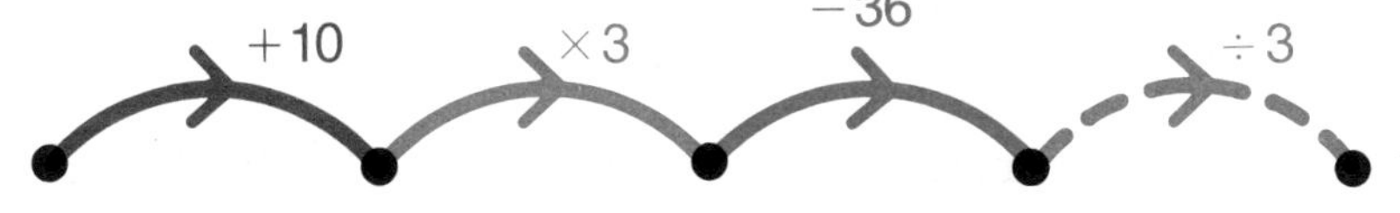

Once they have done so, ask the students to announce their ending numbers. As in the first case, let the class find the two secret starting numbers. In this case, the starting number is always two greater than the ending number.

In the exercises up to this point it is possible that students might attempt to do all the calculations mentally. Encourage this, but require nevertheless that each student draw the arrow diagram, the return arrows and the original arrows suitably color-coded with a different color for each kind of arrow. This encourages good work habits and reduces wild guessing.

Repeat the exercise several times, each time inviting a different pair of students to select secret numbers on which to operate with one of the following sequences of operations:

1.

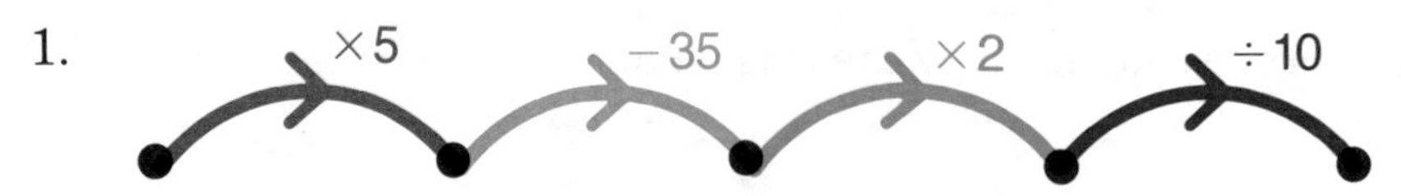

(Starting number is seven greater than ending number.)

2.

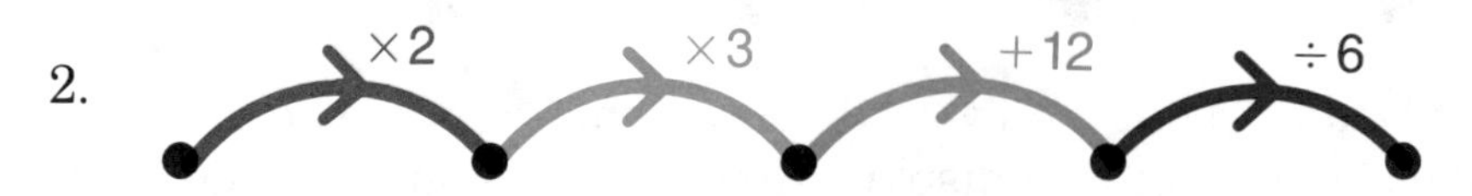

(Starting number is two less than ending number.)

3.

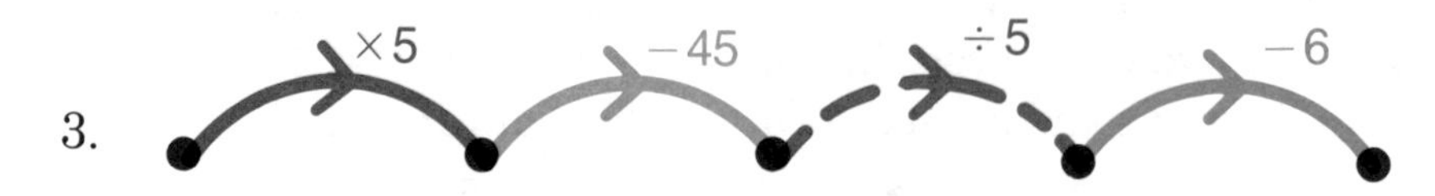

(Starting number is 15 greater than ending number.)

Erase what is written on the board, and replace it with the following equation:

$$(\square - 3) \times 2 + 6 = 20$$

T: What number could we write in the box to make this equation true? Could it be 5?

S: *No; $(5 - 3) \times 2 + 6 = 10$, not 20.*

T: Let's use an arrow road to help us solve this equation.

Invite the class to help you draw an appropriate diagram such as the following:

Then ask students to help you draw return arrows and eventually find a number that could go in the box, that is, a solution of the equation.

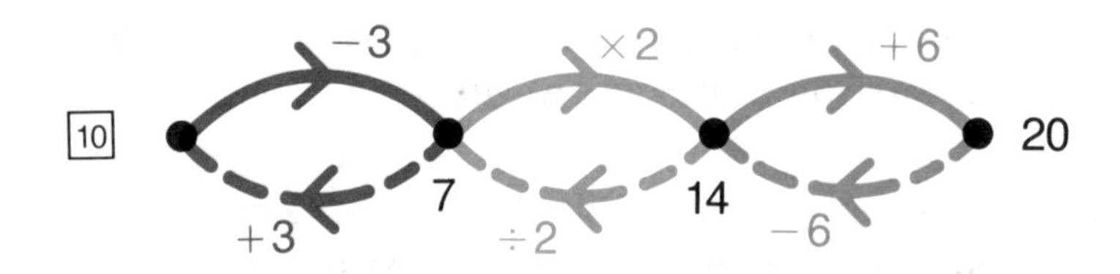

For the remainder of the time available, let the students work individually on the following equations. For each one they should copy the equation from the board, draw a suitable arrow road, and find a number that could go in the box.

1. $(\square + 5) \div 3 - 3 = 1$
2. $(\square \div 4) + 6 = 10$
3. $((3 \times \square) - 7) \div 2 = 7$

Solutions:

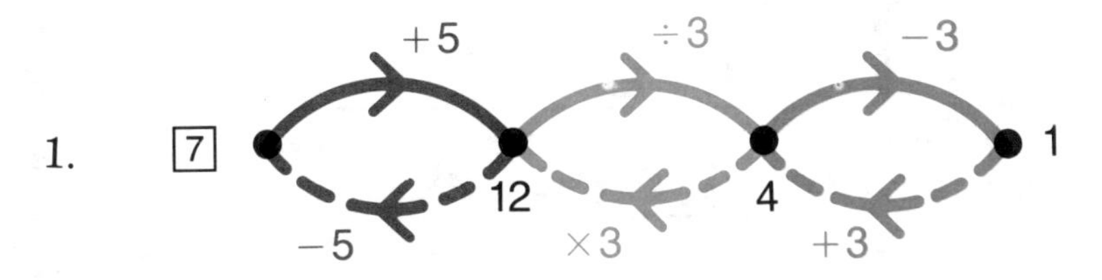

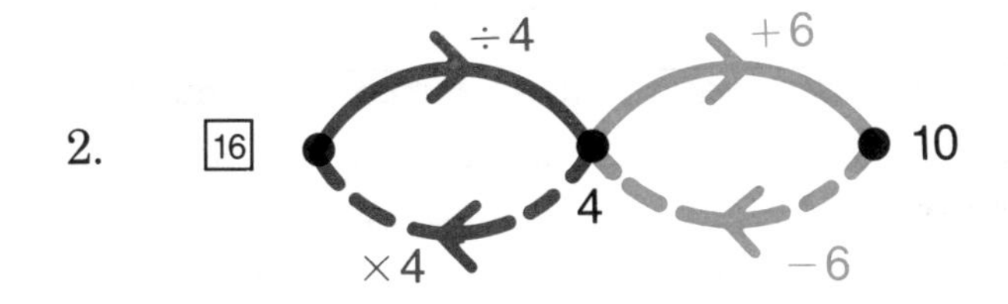

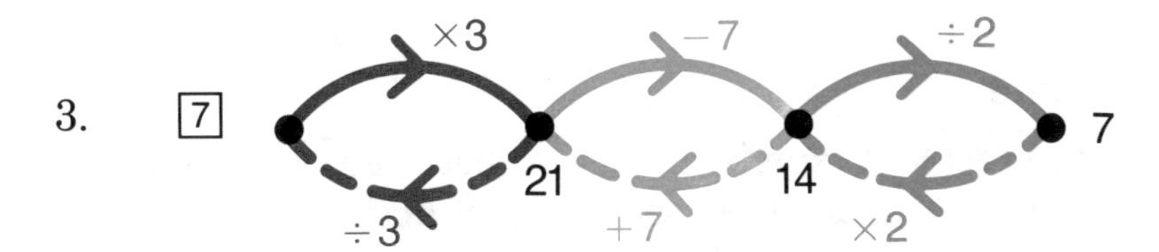

Resources Available

For class use: For those who finish early, Worksheets A5 and A6

For out-of-class use: Any H-worksheets up through H88

ACTIVITY 67
Weighted Checkers 4

Materials Needed
Teacher: Minicomputer kit, chalk
Students: Paper and pencils

Note to the Teacher

You may wish to conduct this exercise as a game between two teams. If so, follow the instructions given at the beginning of Activity 63. However, in this exercise several of the problems have more than one solution. For each such problem, tell the class in advance how many solutions there are. Then continue work on that problem until all the solutions have been found. Award one point for each correct solution, even if it is not the first solution to the problem in question. But no student should give more than one solution to one problem.

Allow the first student to tackle a problem sufficient time for thought. However, subsequent players who might work on the same problem should be limited to about 30 seconds, because they will have had time to think while the first student is at the board. No member of a team should be allowed a second turn before all members of that team have had a first turn.

Display one Minicomputer board, a regular checker, and a 3-checker.

T: Today I'm going to ask you to put various kinds of numbers on the Minicomputer. In each case some checkers will already be on the Minicomputer. You will have to try to get the kind of number I ask for by putting a regular checker or a 3-checker (but not both) on the Minicomputer. In some cases there is more than one way to solve the problem. In those cases we will keep playing the game with that problem until all the possible solutions have been found. I will tell you in advance how many solutions there are. Then while someone is at the board showing one solution, the rest of you can be thinking about finding others. After the first person who is called on for that problem, everybody else will only have 30 seconds to find a solution. Keep alert, and make sure that no solution is given twice. Before you win a point for your team you must fill in the blank correctly as well.

67

Solutions:

(1) An even number

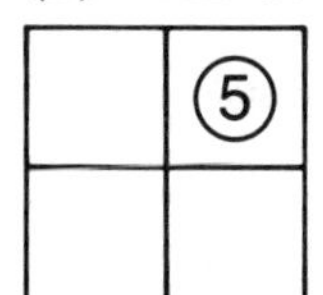

= ______

(six solutions)

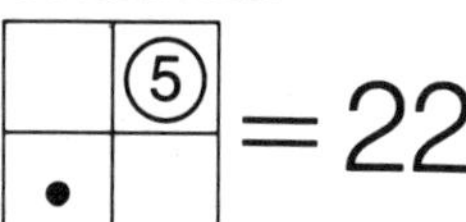

= 24

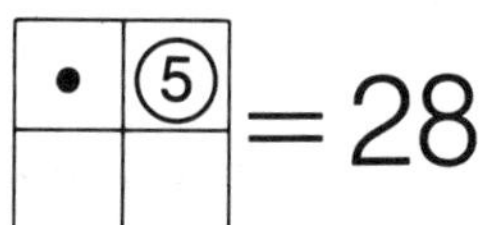

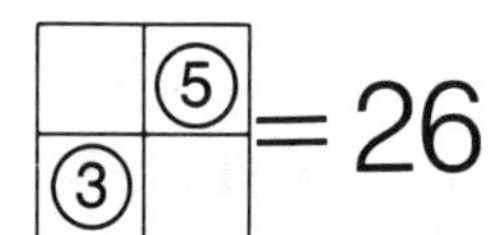

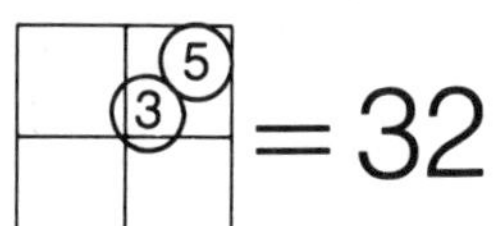

= 44

(2) A multiple of 10

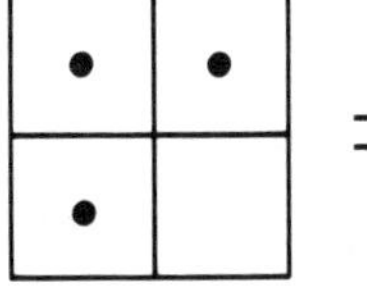

= ______

(one solution)

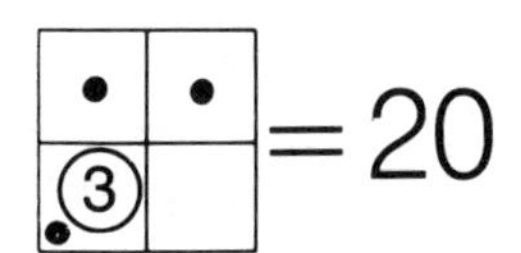

(3) A prime number

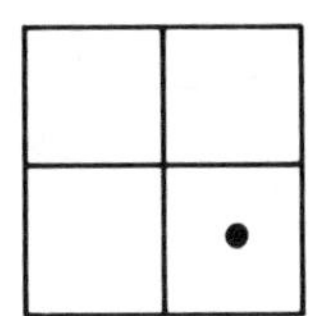

= ______

(five solutions)

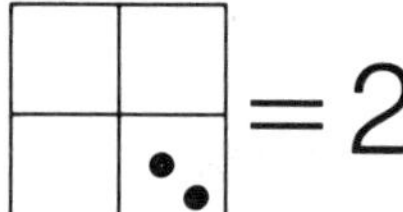

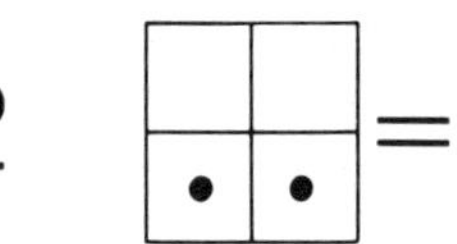

= 5

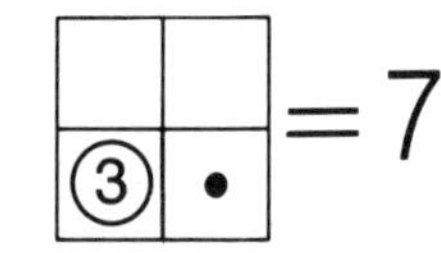

= 13

(4) A positive divisor of 30

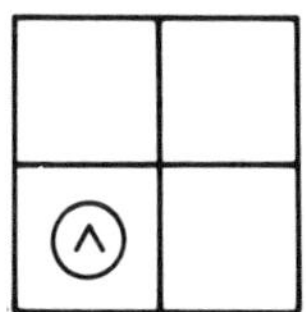

= ______

(four solutions)

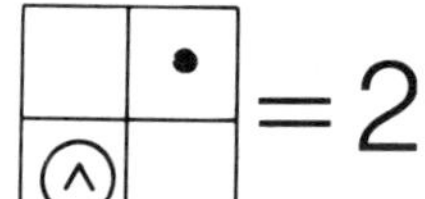

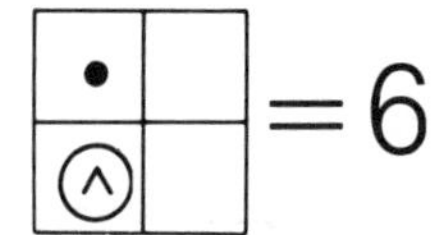

= 1

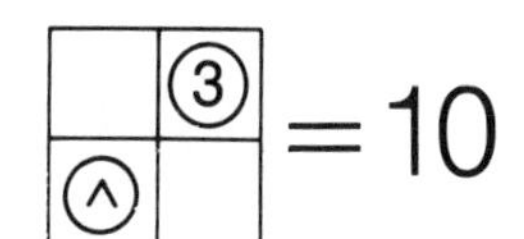

(5) A multiple of 5

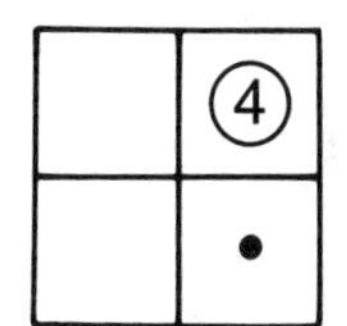

= ______

(two solutions)

= 20

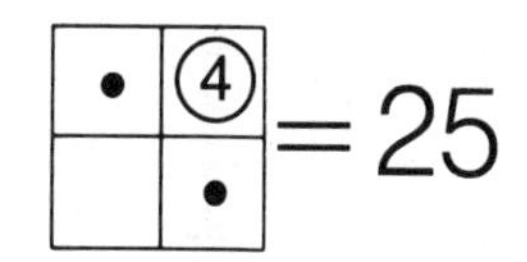

(6) A number greater than 40

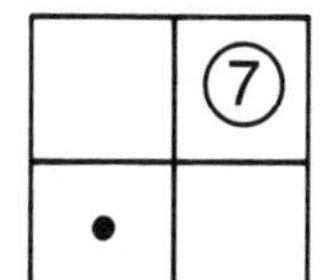

= ______

(two solutions)

= 42

= 54

67

(7) A square number

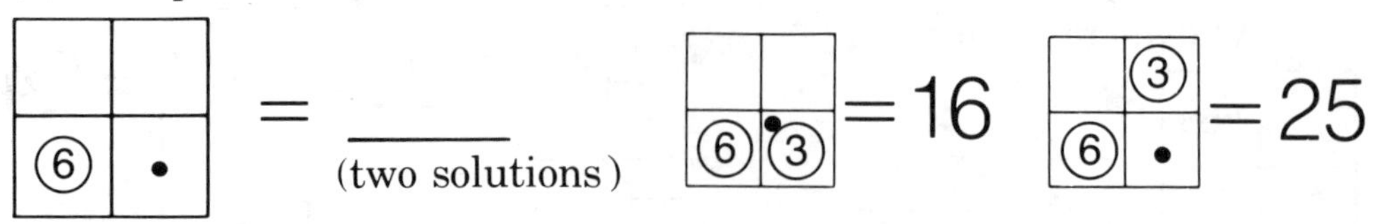

= ______ (two solutions) = 16 = 25

Remove the regular checker and the 3-checker from the board, and display a negative checker.

T: For the rest of these problems you must add exactly one negative checker and nothing else.

(8) An odd number.

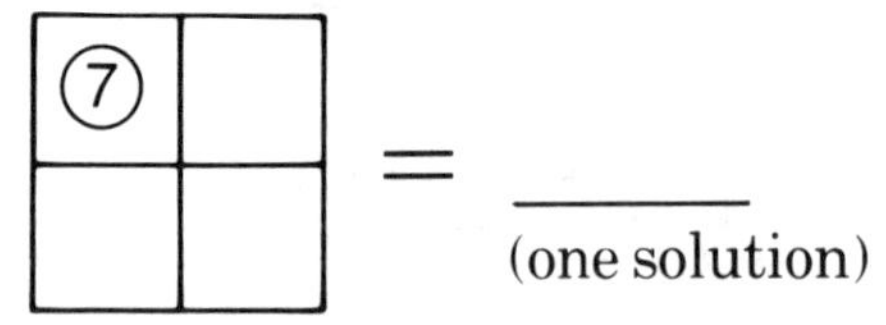

= ______ (one solution) = 55

(9) A multiple of 3

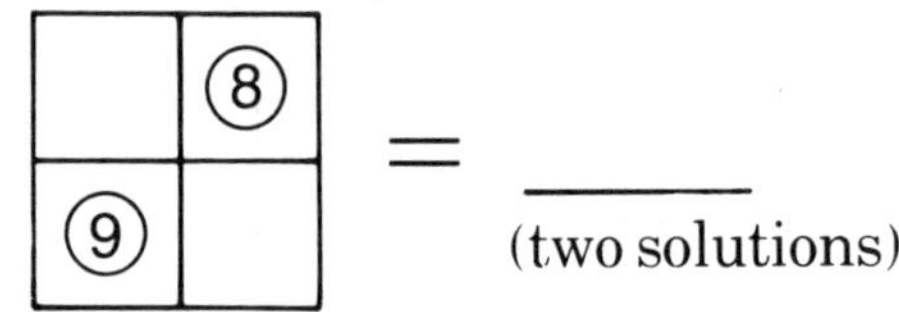

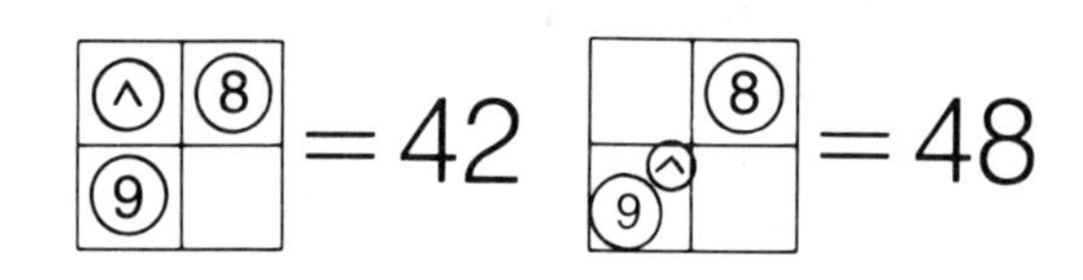

= ______ (two solutions) = 42 = 48

(10) A multiple of 7

= ______ (one solution) = 98

(11) A positive divisor of 72

= ______ (one solution) = 36

(12) A prime number

= ______ (one solution) = 19

(13) A prime number

= ______ (one solution) = 67

(14) A square number

⑤	

= ______ (one solution)

⑤	ⓐ

= 36

(15) A square number

⑥	
	③

= ______ (one solution)

⑥	
ⓐ	③

= 49

Resources Available

For class use: Worksheets L56 and L57
For out-of-class use: Any H-worksheet up through H90

ACTIVITY 68
Calculator 6

Materials Needed
Teacher: Chalk
Students: Paper and pencils, one calculator each

Distribute the calculators to the students, and draw the following symbols on the board:

[3] [5] [+] [−] [×] [÷] [=]

T: Today we're going to pretend that your calculators are broken. The only keys that are working are the ones I've listed on the board. Turn your calculators on and make sure that the display shows 0. Now, using only these keys, try to put 31 on your display. Write down what you do so that we can record some of the solutions on the board.

Let the students work individually for a few minutes, and then ask some of them to write their solutions on the board.

Here are four of the possible solutions. (We are assuming that your calculators have a constant mode for each operation. If this is not the case, refer to the Note to the Teacher at the beginning of Activity 24, where indications are given of some of the adjustments that may be necessary.)

[5] [+] [=] [=] [=] [=] [+] [3] [=] [=]
[5] [×] [=] [+] [3] [=] [=]
[5] [+] [3] [×] [5] [−] [3] [=] [=] [=]
[3] [5] [+] [5] [−] [3] [=] [=] [=]

T: Now let's pretend that it costs 1 cent each time you press a key. Let's see how much the solutions on the board cost.

Calculate the cost of each solution on the board and record it to the right of the solution. For example, for the first solution given above we would have:

[5] [+] [=] [=] [=] [=] [+] [3] [=] [=] 10¢

Challenge the class to find solutions that are cheaper than the ones on the board, if possible. If any such cheaper solutions are found, ask their discoverers to record them on the board.

T: Here's a special offer. If you can find a solution that uses all four operation symbols (+, −, ×, ÷) at least once each, then you will be charged only one-half cent for each key you press.

Now challenge the class to find a solution that is cheaper than any on the board up to this point. For example:

[3] [÷] [3] [+] [3] [×] [5] [−] [3] [+] [=] [−] [3] [=] 7¢

Repeat this exercise for the numbers 62, 103, and $\widehat{41}$.

Resources Available

For out-of-class use: Any H-worksheet up through H90

ACTIVITY 69

String Game Analysis 2

Materials Needed

Teacher: Colored chalk, Numerical String Game kit

Students: Numerical String Game Analysis Sheets (a supply of these is at the back of the workbook), colored pencils

Before the lesson begins, set up your board for the String Game as shown below. The bubbles show what is written on the face-down string cards. Tape Numerical String Game Poster 2 on the board. Head the first two columns "Red" and "Blue," as shown below.

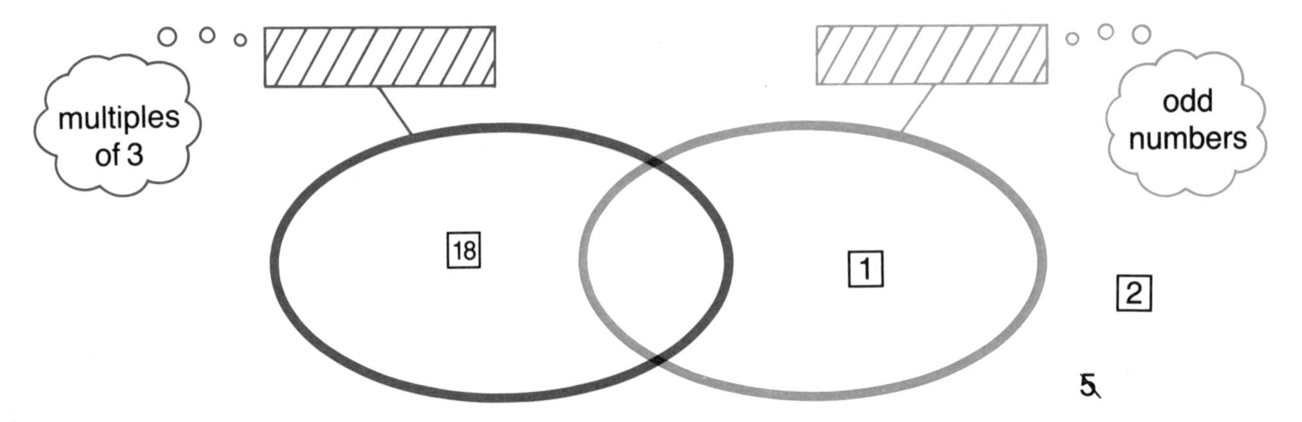

	Red	Blue	
MULTIPLES OF 2			
MULTIPLES OF 3			
MULTIPLES OF 4			
MULTIPLES OF 5			
MULTIPLES OF 10			
ODD NUMBERS			
POSITIVE PRIME NUMBERS			
GREATER THAN 50			
LESS THAN 50			
GREATER THAN 10			
LESS THAN 10			
POSITIVE DIVISORS OF 12			
POSITIVE DIVISORS OF 18			
POSITIVE DIVISORS OF 20			
POSITIVE DIVISORS OF 24			
POSITIVE DIVISORS OF 27			

Distribute Analysis Sheets to the students.

T: Head the first two columns of your analysis sheet "Red" and "Blue" as I have here on the board. Work through the clues I have given you here. Work out which labels are impossible for each string and mark them with crosses in the correct columns of your analysis sheet . As soon as you have only one possibility left for a string, put a check mark next to that label in the correct column. When you know both string labels, raise your hand and I'll check your work.

Let the students work individually for about 5 to 10 minutes. As they finish, check their work and let them know if they have both string labels correct. If one or both labels are incorrect, simply say, "Your answers are not completely correct yet. Check your work again."

After about ten minutes, or earlier if more than half your class has correctly solved the problem, briefly discuss the problem. Begin by considering the 18-clue. Cross off labels from your board poster using red and blue crosses. After considering this clue your poster should look like this:

	Red	Blue	
MULTIPLES OF 2		X	
MULTIPLES OF 3		X	
MULTIPLES OF 4	X		
MULTIPLES OF 5	X		
MULTIPLES OF 10	X		
ODD NUMBERS	X		
POSITIVE PRIME NUMBERS	X		
GREATER THAN 50	X		
LESS THAN 50		X	
GREATER THAN $\widehat{10}$		X	
LESS THAN $\widehat{10}$	X		
POSITIVE DIVISORS OF 12	X		
POSITIVE DIVISORS OF 18		X	
POSITIVE DIVISORS OF 20	X		
POSITIVE DIVISORS OF 24	X		
POSITIVE DIVISORS OF 27	X		

Consider the 1-clue next. After you have done so your poster should be as shown in the top figure on page 180. Now take up the 2-clue, and you should arrive at the result shown in the bottom figure on page 180.

	Red	Blue	
MULTIPLES OF 2		×	
MULTIPLES OF 3		×	
MULTIPLES OF 4	×	×	
MULTIPLES OF 5	×	×	
MULTIPLES OF 10	×	×	
ODD NUMBERS	×		
POSITIVE PRIME NUMBERS	×	×	
GREATER THAN 50	×	×	
LESS THAN 50	×	×	
GREATER THAN $\widehat{10}$	×	×	
LESS THAN $\widehat{10}$	×	×	
POSITIVE DIVISORS OF 12	×		
POSITIVE DIVISORS OF 18	×	×	
POSITIVE DIVISORS OF 20	×		
POSITIVE DIVISORS OF 24	×		
POSITIVE DIVISORS OF 27	×		

	Red	Blue	
MULTIPLES OF 2	×	×	
MULTIPLES OF 3	✓	×	
MULTIPLES OF 4	×	×	
MULTIPLES OF 5	×	×	
MULTIPLES OF 10	×	×	
ODD NUMBERS	×		
POSITIVE PRIME NUMBERS	×	×	
GREATER THAN 50	×	×	
LESS THAN 50	×	×	
GREATER THAN $\widehat{10}$	×	×	
LESS THAN $\widehat{10}$	×	×	
POSITIVE DIVISORS OF 12	×	×	
POSITIVE DIVISORS OF 18	×	×	
POSITIVE DIVISORS OF 20	×	×	
POSITIVE DIVISORS OF 24	×	×	
POSITIVE DIVISORS OF 27	×		

Show the class that the red string's label does indeed read "Multiples of 3."

T: So now we know that the red string is for the multiples of 3 and that the blue string is for either the positive divisors of 27 or the odd numbers. How can we decide what the blue string is for from the last clue? All it tells us is that 5 is not on the outside.

S: *That means that 5 belongs somewhere in the strings. But the red string is for the multiples of 3, and 5 is not a multiple of 3. So 5 has to go in the part of the blue string that's outside the red string.*

Place the 5-card in the right-hand region of the string diagram on the board.

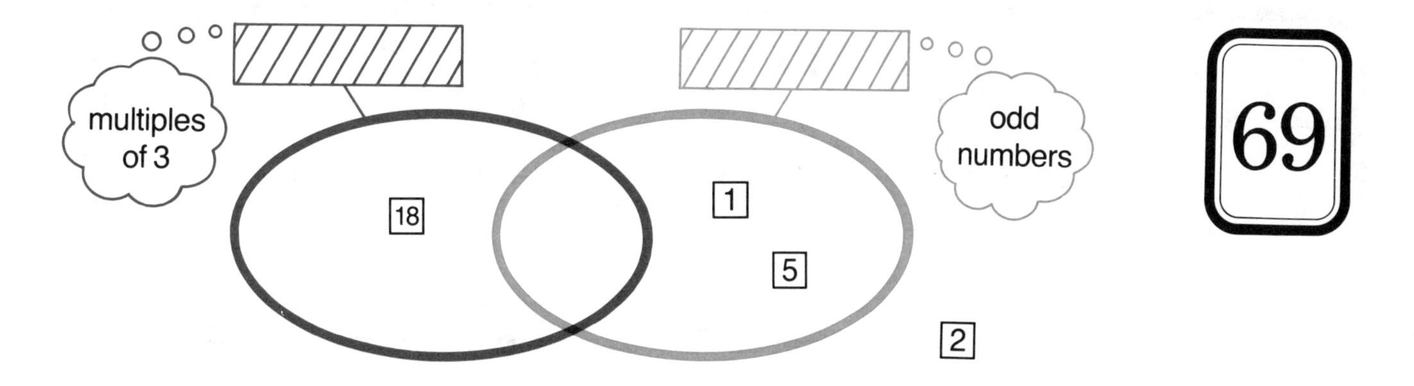

S: *The number 5 isn't a positive divisor of 27, so the blue string must be for the odd numbers.*

Show the class that the blue string's label does indeed read "odd numbers."

Resources Available

For class use: Worksheets L58 and L59
For out-of-class use: Any H-worksheet up through H91

ACTIVITY 70
Numerical String Game 6

Materials Needed

Teacher: Numerical String Game kit, colored chalk
Students: Numerical String Game Analysis Sheets, pencils

Note to the Teacher

In order to increase your students' incentive to analyze each play as well as the starting clues, it is suggested that you use the following special scoring rules.

We call two plays, one by each team, a round. After each round, ask the students if they wish to say at that point what the string labels are. Those who do should check one label for each string on their analysis sheets and give the sheets to you. Those who do not wish to commit themselves at that point should keep their analysis sheets for the next round.

Note on which round you receive each analysis sheet. Score them as follows:

If both strings are correct on round 1: 200 points
round 2: 150 points
round 3: 100 points
round 4: 75 points
round 5: 50 points
round 6: 25 points
If either string is incorrect: 0 points

Students have only one opportunity to score in this fashion.

After round 6 the game continues in the usual manner until completed. In the usual way, the team that first exhausts all its pieces and correctly identifies the strings is awarded 100 points, plus 10 points for each unplaced piece still on the opposing team's side of the playing board. Once this has occurred, all the points scored by the members of both teams are added together and the team with the most points is declared the winner.

Play two games using the starting clues on page 183. In the early stages of the game provide sufficient time for the students to do the analysis. When a number is placed incorrectly, remember to write that number in the region where it was placed and then draw a cross through it.

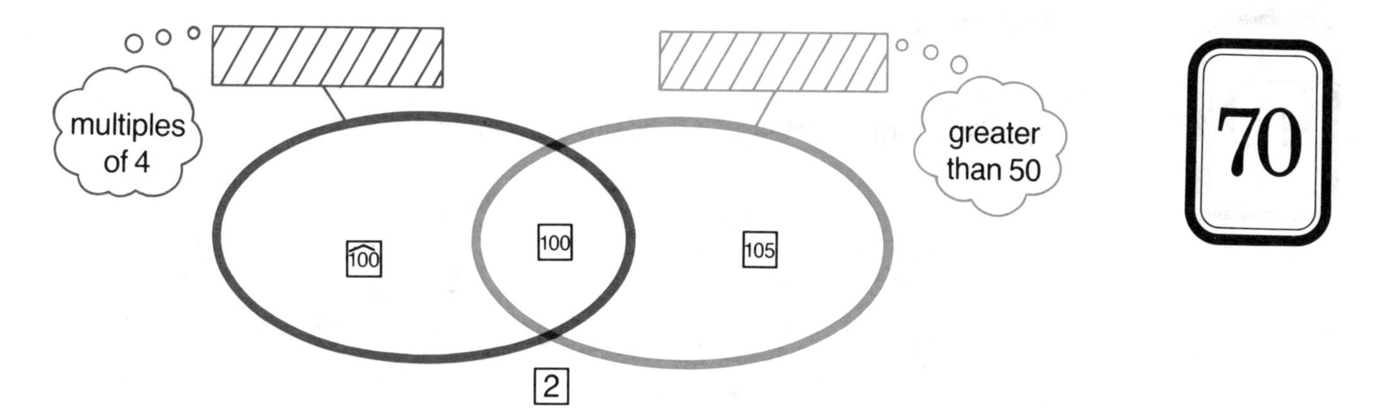

Crib sheet:

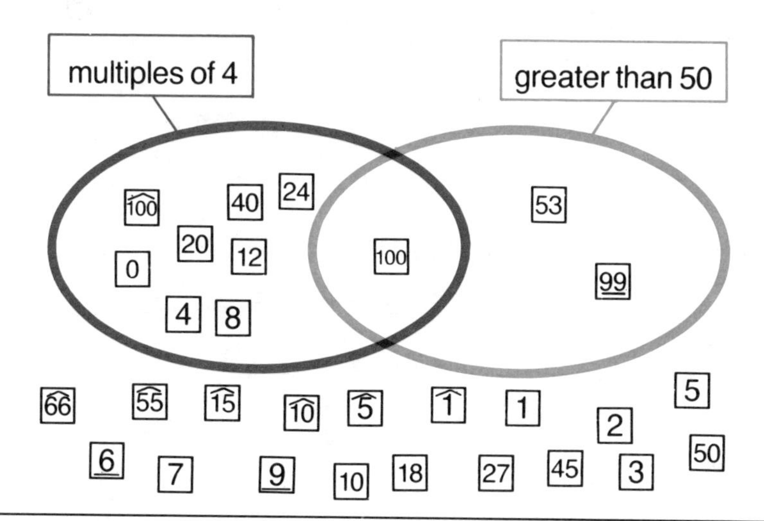

Note to the Teacher

If you think it necessary, remind your class that in the following starting clues the hatching, the dot, and the 3-card in the middle region mean that there are exactly two numbers in the middle region and that one of them is 3.

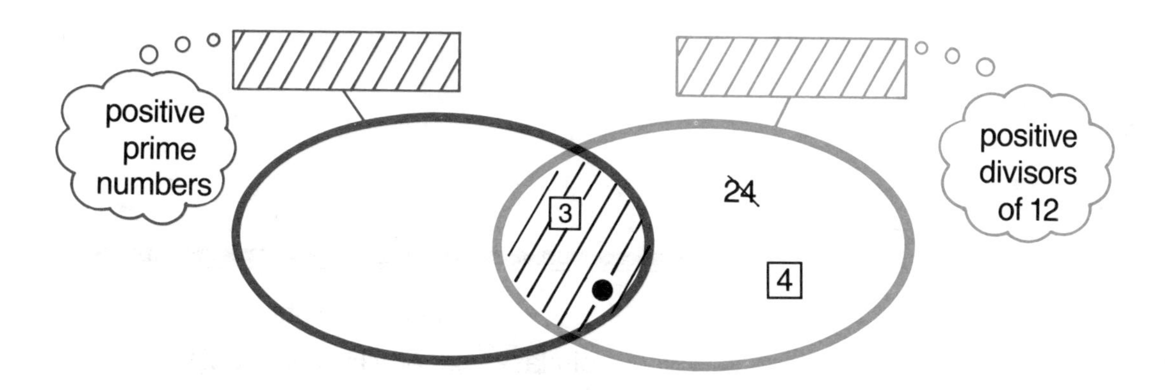

70

Crib sheet:

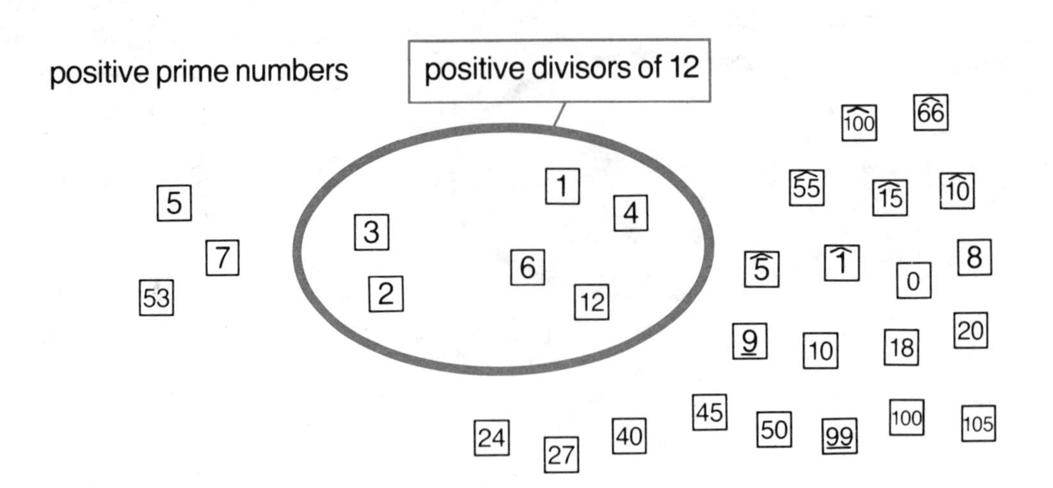

Resources Available

For out-of-class use: Any H-worksheet up through H91

L1

Name ____________________

There are a lot of numbers that could go in the little square.

positive divisors of □

Write some of them here: *8, 27, 125,... or the cube of any prime*
6, 10, 15, 14, 21,... or the product of 2 different primes

There are a lot of numbers that could go in the little triangle.

positive divisors of △

Write some of them here: *16, 81, 625,... or the 4th power of any prime*

Reminder: **Prime numbers** are numbers that have exactly two positive divisors. Try to write down all the prime numbers that are less than 50.

2, 3, 5, *7*, *11*, *13*, *17*, *19*, *23*, *29*, *31*, *37*, *41*, *43*, *47*.

L2

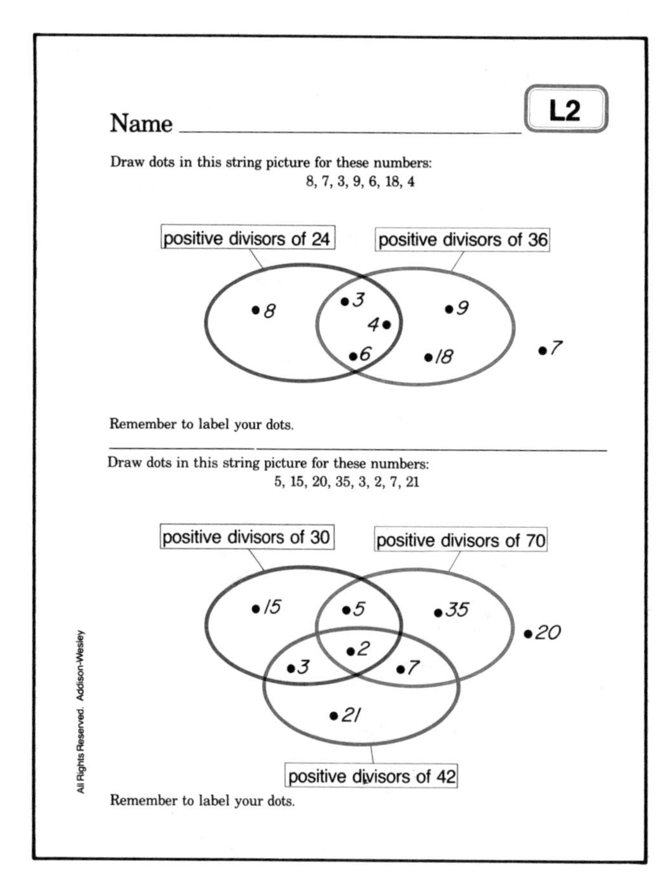

L3

Name ____________________

Draw one "sunny day" route from Bill's house (**B**) to Amy's house (**A**).
Draw four or five "rainy day" routes from **B** to **A**.
Use a different color for each route.

B
A
1
sunny day
rainy day
rainy day

The taxidistance from **A** to **B** is *13* blocks.
The taxidistance from **B** to **A** is *13* blocks.

Many other answers are possible.

L4

Name ____________________

Mike lives at **M**. He has some errands to run.
He has to go the post office (**P**) and the store (**S**).

1
P
S
M

The taxidistance from **M** to **P** is *11* blocks.
The taxidistance from **P** to **S** is *12* blocks.
The taxidistance from **S** to **M** is *13* blocks.

It is raining. How many blocks long is the shortest trip Mike can make from his house to the post office, on to the store, and then back home? *36*

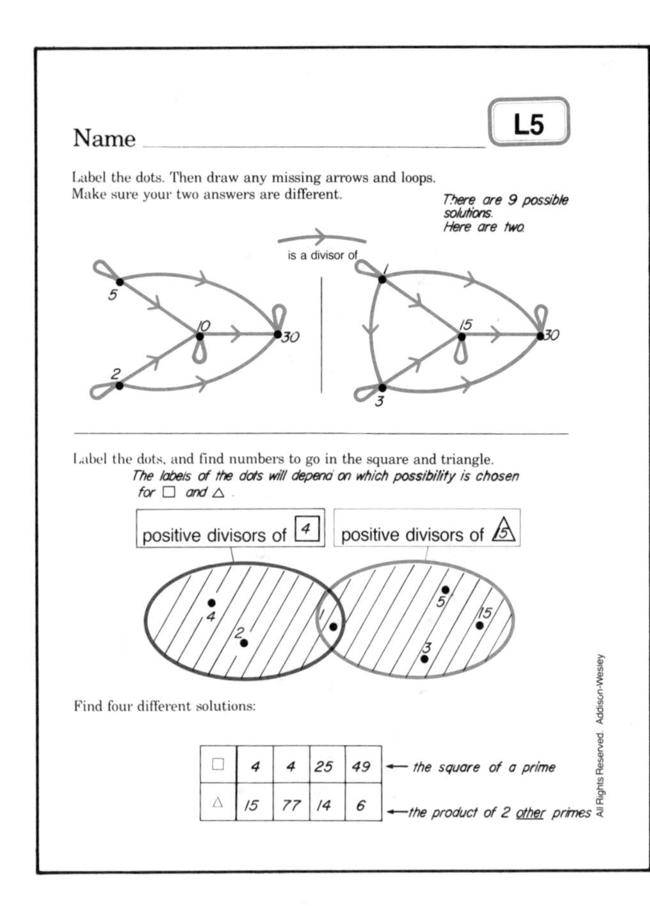

L5

Name ____________________

Label the dots. Then draw any missing arrows and loops.
Make sure your two answers are different.

There are 9 possible solutions. Here are two.

Label the dots, and find numbers to go in the square and triangle.

The labels of the dots will depend on which possibility is chosen for □ and △.

Find four different solutions:

□	4	4	25	49	← *the square of a prime*
△	15	77	14	6	← *the product of 2 other primes*

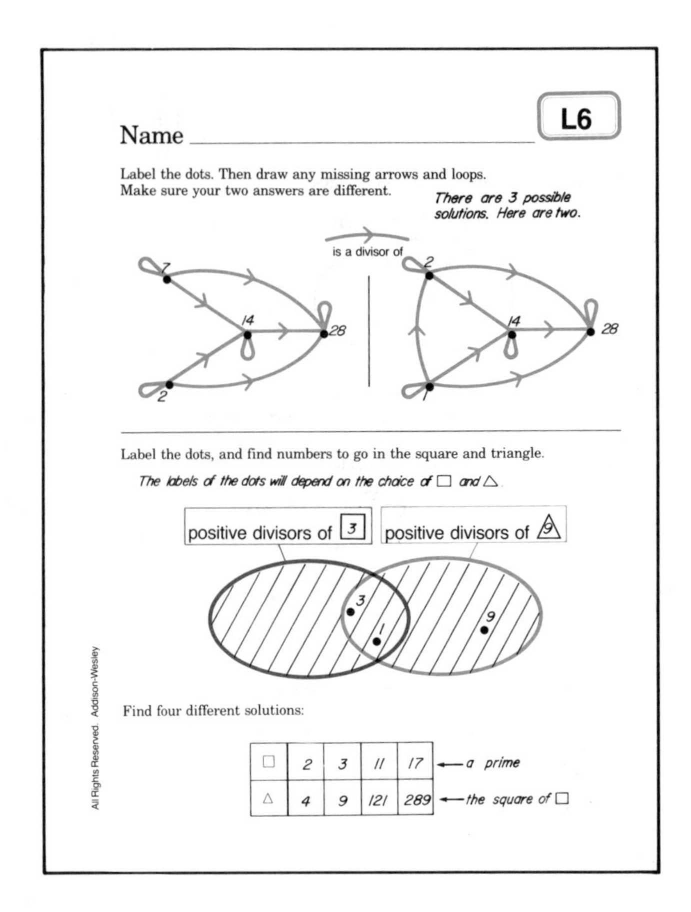

L6

Name ____________________

Label the dots. Then draw any missing arrows and loops.
Make sure your two answers are different.

There are 3 possible solutions. Here are two.

Label the dots, and find numbers to go in the square and triangle.

The labels of the dots will depend on the choice of □ and △.

Find four different solutions:

□	2	3	11	17	← *a prime*
△	4	9	121	289	← *the square of □*

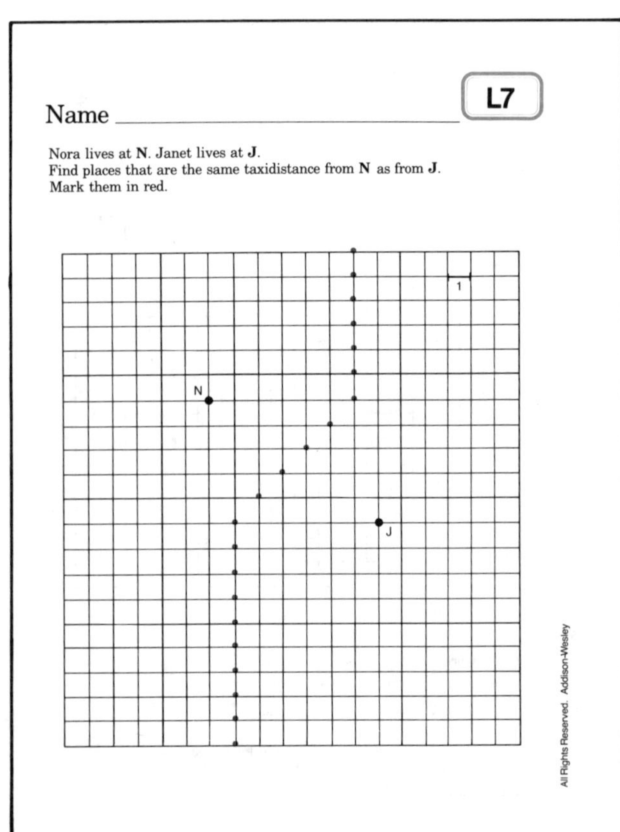

L7

Name ____________________

Nora lives at **N**. Janet lives at **J**.
Find places that are the same taxidistance from **N** as from **J**.
Mark them in red.

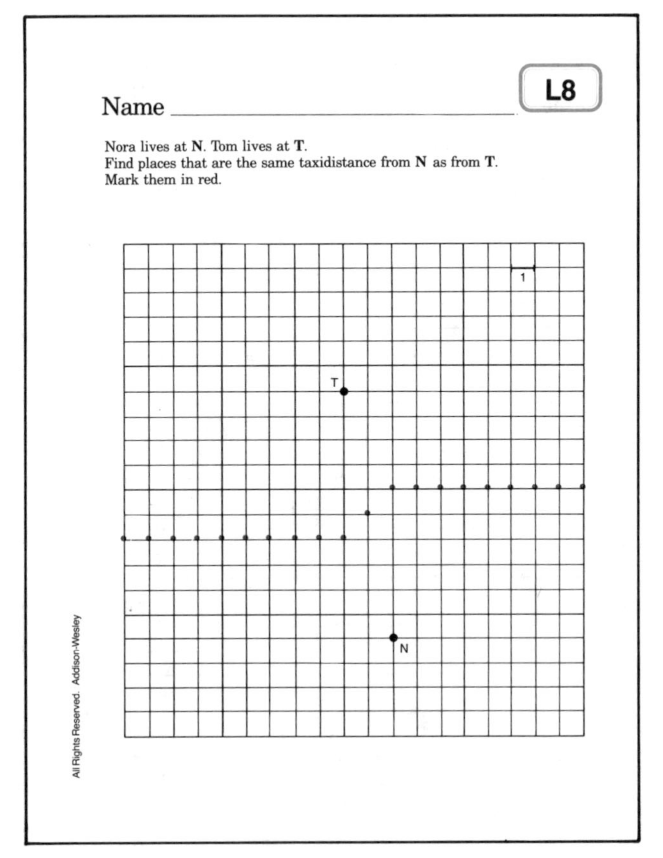

L8

Name ____________________

Nora lives at **N**. Tom lives at **T**.
Find places that are the same taxidistance from **N** as from **T**.
Mark them in red.

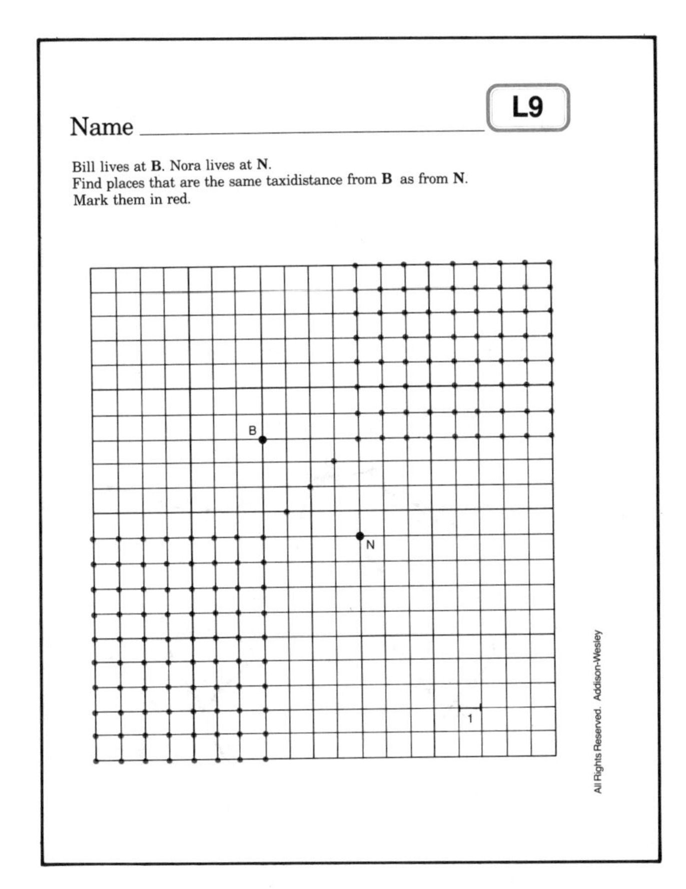

Name ____________________ **L9**

Bill lives at **B**. Nora lives at **N**.
Find places that are the same taxidistance from **B** as from **N**.
Mark them in red.

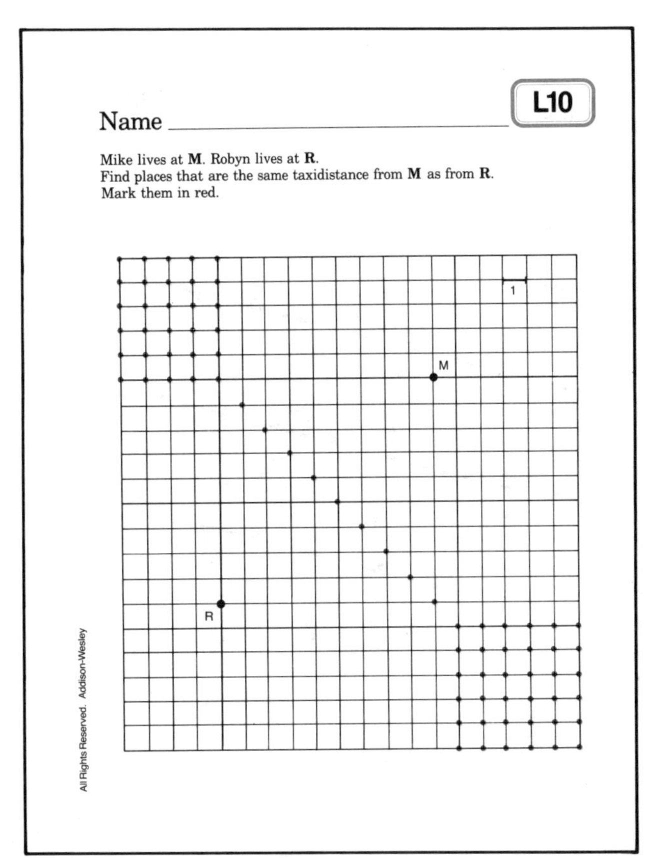

Name ____________________ **L10**

Mike lives at **M**. Robyn lives at **R**.
Find places that are the same taxidistance from **M** as from **R**.
Mark them in red.

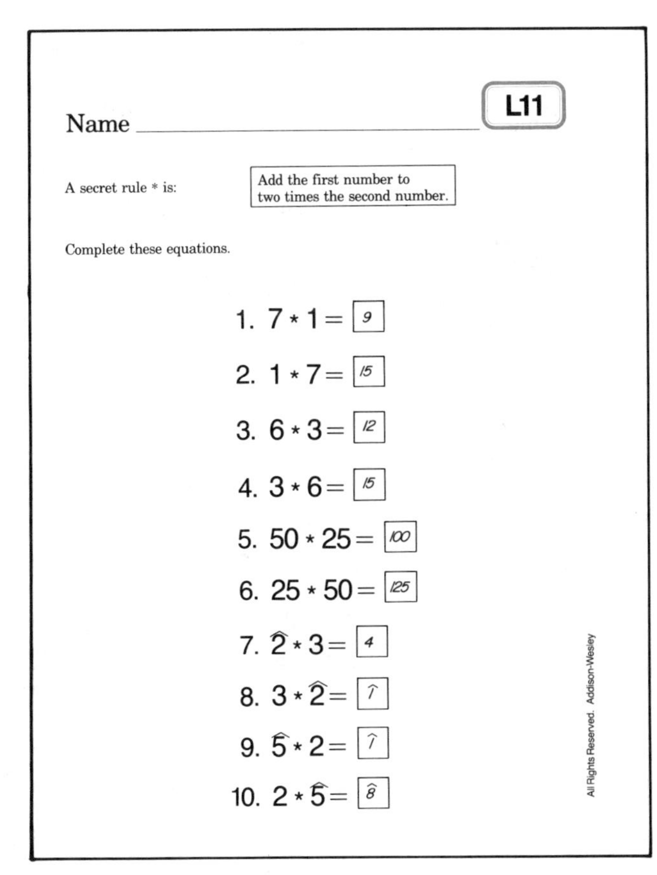

Name ____________________ **L11**

A secret rule * is: Add the first number to two times the second number.

Complete these equations.

1. 7 * 1 = [9]
2. 1 * 7 = [15]
3. 6 * 3 = [12]
4. 3 * 6 = [15]
5. 50 * 25 = [100]
6. 25 * 50 = [125]
7. $\hat{2}$ * 3 = [4]
8. 3 * $\hat{2}$ = [7]
9. $\hat{5}$ * 2 = [7]
10. 2 * $\hat{5}$ = [8]

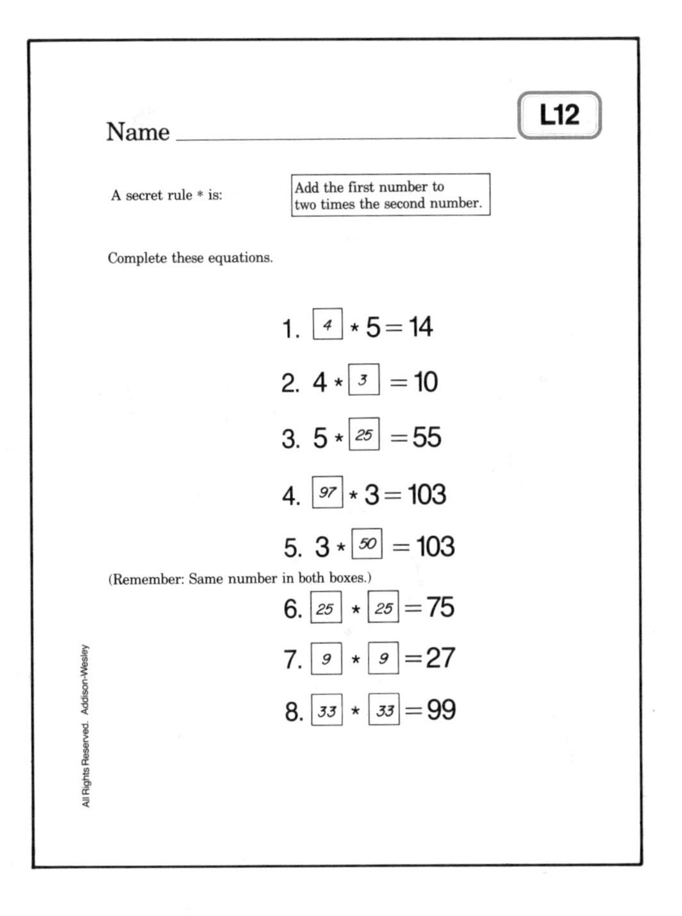

Name ____________________ **L12**

A secret rule * is: Add the first number to two times the second number.

Complete these equations.

1. [4] * 5 = 14
2. 4 * [3] = 10
3. 5 * [25] = 55
4. [97] * 3 = 103
5. 3 * [50] = 103

(Remember: Same number in both boxes.)

6. [25] * [25] = 75
7. [9] * [9] = 27
8. [33] * [33] = 99

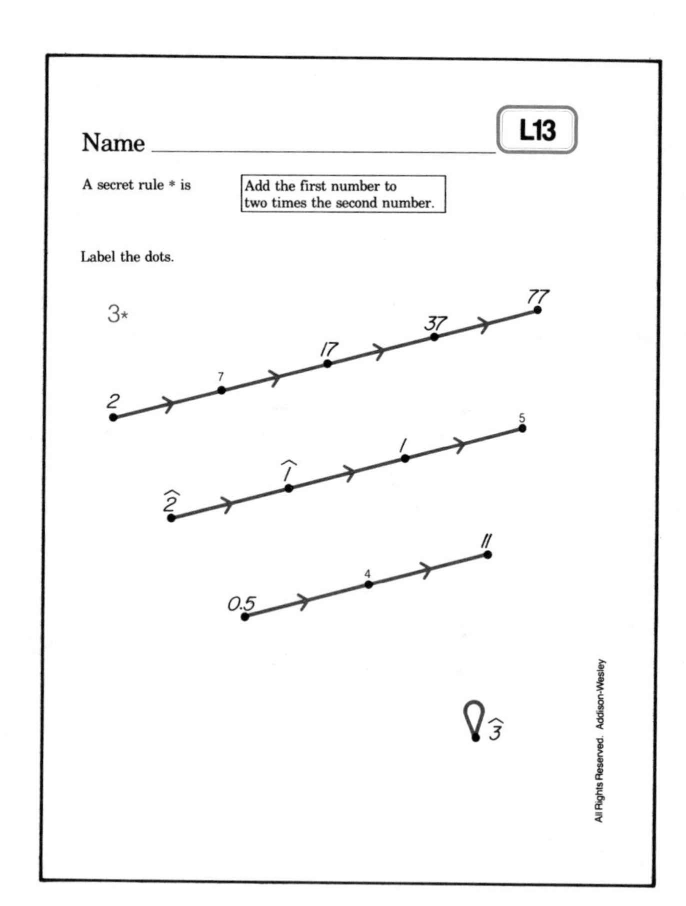

Name ____________ **L13**

A secret rule * is: Add the first number to two times the second number.

Label the dots.

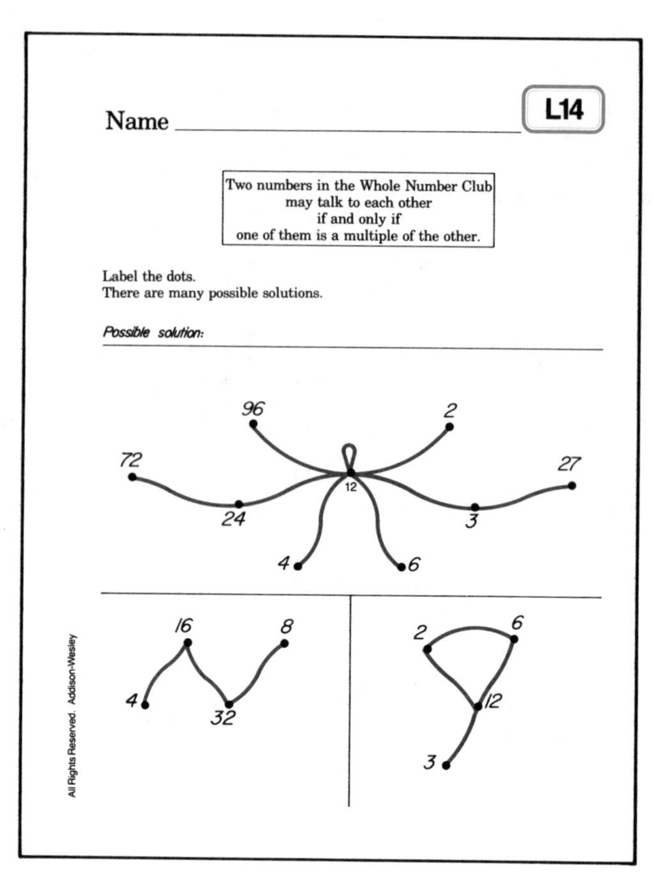

Name ____________ **L14**

Two numbers in the Whole Number Club may talk to each other if and only if one of them is a multiple of the other.

Label the dots.
There are many possible solutions.

Possible solution:

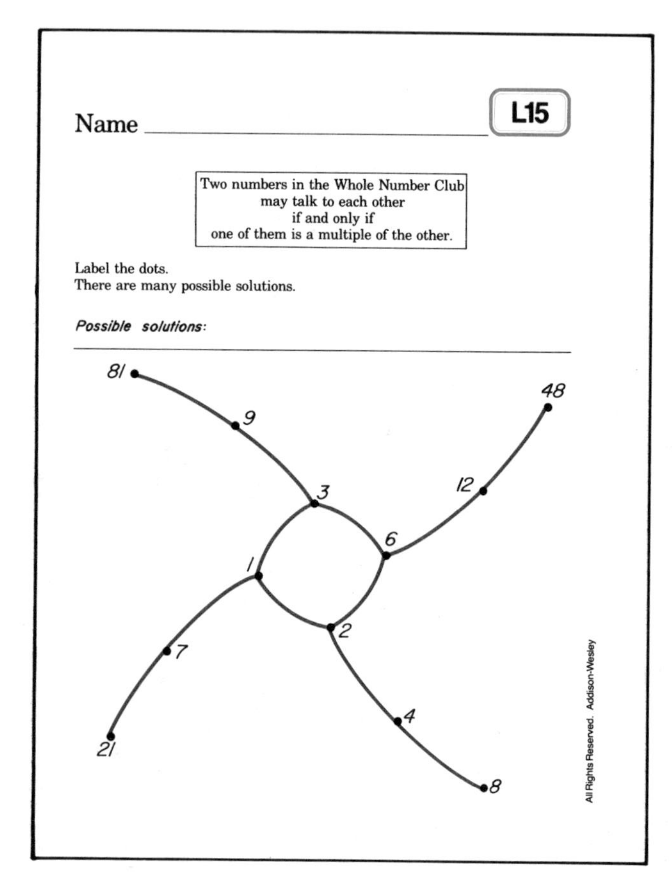

Name ____________ **L15**

Two numbers in the Whole Number Club may talk to each other if and only if one of them is a multiple of the other.

Label the dots.
There are many possible solutions.

Possible solutions:

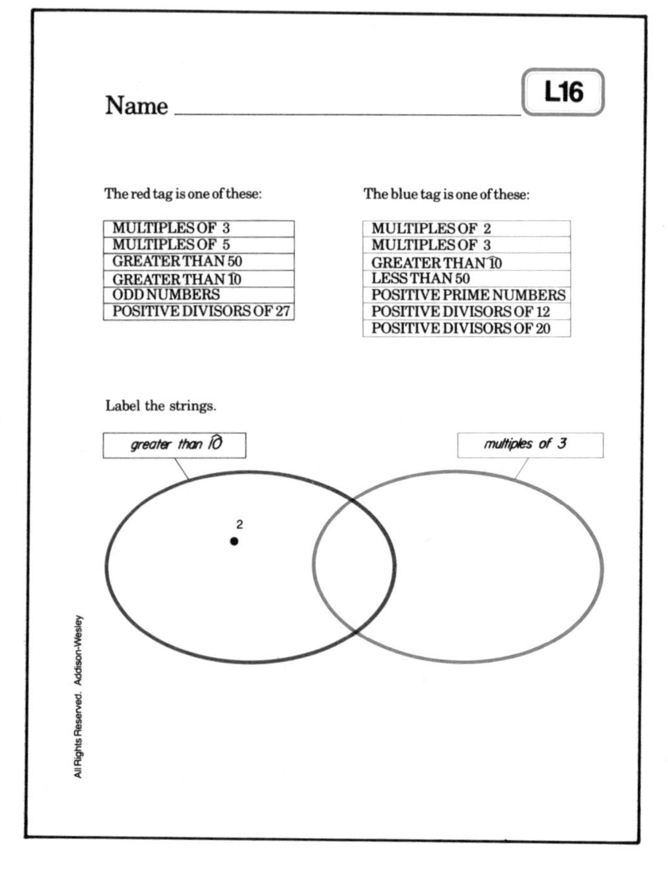

Name ____________ **L16**

The red tag is one of these:

MULTIPLES OF 3
MULTIPLES OF 5
GREATER THAN 50
GREATER THAN 10̂
ODD NUMBERS
POSITIVE DIVISORS OF 27

The blue tag is one of these:

MULTIPLES OF 2
MULTIPLES OF 3
GREATER THAN 10̂
LESS THAN 50
POSITIVE PRIME NUMBERS
POSITIVE DIVISORS OF 12
POSITIVE DIVISORS OF 20

Label the strings.

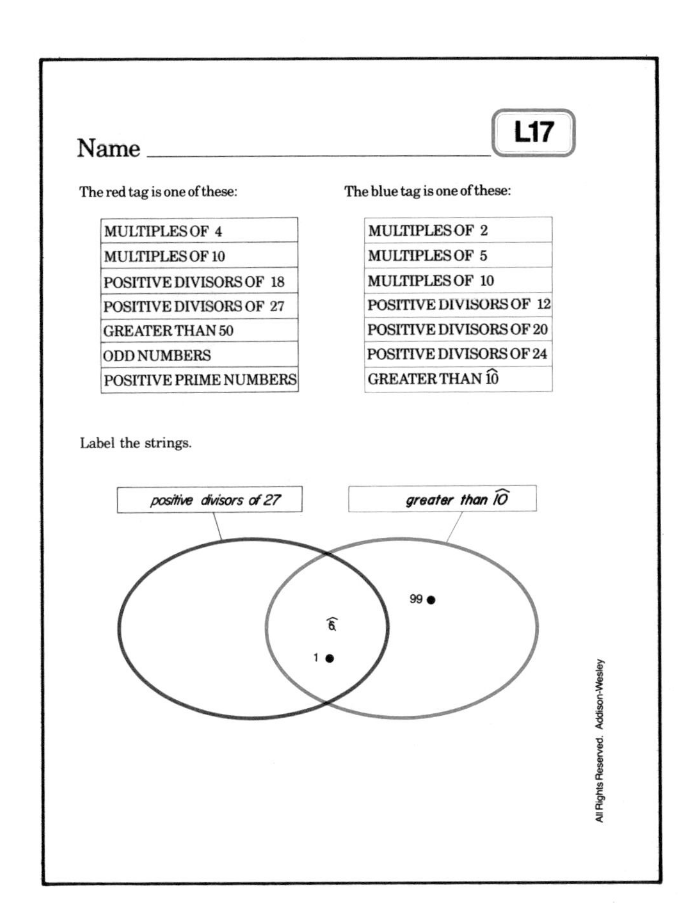

Name ______________________ **L17**

The red tag is one of these:

MULTIPLES OF 4
MULTIPLES OF 10
POSITIVE DIVISORS OF 18
POSITIVE DIVISORS OF 27
GREATER THAN 50
ODD NUMBERS
POSITIVE PRIME NUMBERS

The blue tag is one of these:

MULTIPLES OF 2
MULTIPLES OF 5
MULTIPLES OF 10
POSITIVE DIVISORS OF 12
POSITIVE DIVISORS OF 20
POSITIVE DIVISORS OF 24
GREATER THAN $\widehat{10}$

Label the strings.

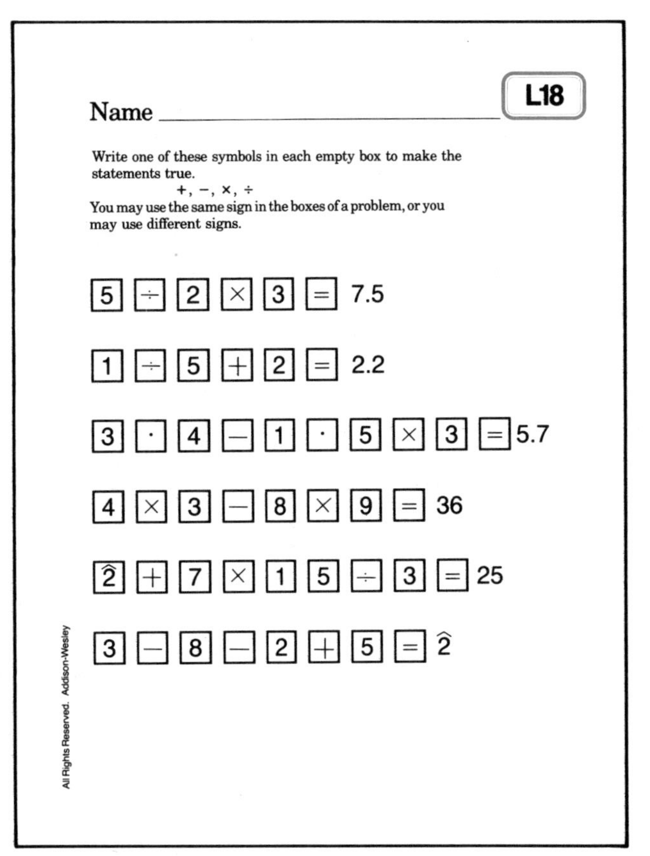

Name ______________________ **L18**

Write one of these symbols in each empty box to make the statements true.

+, −, ×, ÷

You may use the same sign in the boxes of a problem, or you may use different signs.

5 ÷ 2 × 3 = 7.5

1 ÷ 5 + 2 = 2.2

3 . 4 − 1 . 5 × 3 = 5.7

4 × 3 − 8 × 9 = 36

$\hat{2}$ + 7 × 1 5 ÷ 3 = 25

3 − 8 − 2 + 5 = $\hat{2}$

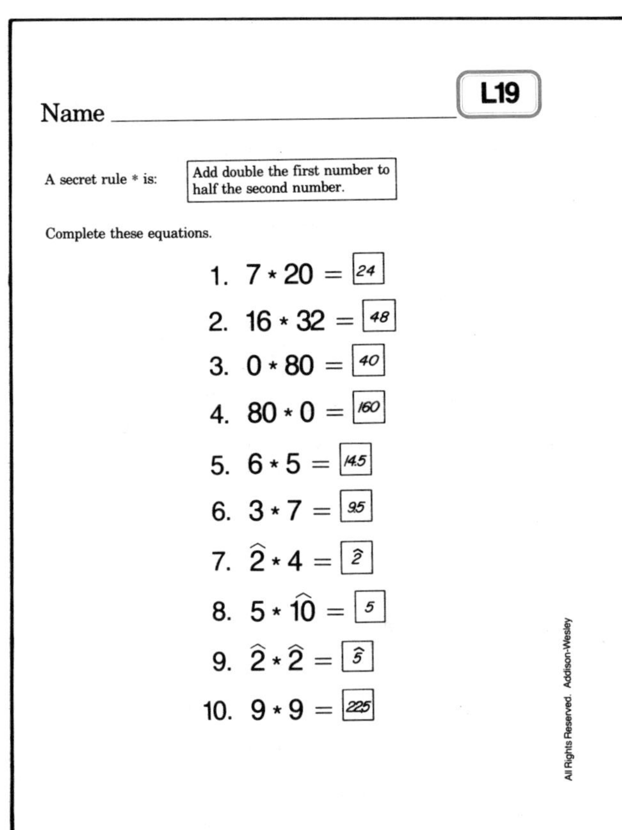

Name ______________________ **L19**

A secret rule * is: Add double the first number to half the second number.

Complete these equations.

1. 7 * 20 = 24
2. 16 * 32 = 48
3. 0 * 80 = 40
4. 80 * 0 = 160
5. 6 * 5 = 14.5
6. 3 * 7 = 9.5
7. $\hat{2}$ * 4 = $\hat{2}$
8. 5 * $\widehat{10}$ = 5
9. $\hat{2}$ * $\hat{2}$ = $\hat{5}$
10. 9 * 9 = 22.5

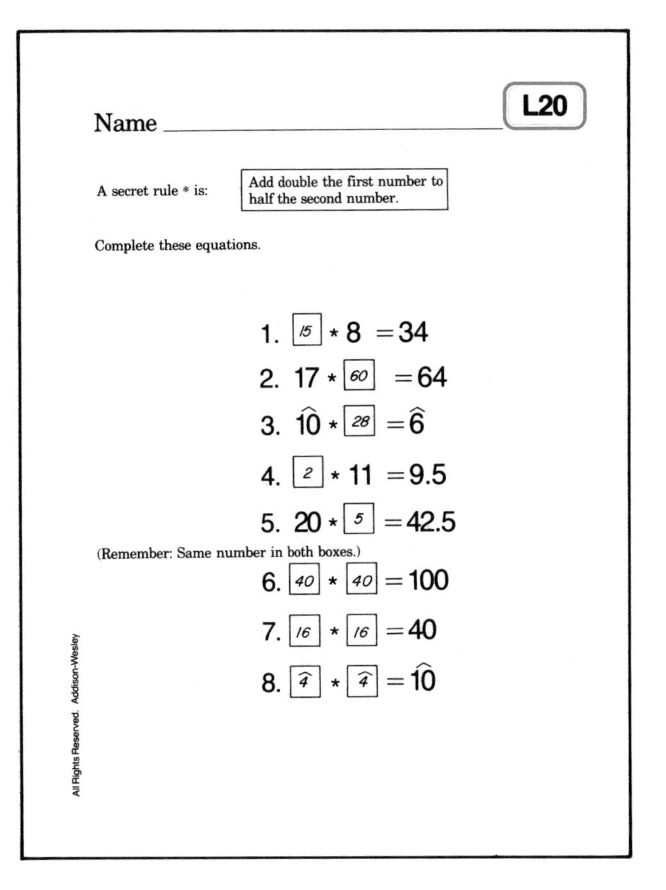

Name ______________________ **L20**

A secret rule * is: Add double the first number to half the second number.

Complete these equations.

1. 15 * 8 = 34
2. 17 * 60 = 64
3. $\widehat{10}$ * 28 = $\hat{6}$
4. 2 * 11 = 9.5
5. 20 * 5 = 42.5

(Remember: Same number in both boxes.)

6. 40 * 40 = 100
7. 16 * 16 = 40
8. $\hat{4}$ * $\hat{4}$ = $\widehat{10}$

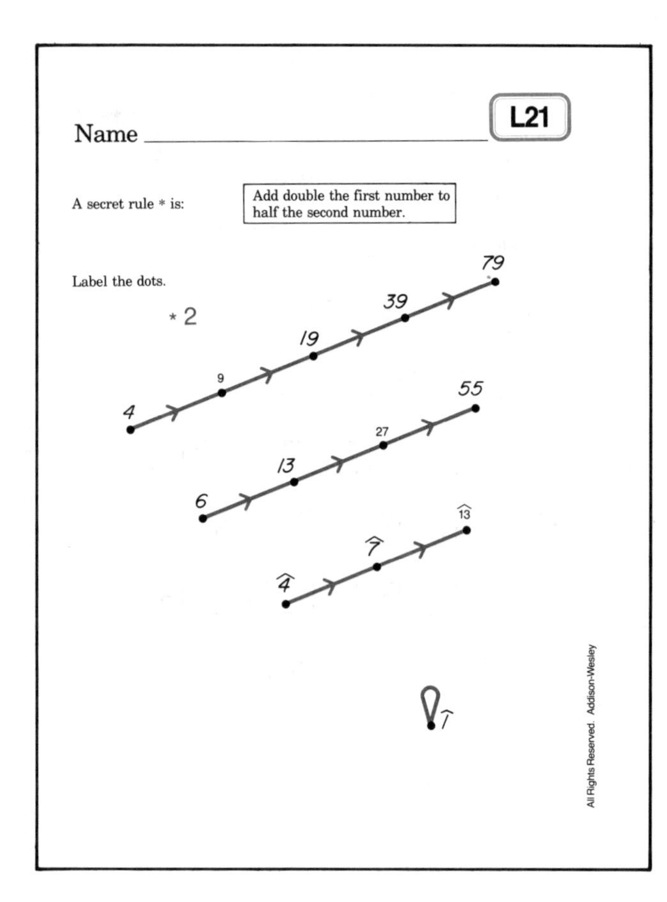
Name ____________ **L21**

A secret rule * is: Add double the first number to half the second number.

Label the dots.

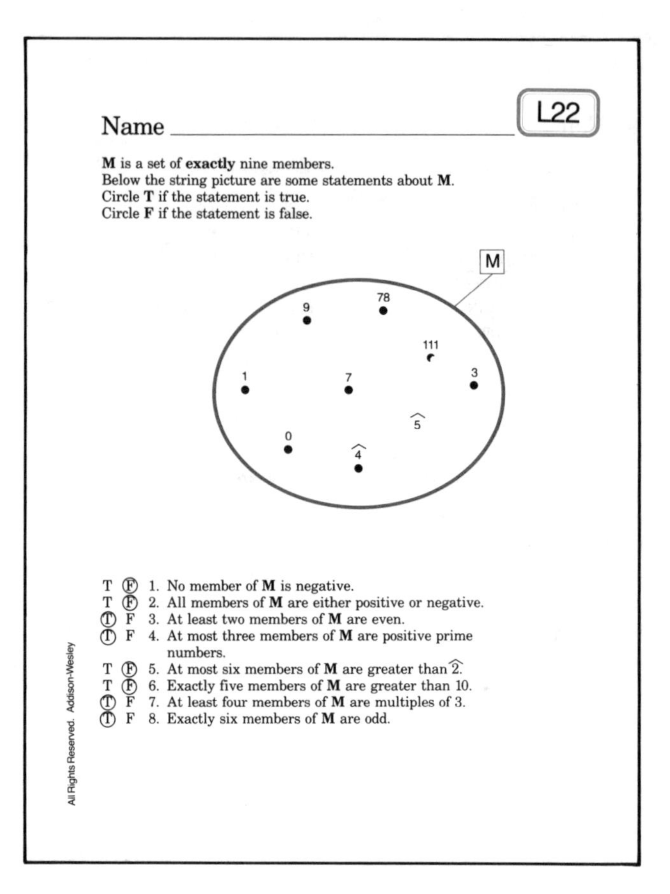
Name ____________ **L22**

M is a set of **exactly** nine members.
Below the string picture are some statements about **M**.
Circle **T** if the statement is true.
Circle **F** if the statement is false.

T (F) 1. No member of **M** is negative.
T (F) 2. All members of **M** are either positive or negative.
(T) F 3. At least two members of **M** are even.
(T) F 4. At most three members of **M** are positive prime numbers.
T (F) 5. At most six members of **M** are greater than 2.
T (F) 6. Exactly five members of **M** are greater than 10.
(T) F 7. At least four members of **M** are multiples of 3.
(T) F 8. Exactly six members of **M** are odd.

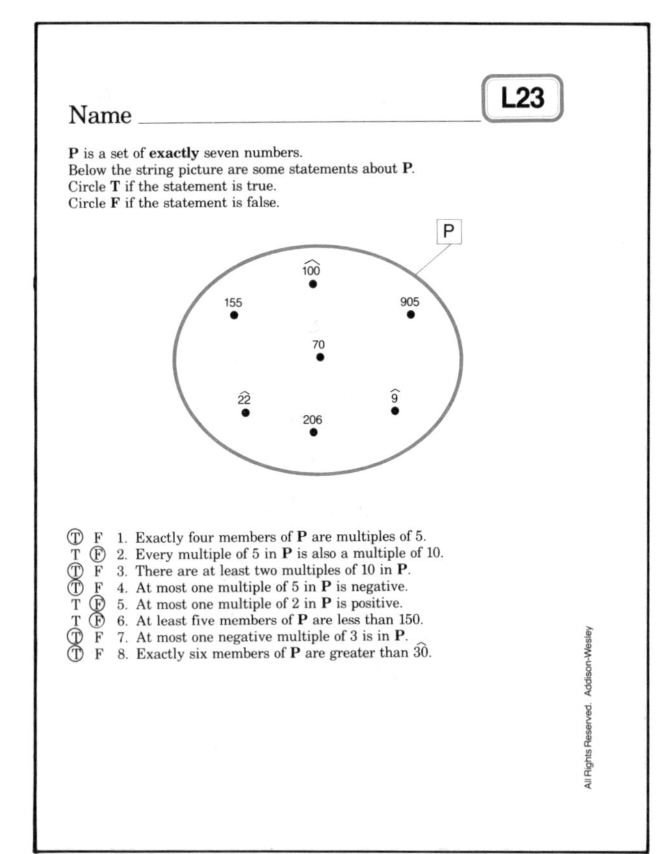
Name ____________ **L23**

P is a set of **exactly** seven numbers.
Below the string picture are some statements about **P**.
Circle **T** if the statement is true.
Circle **F** if the statement is false.

(T) F 1. Exactly four members of **P** are multiples of 5.
T (F) 2. Every multiple of 5 in **P** is also a multiple of 10.
(T) F 3. There are at least two multiples of 10 in **P**.
(T) F 4. At most one multiple of 5 in **P** is negative.
T (F) 5. At most one multiple of 2 in **P** is positive.
T (F) 6. At least five members of **P** are less than 150.
(T) F 7. At most one negative multiple of 3 is in **P**.
(T) F 8. Exactly six members of **P** are greater than 30.

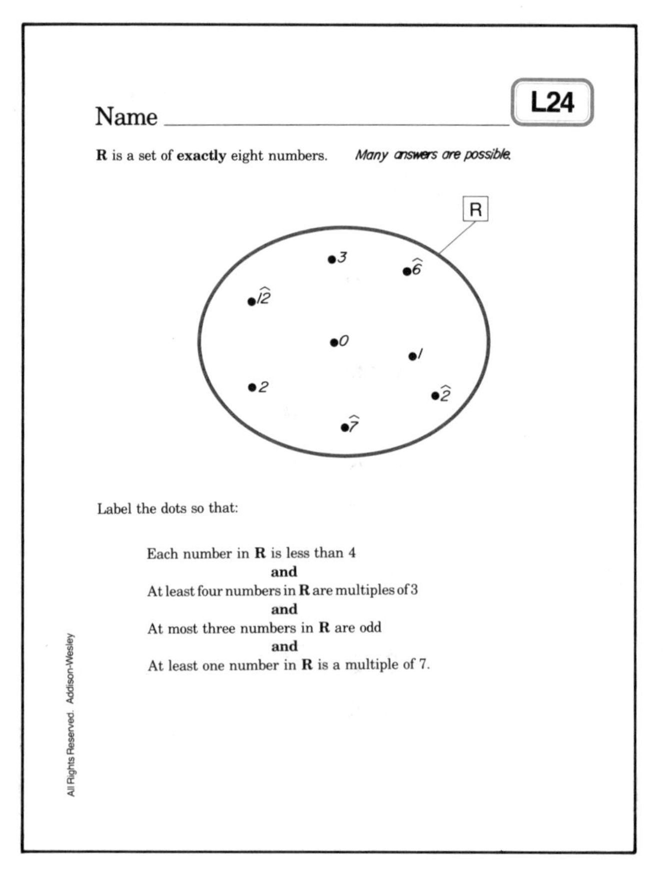
Name ____________ **L24**

R is a set of **exactly** eight numbers. *Many answers are possible.*

Label the dots so that:

Each number in **R** is less than 4
and
At least four numbers in **R** are multiples of 3
and
At most three numbers in **R** are odd
and
At least one number in **R** is a multiple of 7.

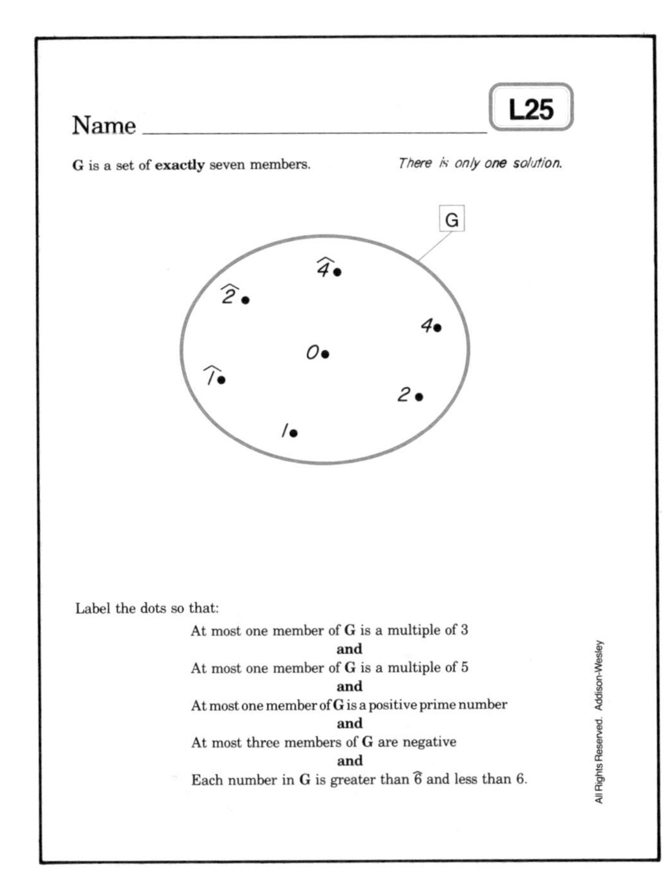

Name ______________________ **L25**

G is a set of **exactly** seven members. *There is only one solution.*

Label the dots so that:

At most one member of **G** is a multiple of 3
and
At most one member of **G** is a multiple of 5
and
At most one member of **G** is a positive prime number
and
At most three members of **G** are negative
and
Each number in **G** is greater than $\hat{6}$ and less than 6.

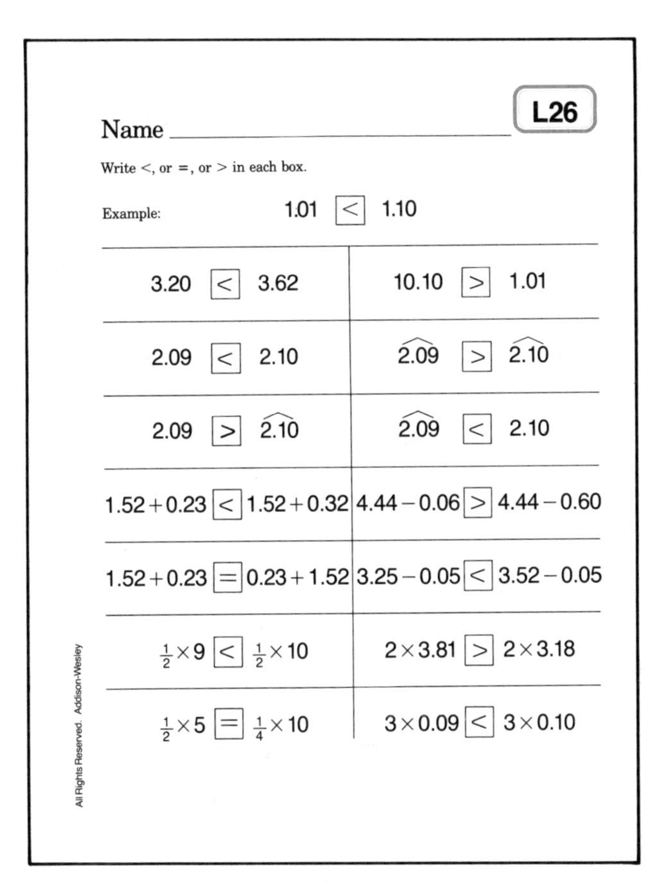

Name ______________________ **L26**

Write <, or =, or > in each box.

Example: 1.01 [<] 1.10

3.20 [<] 3.62	10.10 [>] 1.01
2.09 [<] 2.10	$\hat{2.09}$ [>] $\hat{2.10}$
2.09 [>] $\hat{2.10}$	$\hat{2.09}$ [<] 2.10
1.52 + 0.23 [<] 1.52 + 0.32	4.44 − 0.06 [>] 4.44 − 0.60
1.52 + 0.23 [=] 0.23 + 1.52	3.25 − 0.05 [<] 3.52 − 0.05
$\frac{1}{2} \times 9$ [<] $\frac{1}{2} \times 10$	2 × 3.81 [>] 2 × 3.18
$\frac{1}{2} \times 5$ [=] $\frac{1}{4} \times 10$	3 × 0.09 [<] 3 × 0.10

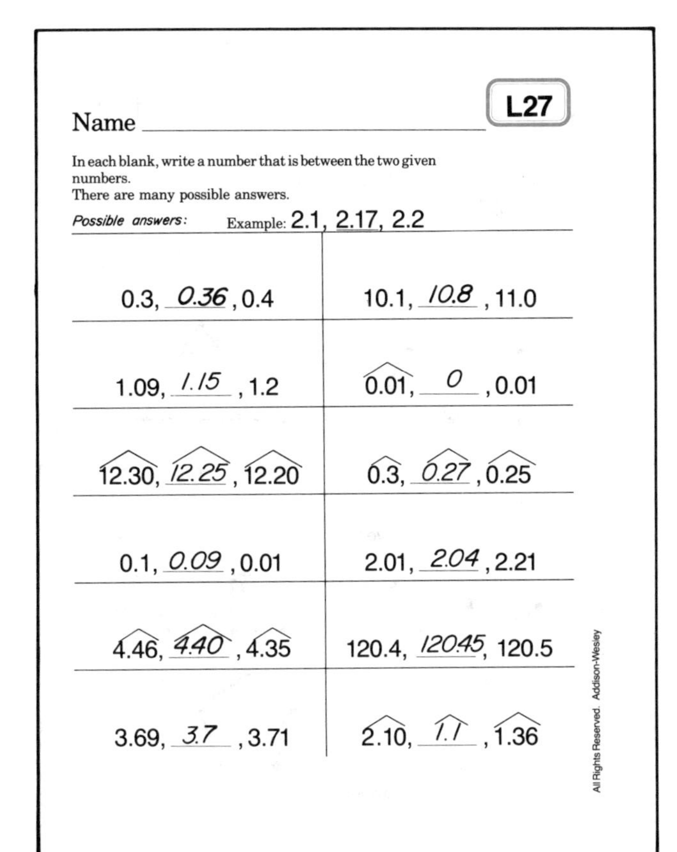

Name ______________________ **L27**

In each blank, write a number that is between the two given numbers.
There are many possible answers.

Possible answers: Example: 2.1, 2.17, 2.2

0.3, *0.36*, 0.4	10.1, *10.8*, 11.0
1.09, *1.15*, 1.2	$\hat{0.01}$, *0*, 0.01
$\hat{12.30}$, *$\hat{12.25}$*, $\hat{12.20}$	$\hat{0.3}$, *$\hat{0.27}$*, $\hat{0.25}$
0.1, *0.09*, 0.01	2.01, *2.04*, 2.21
$\hat{4.46}$, *$\hat{4.40}$*, $\hat{4.35}$	120.4, *120.45*, 120.5
3.69, *3.7*, 3.71	$\hat{2.10}$, *$\hat{1.1}$*, $\hat{1.36}$

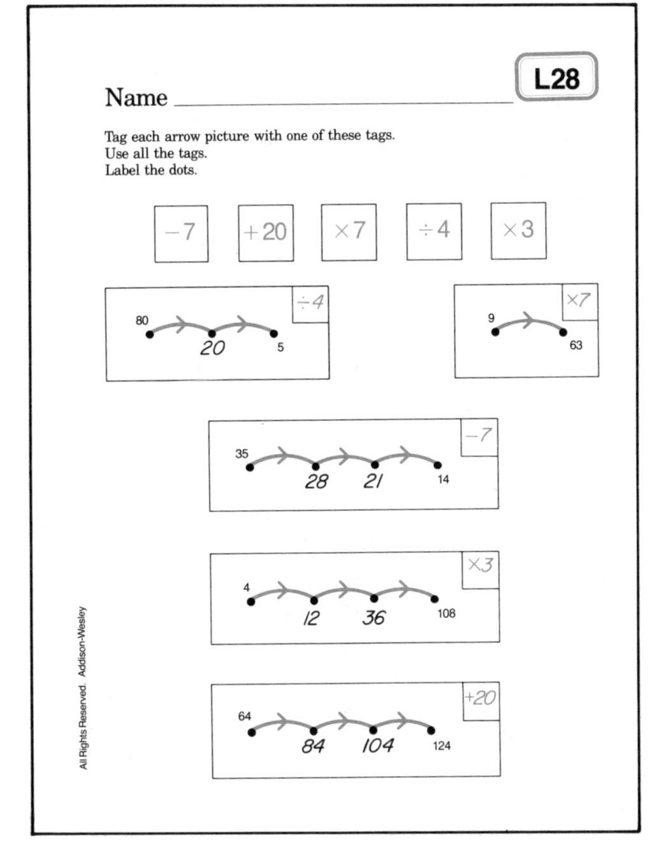

Name ______________________ **L28**

Tag each arrow picture with one of these tags.
Use all the tags.
Label the dots.

[−7] [+20] [×7] [÷4] [×3]

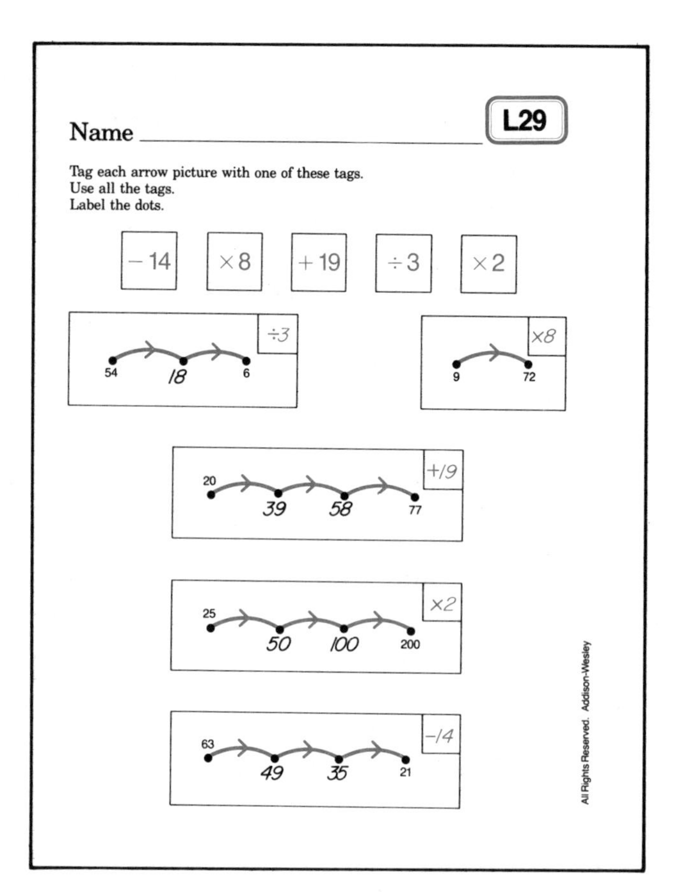
Name
L29
Tag each arrow picture with one of these tags.
Use all the tags.
Label the dots.
− 14
× 8
+ 19
÷ 3
× 2
÷3
54
18
6
×8
9
72
+19
20
39
58
77
×2
25
50
100
200
−14
63
49
35
21
All Rights Reserved. Addison-Wesley

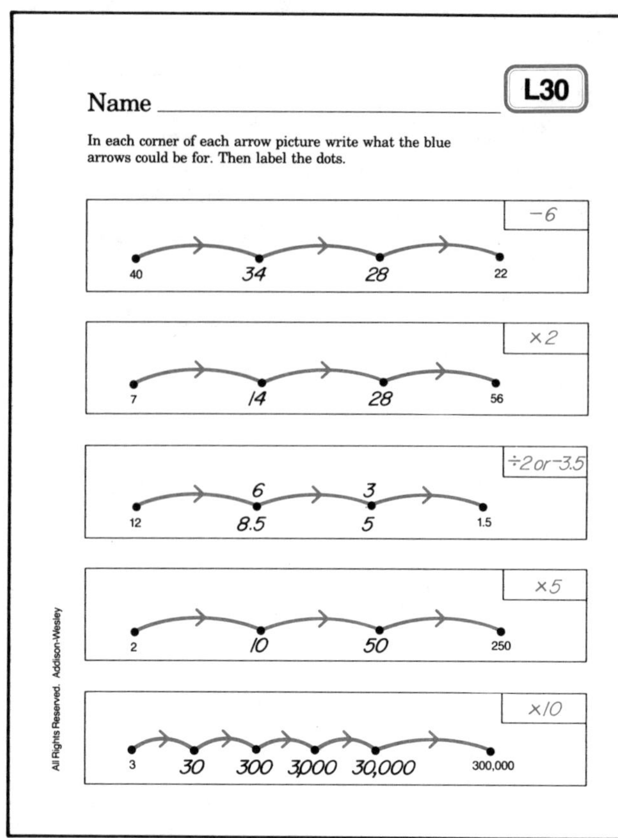
Name
L30
In each corner of each arrow picture write what the blue arrows could be for. Then label the dots.
−6
40
34
28
22
×2
7
14
28
56
÷2 or −3.5
12
6
8.5
3
5
1.5
×5
2
10
50
250
×10
3
30
300
3,000
30,000
300,000
All Rights Reserved. Addison-Wesley

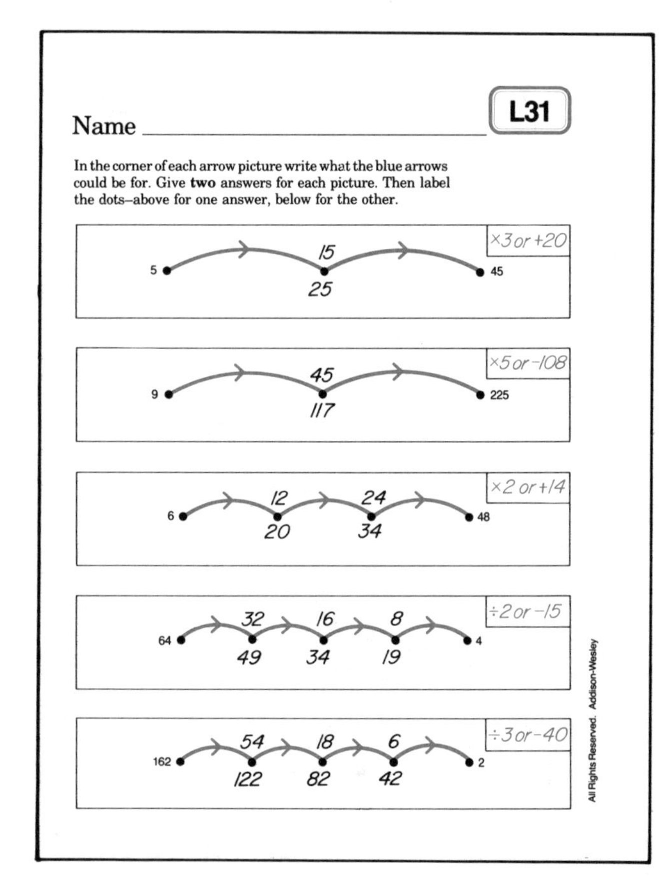
Name
L31
In the corner of each arrow picture write what the blue arrows could be for. Give two answers for each picture. Then label the dots–above for one answer, below for the other.
×3 or +20
5
15
25
45
×5 or −108
9
45
117
225
×2 or +14
6
12
20
24
34
48
÷2 or −15
64
32
49
16
34
8
19
4
÷3 or −40
162
54
122
18
82
6
42
2
All Rights Reserved. Addison-Wesley

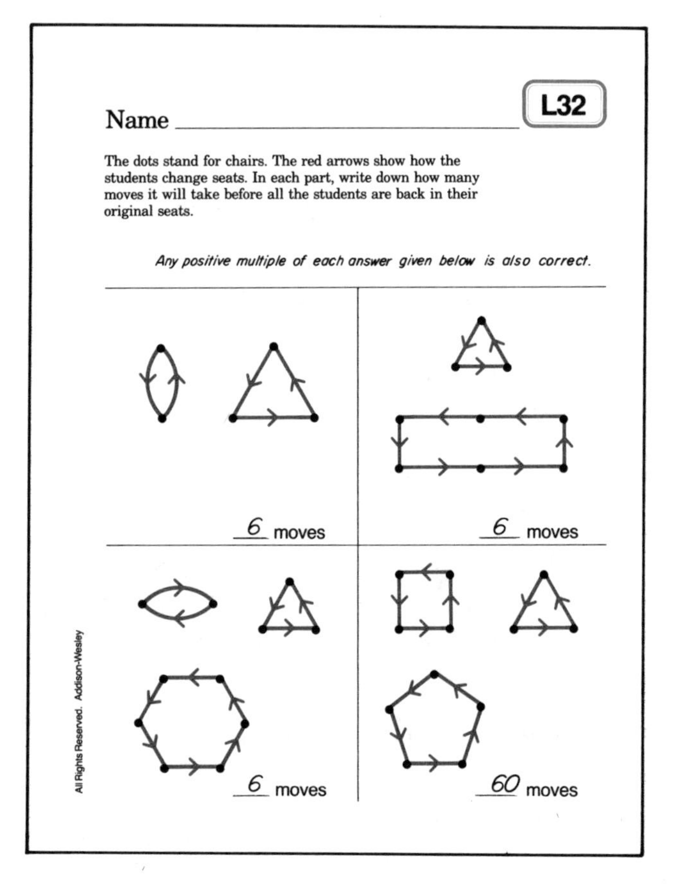
Name
L32
The dots stand for chairs. The red arrows show how the students change seats. In each part, write down how many moves it will take before all the students are back in their original seats.
Any positive multiple of each answer given below is also correct.
6 moves
6 moves
6 moves
60 moves
All Rights Reserved. Addison-Wesley

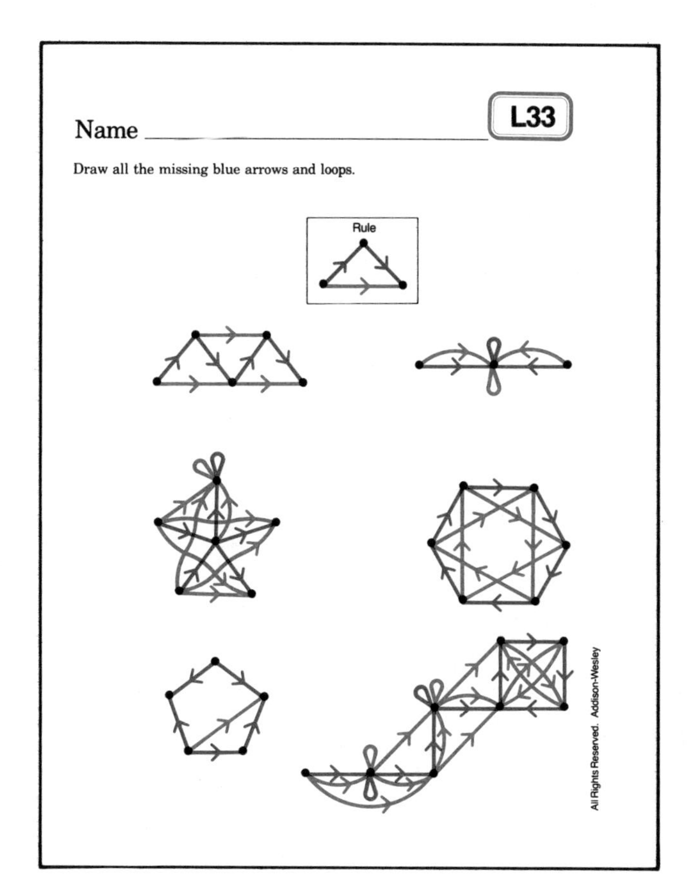

Name ______________ **L33**

Draw all the missing blue arrows and loops.

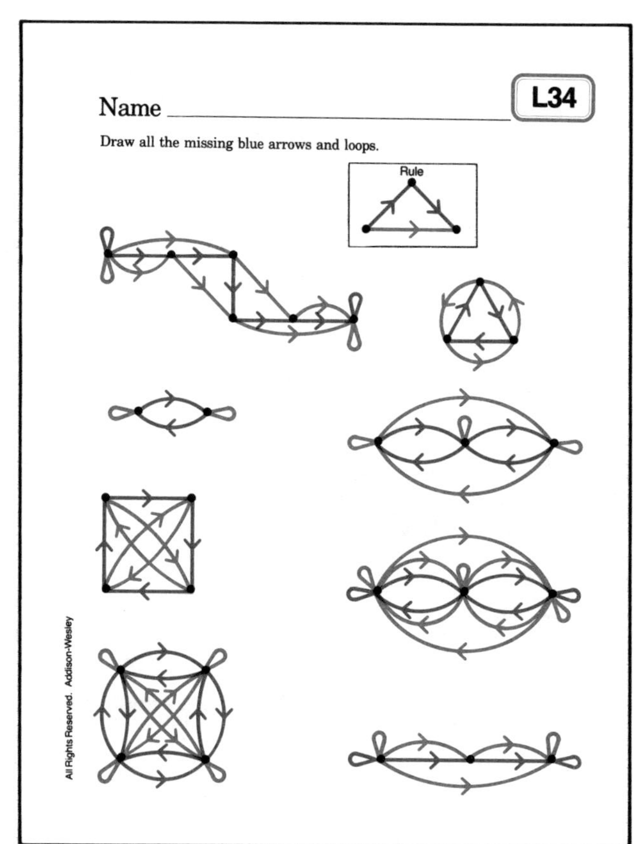

Name ______________ **L34**

Draw all the missing blue arrows and loops.

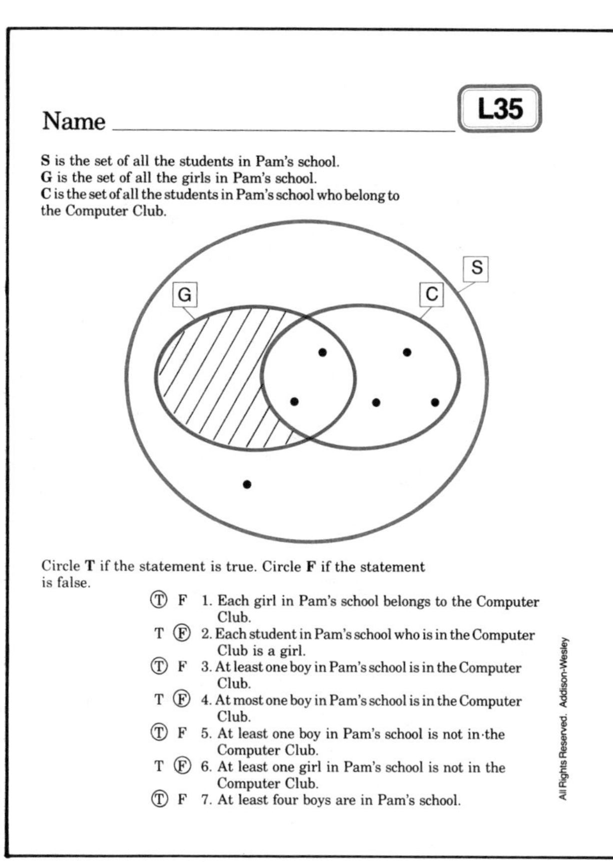

Name ______________ **L35**

S is the set of all the students in Pam's school.
G is the set of all the girls in Pam's school.
C is the set of all the students in Pam's school who belong to the Computer Club.

Circle **T** if the statement is true. Circle **F** if the statement is false.

(T) F 1. Each girl in Pam's school belongs to the Computer Club.
T (F) 2. Each student in Pam's school who is in the Computer Club is a girl.
(T) F 3. At least one boy in Pam's school is in the Computer Club.
T (F) 4. At most one boy in Pam's school is in the Computer Club.
(T) F 5. At least one boy in Pam's school is not in the Computer Club.
T (F) 6. At least one girl in Pam's school is not in the Computer Club.
(T) F 7. At least four boys are in Pam's school.

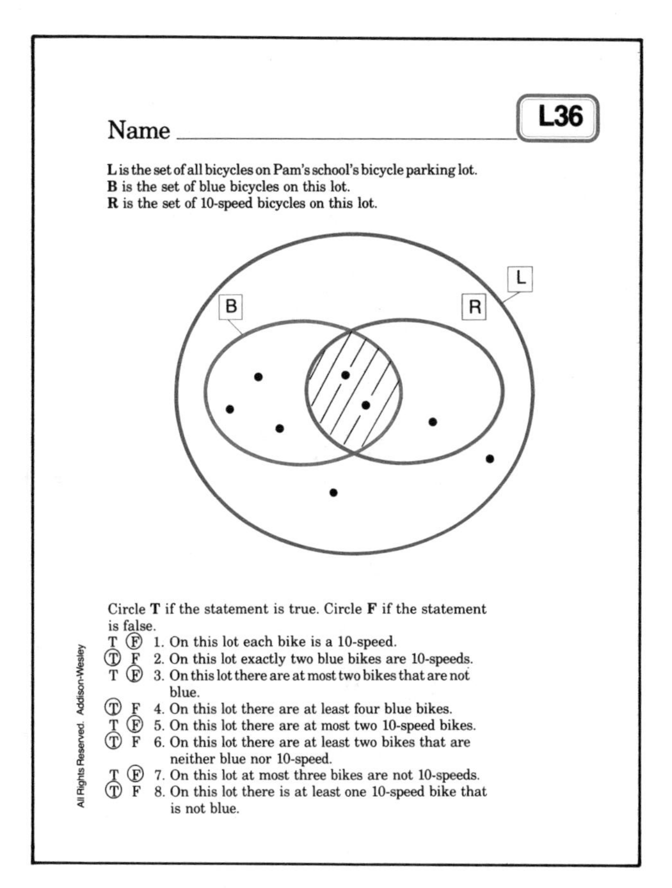

Name ______________ **L36**

L is the set of all bicycles on Pam's school's bicycle parking lot.
B is the set of blue bicycles on this lot.
R is the set of 10-speed bicycles on this lot.

Circle **T** if the statement is true. Circle **F** if the statement is false.

T (F) 1. On this lot each bike is a 10-speed.
(T) F 2. On this lot exactly two blue bikes are 10-speeds.
T (F) 3. On this lot there are at most two bikes that are not blue.
(T) F 4. On this lot there are at least four blue bikes.
T (F) 5. On this lot there are at most two 10-speed bikes.
(T) F 6. On this lot there are at least two bikes that are neither blue nor 10-speed.
T (F) 7. On this lot at most three bikes are not 10-speeds.
(T) F 8. On this lot there is at least one 10-speed bike that is not blue.

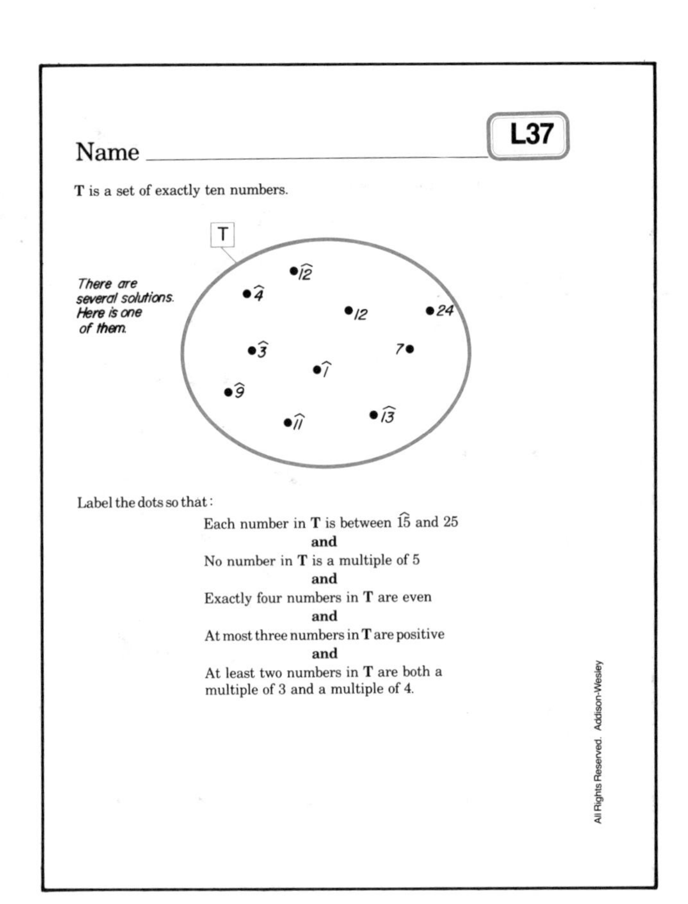

Name ____________________ **L37**

T is a set of exactly ten numbers.

Label the dots so that:

Each number in **T** is between $\widehat{15}$ and 25
and
No number in **T** is a multiple of 5
and
Exactly four numbers in **T** are even
and
At most three numbers in **T** are positive
and
At least two numbers in **T** are both a multiple of 3 and a multiple of 4.

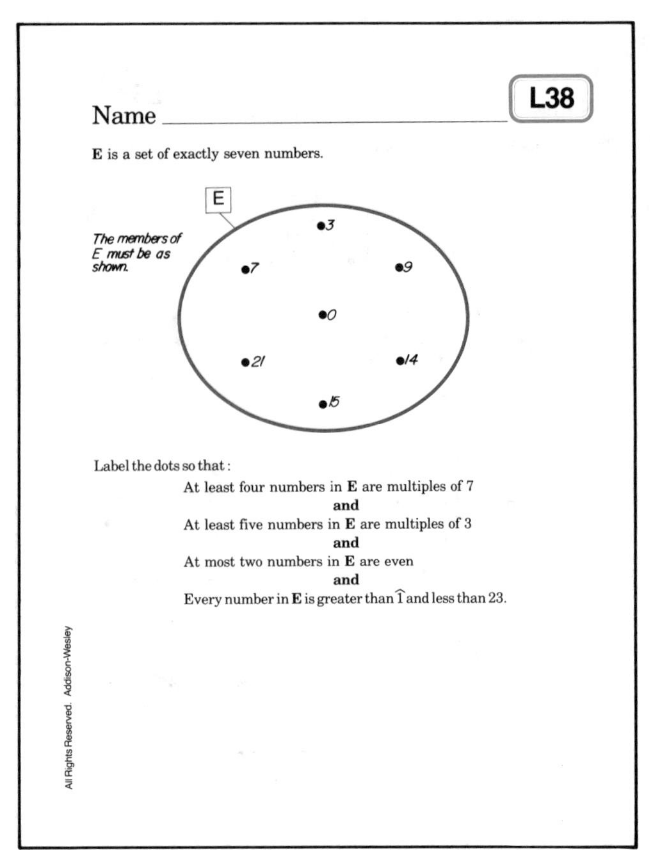

Name ____________________ **L38**

E is a set of exactly seven numbers.

Label the dots so that:

At least four numbers in **E** are multiples of 7
and
At least five numbers in **E** are multiples of 3
and
At most two numbers in **E** are even
and
Every number in **E** is greater than $\widehat{1}$ and less than 23.

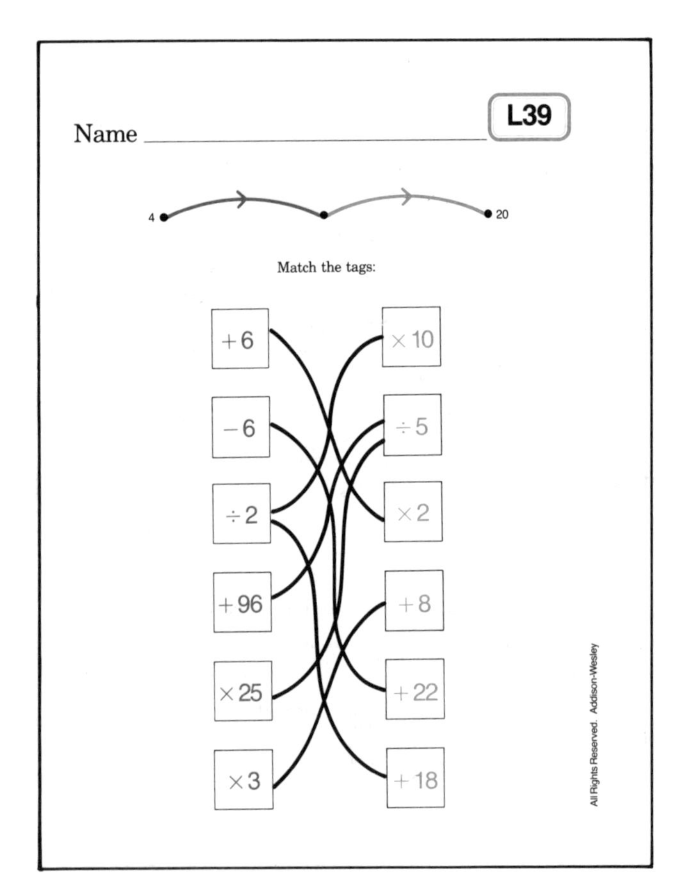

Name ____________________ **L39**

Match the tags:

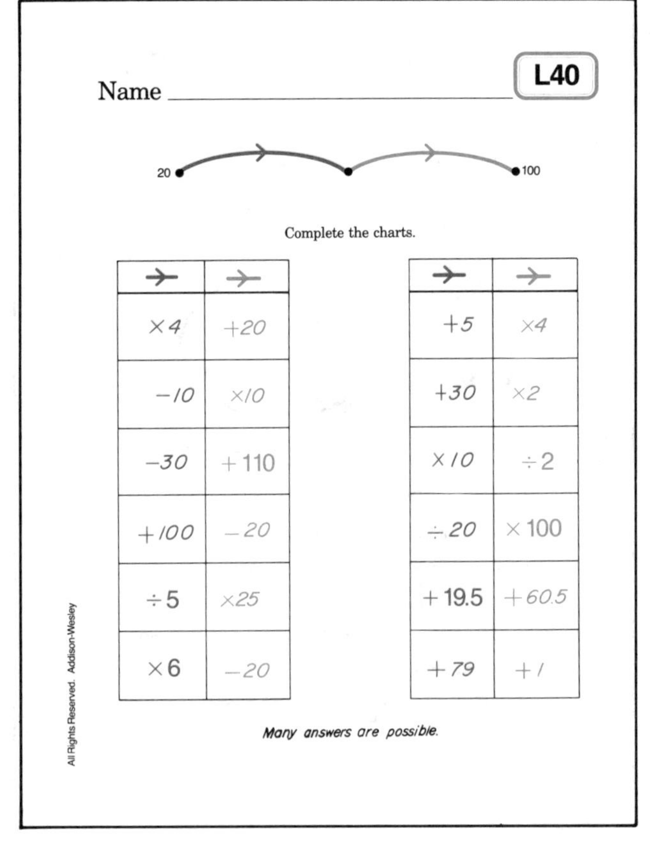

Name ____________________ **L40**

Complete the charts.

→	→
×4	+20
−10	×10
−30	+110
+100	−20
÷5	×25
×6	−20

→	→
+5	×4
+30	×2
×10	÷2
÷20	×100
+19.5	+60.5
+79	+1

Many answers are possible.

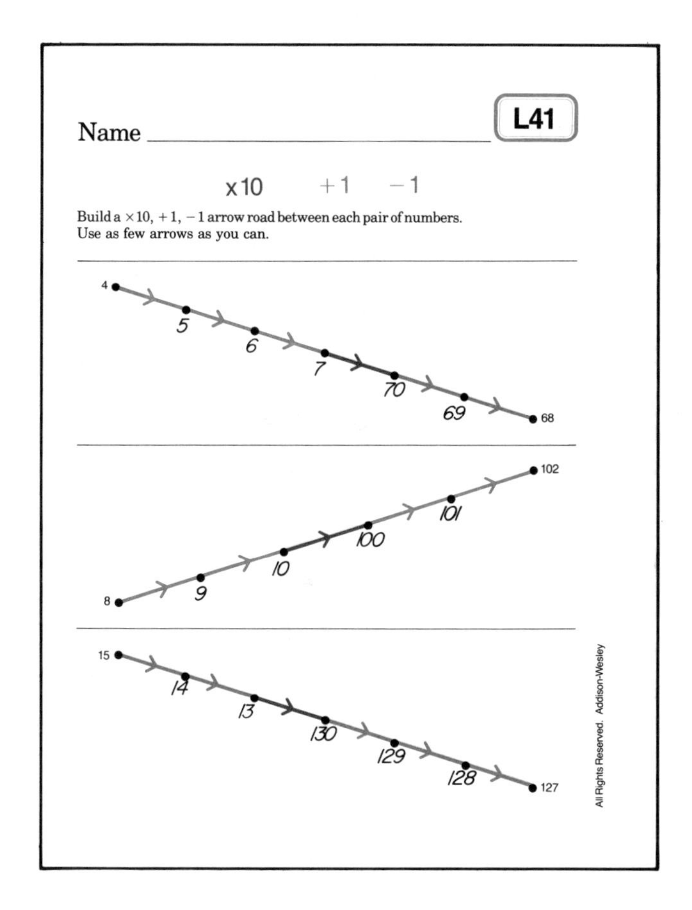

Name
L41
x10 +1 −1
Build a ×10, +1, −1 arrow road between each pair of numbers.
Use as few arrows as you can.
4 5 6 7 70 69 68
8 9 10 100 101 102
15 14 13 130 129 128 127
All Rights Reserved. Addison-Wesley

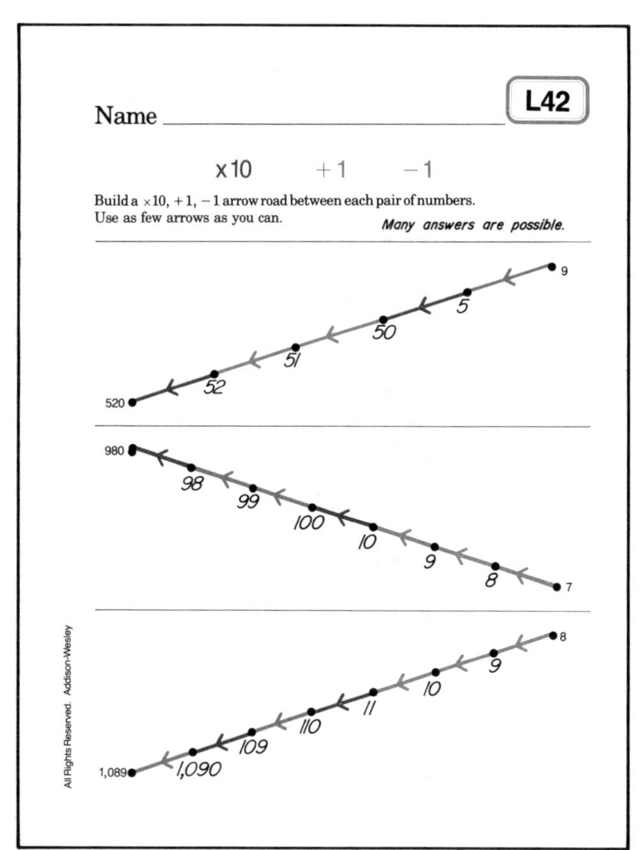

Name
L42
x10 +1 −1
Build a ×10, +1, −1 arrow road between each pair of numbers.
Use as few arrows as you can.
Many answers are possible.
9 5 50 51 52 520
980 98 99 100 10 9 8 7
8 9 10 11 110 109 1,090 1,089
All Rights Reserved. Addison-Wesley

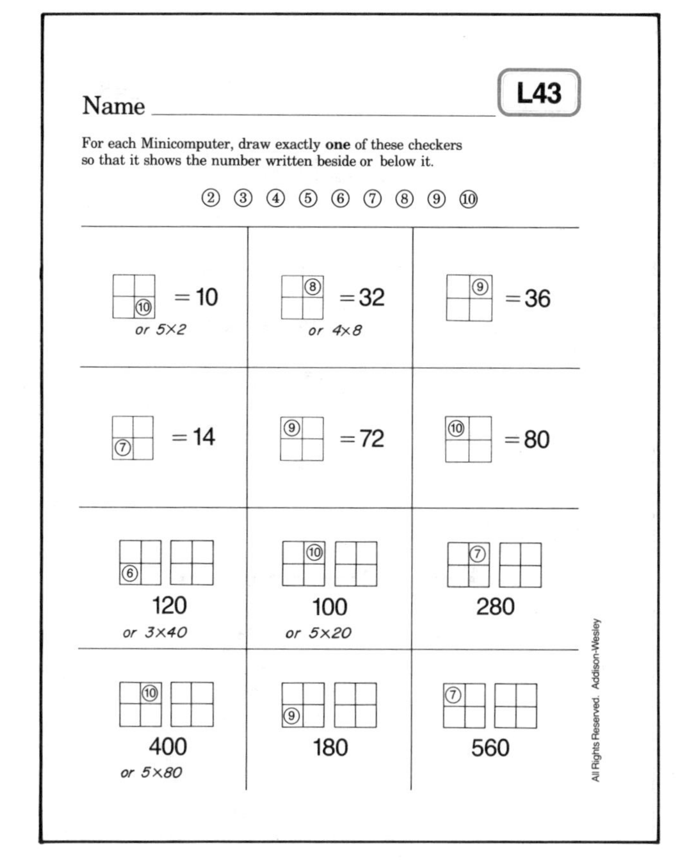

Name
L43
For each Minicomputer, draw exactly one of these checkers
so that it shows the number written beside or below it.
② ③ ④ ⑤ ⑥ ⑦ ⑧ ⑨ ⑩
= 10
or 5×2
= 32
or 4×8
= 36
= 14
= 72
= 80
120
or 3×40
100
or 5×20
280
400
or 5×80
180
560
All Rights Reserved. Addison-Wesley

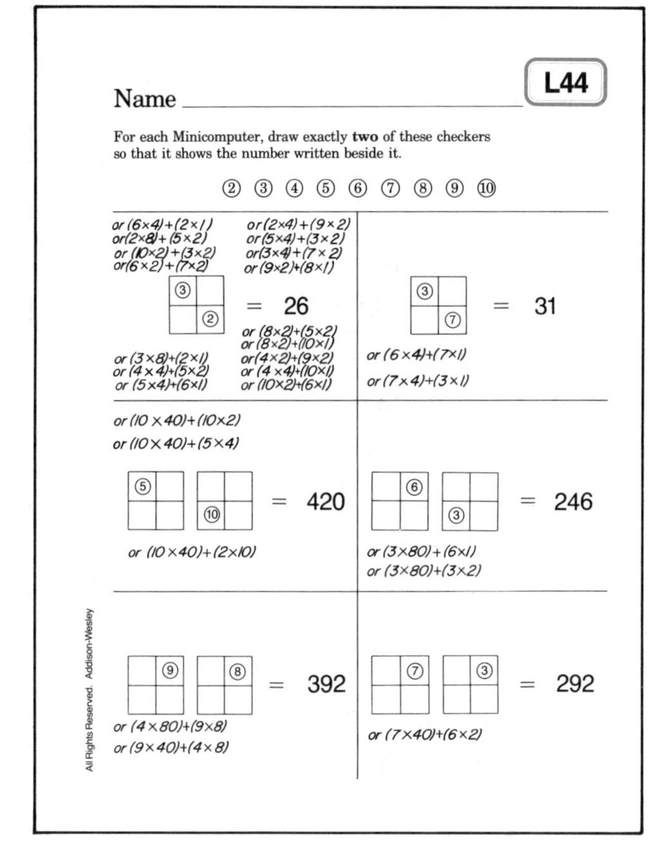

Name
L44
For each Minicomputer, draw exactly two of these checkers
so that it shows the number written beside it.
② ③ ④ ⑤ ⑥ ⑦ ⑧ ⑨ ⑩
or (6×4)+(2×1)
or (2×8)+(5×2)
or (10×2)+(3×2)
or (6×2)+(7×2)
or (2×4)+(9×2)
or (5×4)+(3×2)
or (3×4)+(7×2)
or (9×2)+(8×1)
= 26
or (8×2)+(5×2)
or (8×2)+(10×1)
or (4×2)+(9×2)
or (4×4)+(10×1)
or (10×2)+(6×1)
or (3×8)+(2×1)
or (4×4)+(5×2)
or (5×4)+(6×1)
= 31
or (6×4)+(7×1)
or (7×4)+(3×1)
or (10×40)+(10×2)
or (10×40)+(5×4)
= 420
or (10×40)+(2×10)
= 246
or (3×80)+(6×1)
or (3×80)+(3×2)
= 392
or (4×80)+(9×8)
or (9×40)+(4×8)
= 292
or (7×40)+(6×2)
All Rights Reserved. Addison-Wesley

Name ______________________ **L45**

Complete these equations.

1. $7-\widehat{3}=$ [10]
2. $2-5=$ [$\widehat{3}$]
3. $\widehat{4}-6=$ [$\widehat{10}$]
4. $\widehat{8}-\widehat{12}=$ [4]
5. $\widehat{12}-\widehat{8}=$ [$\widehat{4}$]
6. $13-\widehat{17}=$ [30]
7. $\widehat{21}-15=$ [$\widehat{36}$]
8. $0-8=$ [$\widehat{8}$]
9. $0-\widehat{8}=$ [8]

Name ______________________ **L46**

Complete these equations.

1. $5-$ [7] $=\widehat{2}$
2. $10-$ [3] $=7$
3. $10-$ [17] $=\widehat{7}$
4. $\widehat{10}-$ [$\widehat{17}$] $=7$
5. [8] $-5=3$
6. [2] $-5=\widehat{3}$
7. [5] $-\widehat{2}=7$
8. [$\widehat{12}$] $-\widehat{12}=0$

Name ______________________ **L47**

A secret rule * is: Add the two numbers and then take one-half of the sum.

Complete these equations.

1. $4 * 14=$ 9
2. $20 * 32=$ 26
3. $18 * 18=$ 18
4. $\widehat{5} * 13=$ 4
5. $\widehat{50} * 20=$ $\widehat{15}$
6. $\widehat{3} * \widehat{9}=$ $\widehat{6}$
7. $8 * 3=$ 5.5
8. $8 * \widehat{3}=$ 2.5
9. $3 * \widehat{8}=$ $\widehat{2.5}$
10. $9 * 9=$ 9
11. $105 * 105=$ 105
12. $\widehat{15} * \widehat{15}=$ $\widehat{15}$

Name ______________________ **L48**

A secret rule * is: Add the two numbers and then take one-half of the sum.

Complete these equations.

[16] $* 8 = 12$	[12] $* 1 = 6.5$
$16 *$ [2] $= 9$	[100] $*$ [100] $= 100$
$6 *$ [$\widehat{10}$] $=\widehat{2}$	[$\widehat{9}$] $*$ [$\widehat{9}$] $=\widehat{9}$
[7] $* 2 = 4.5$	[31.5] $*$ [31.5] $= 31.5$

Label the dots: *2

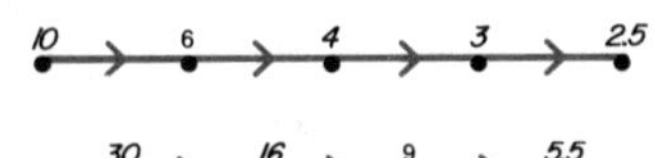

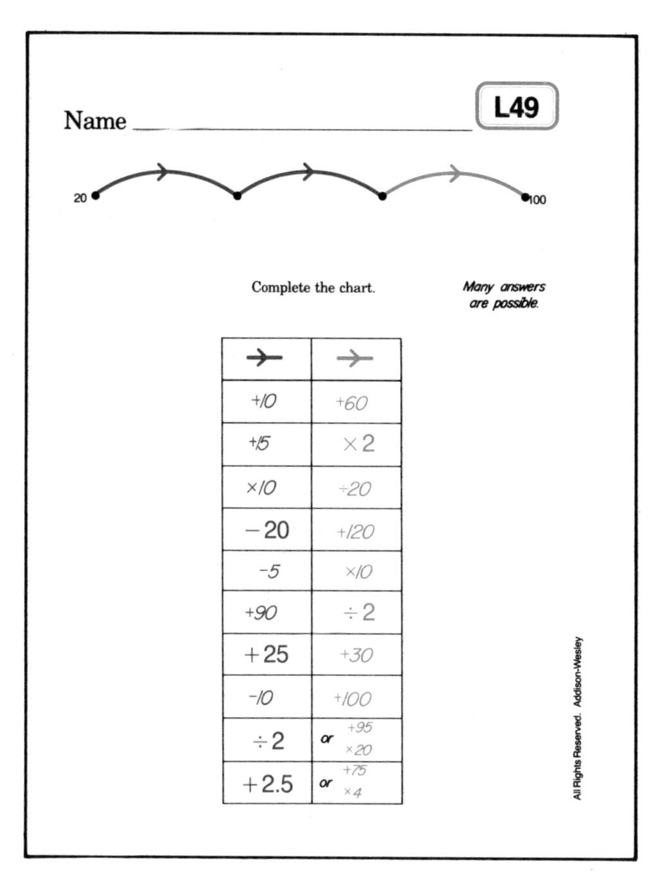
Name ______________________ **L49**

Complete the chart.

Many answers are possible.

→	→
+10	+60
+15	×2
×10	÷20
−20	+120
−5	×10
+90	÷2
+25	+30
−10	+100
÷2	or +95 ×20
+2.5	or +75 ×4

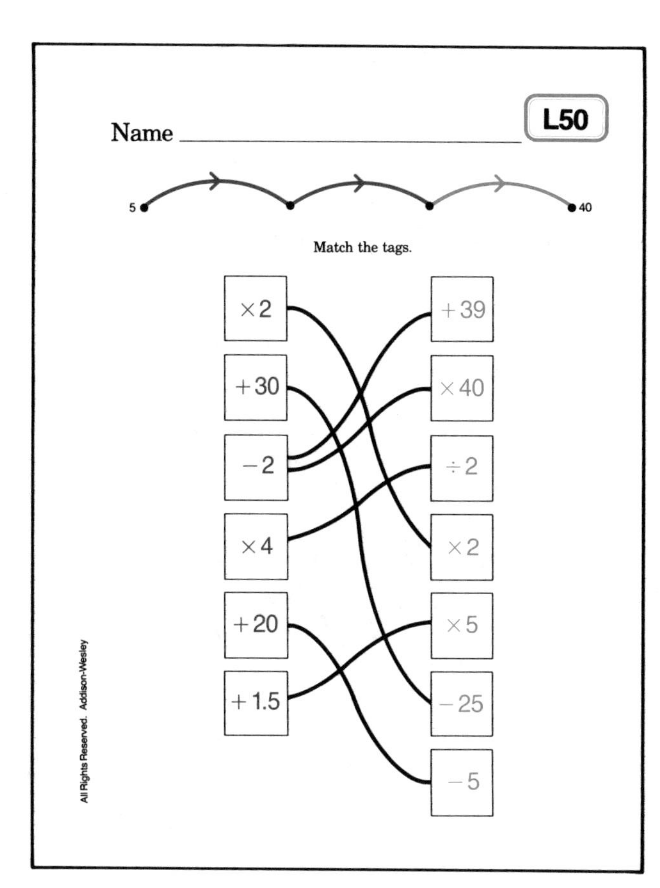
Name ______________________ **L50**

Match the tags.

×2	+39
+30	×40
−2	÷2
×4	×2
+20	×5
+1.5	−25
	−5

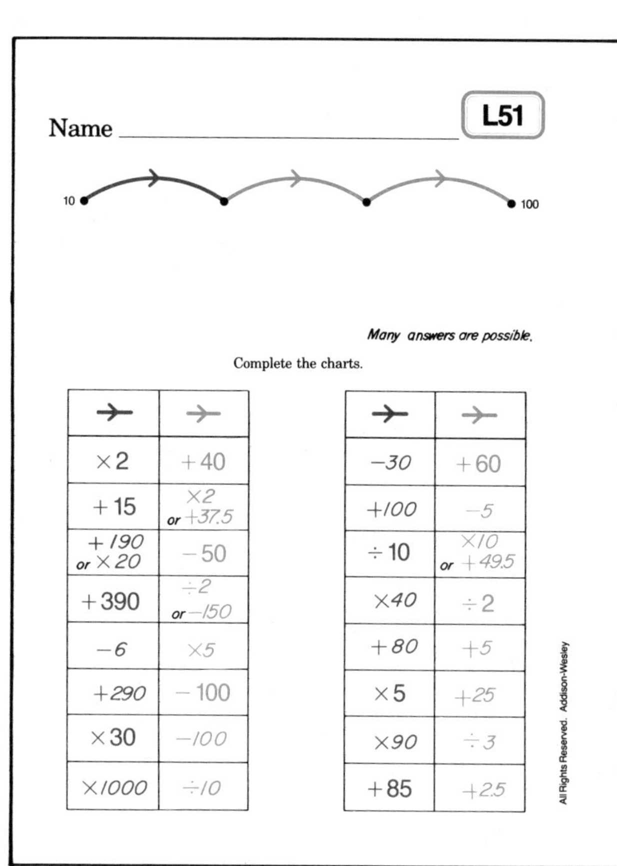
Name ______________________ **L51**

Many answers are possible.

Complete the charts.

→	→
×2	+40
+15	×2 or +37.5
+190 or ×20	−50
+390	÷2 or −150
−6	×5
+290	−100
×30	−100
×1000	÷10

→	→
−30	+60
+100	−5
÷10	×10 or +49.5
×40	÷2
+80	+5
×5	+25
×90	÷3
+85	+2.5

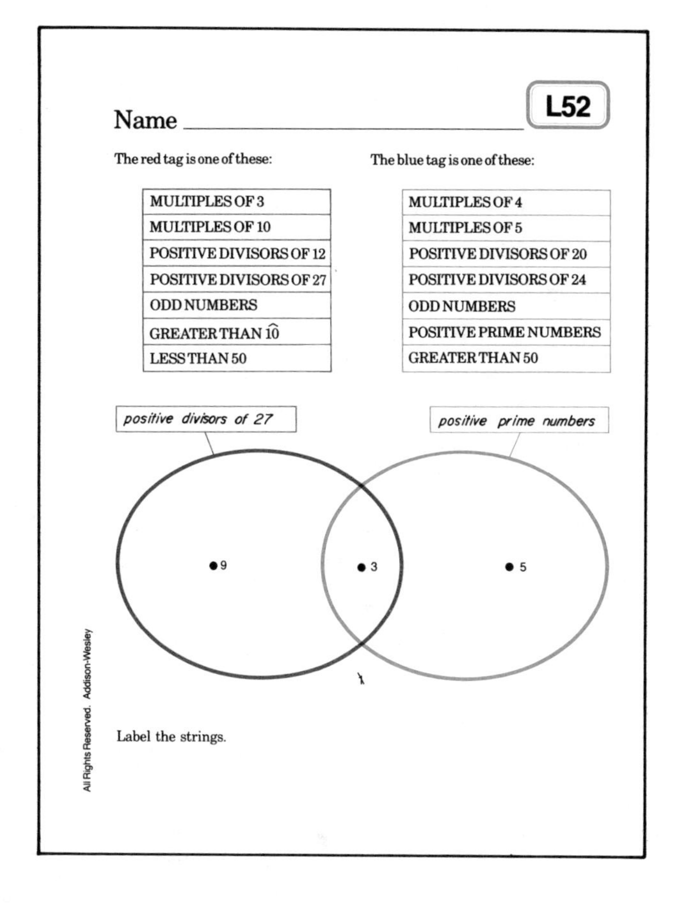
Name ______________________ **L52**

The red tag is one of these:	The blue tag is one of these:
MULTIPLES OF 3	MULTIPLES OF 4
MULTIPLES OF 10	MULTIPLES OF 5
POSITIVE DIVISORS OF 12	POSITIVE DIVISORS OF 20
POSITIVE DIVISORS OF 27	POSITIVE DIVISORS OF 24
ODD NUMBERS	ODD NUMBERS
GREATER THAN 10	POSITIVE PRIME NUMBERS
LESS THAN 50	GREATER THAN 50

Label the strings.

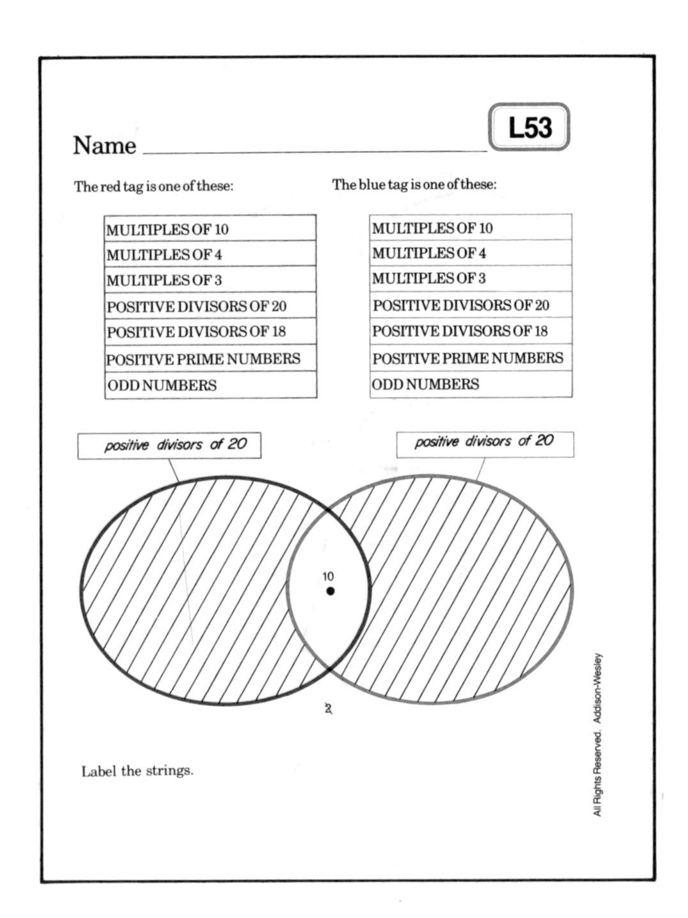

L53

Name ____________

The red tag is one of these:

MULTIPLES OF 10
MULTIPLES OF 4
MULTIPLES OF 3
POSITIVE DIVISORS OF 20
POSITIVE DIVISORS OF 18
POSITIVE PRIME NUMBERS
ODD NUMBERS

The blue tag is one of these:

MULTIPLES OF 10
MULTIPLES OF 4
MULTIPLES OF 3
POSITIVE DIVISORS OF 20
POSITIVE DIVISORS OF 18
POSITIVE PRIME NUMBERS
ODD NUMBERS

Label the strings.

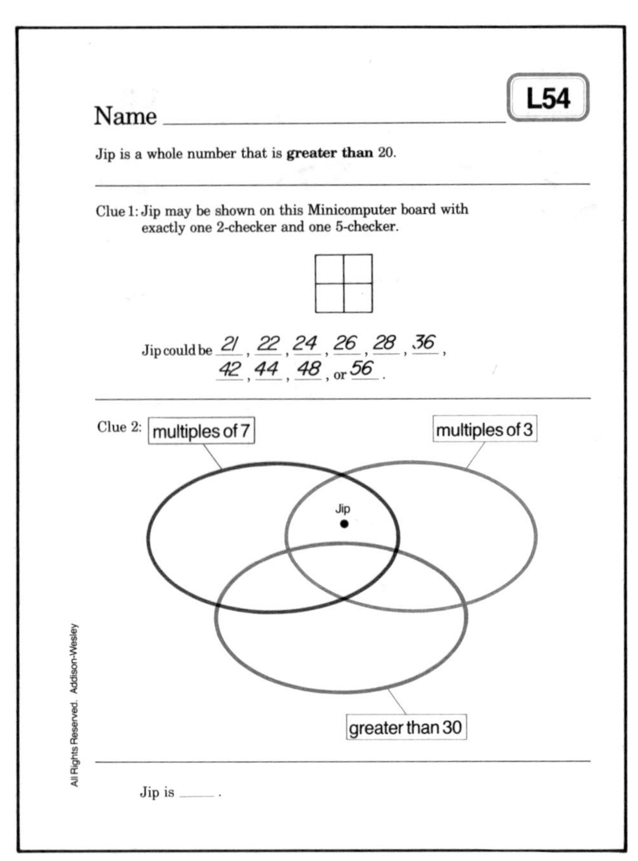

L54

Name ____________

Jip is a whole number that is **greater than** 20.

Clue 1: Jip may be shown on this Minicomputer board with exactly one 2-checker and one 5-checker.

Jip could be 21, 22, 24, 26, 28, 36, 42, 44, 48, or 56.

Clue 2:

Jip is ____.

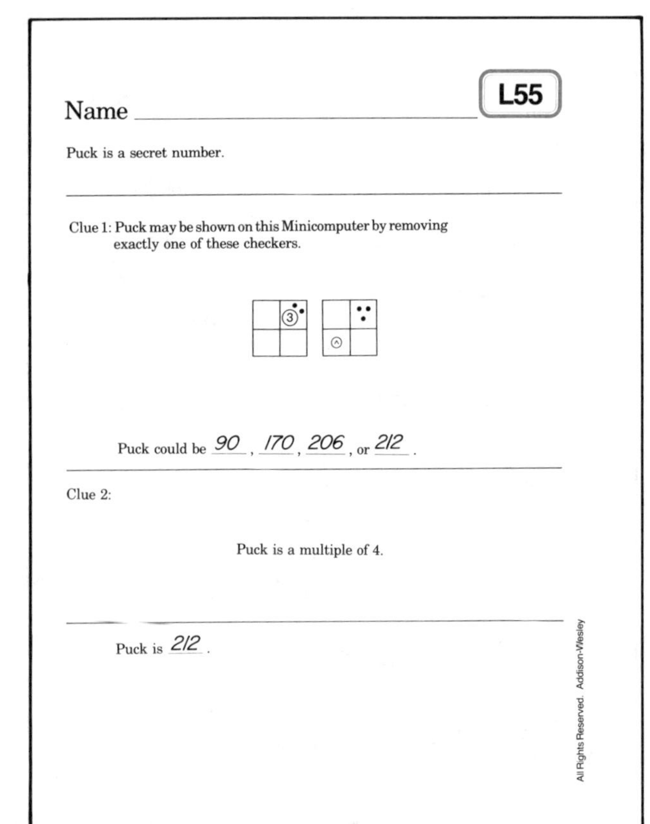

L55

Name ____________

Puck is a secret number.

Clue 1: Puck may be shown on this Minicomputer by removing exactly one of these checkers.

Puck could be 90, 170, 206, or 212.

Clue 2:

Puck is a multiple of 4.

Puck is 212.

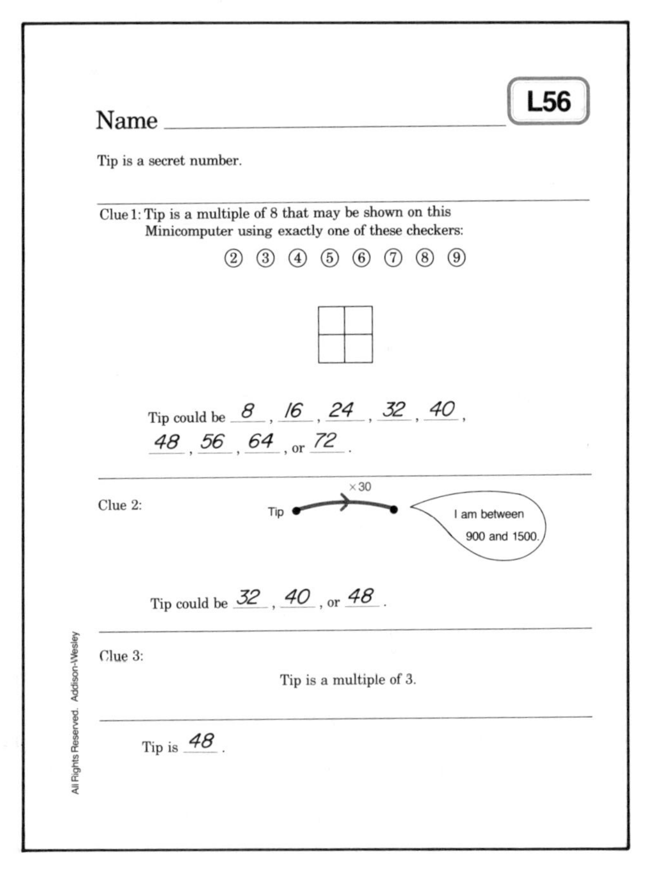

L56

Name ____________

Tip is a secret number.

Clue 1: Tip is a multiple of 8 that may be shown on this Minicomputer using exactly one of these checkers:

② ③ ④ ⑤ ⑥ ⑦ ⑧ ⑨

Tip could be 8, 16, 24, 32, 40, 48, 56, 64, or 72.

Clue 2:

Tip could be 32, 40, or 48.

Clue 3:

Tip is a multiple of 3.

Tip is 48.

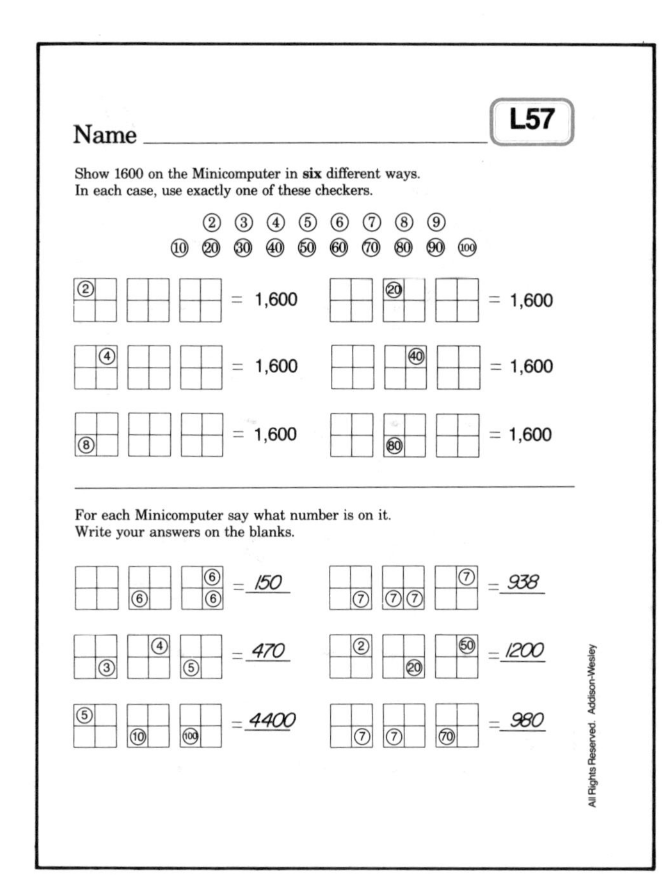

Name ____________ **L57**

Show 1600 on the Minicomputer in **six** different ways.
In each case, use exactly one of these checkers.

② ③ ④ ⑤ ⑥ ⑦ ⑧ ⑨
⑩ ⑳ ㉚ ㊵ ㊿ 60 70 80 90 100

= 1,600 = 1,600
= 1,600 = 1,600
= 1,600 = 1,600

For each Minicomputer say what number is on it.
Write your answers on the blanks.

= 150 = 938
= 470 = 1200
= 4400 = 980

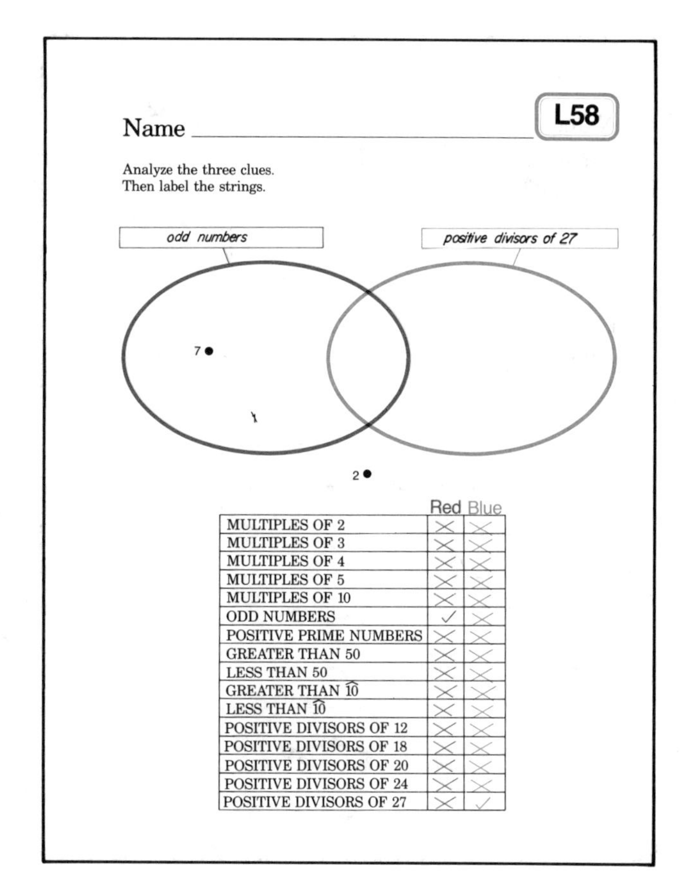

Name ____________ **L58**

Analyze the three clues.
Then label the strings.

	Red	Blue
MULTIPLES OF 2	X	X
MULTIPLES OF 3	X	X
MULTIPLES OF 4	X	X
MULTIPLES OF 5	X	X
MULTIPLES OF 10	X	X
ODD NUMBERS	✓	X
POSITIVE PRIME NUMBERS	X	X
GREATER THAN 50	X	X
LESS THAN 50	X	X
GREATER THAN $\widehat{10}$	X	X
LESS THAN $\widehat{10}$	X	X
POSITIVE DIVISORS OF 12	X	X
POSITIVE DIVISORS OF 18	X	X
POSITIVE DIVISORS OF 20	X	X
POSITIVE DIVISORS OF 24	X	X
POSITIVE DIVISORS OF 27	X	✓

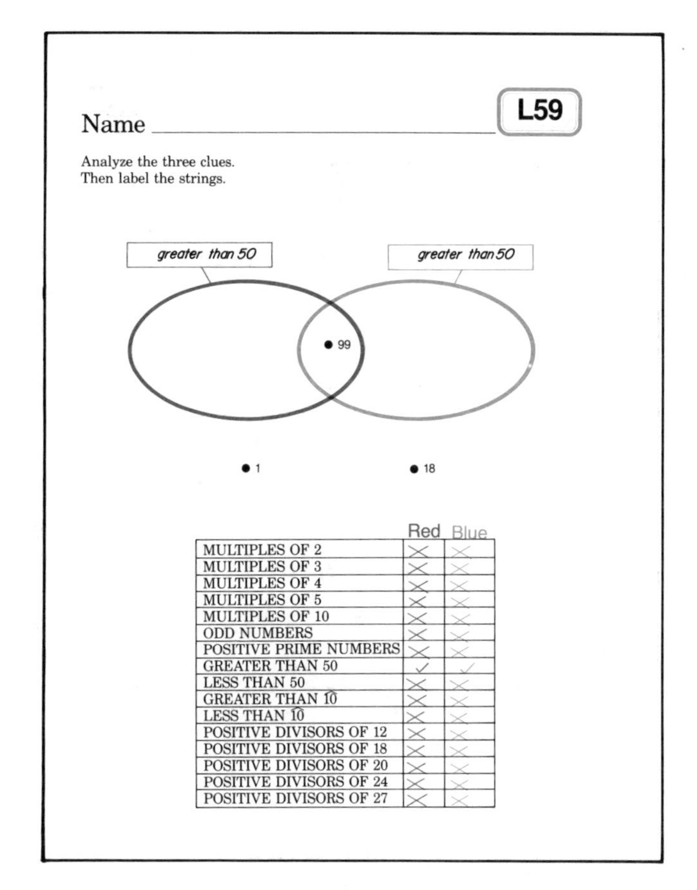

Name ____________ **L59**

Analyze the three clues.
Then label the strings.

	Red	Blue
MULTIPLES OF 2	X	X
MULTIPLES OF 3	X	X
MULTIPLES OF 4	X	X
MULTIPLES OF 5	X	X
MULTIPLES OF 10	X	X
ODD NUMBERS	X	X
POSITIVE PRIME NUMBERS	X	X
GREATER THAN 50	✓	✓
LESS THAN 50	X	X
GREATER THAN $\widehat{10}$	X	X
LESS THAN $\widehat{10}$	X	X
POSITIVE DIVISORS OF 12	X	X
POSITIVE DIVISORS OF 18	X	X
POSITIVE DIVISORS OF 20	X	X
POSITIVE DIVISORS OF 24	X	X
POSITIVE DIVISORS OF 27	X	X

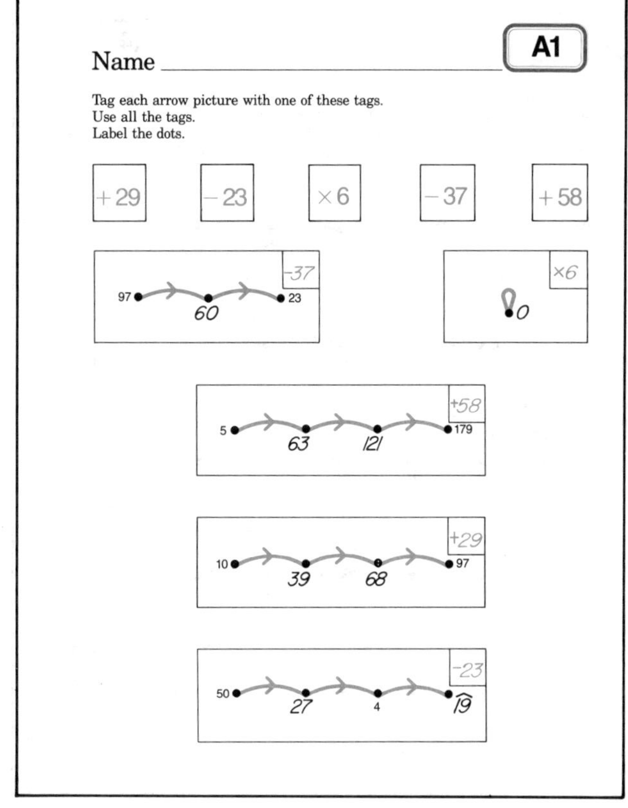

Name ____________ **A1**

Tag each arrow picture with one of these tags.
Use all the tags.
Label the dots.

+29 −23 ×6 −37 +58

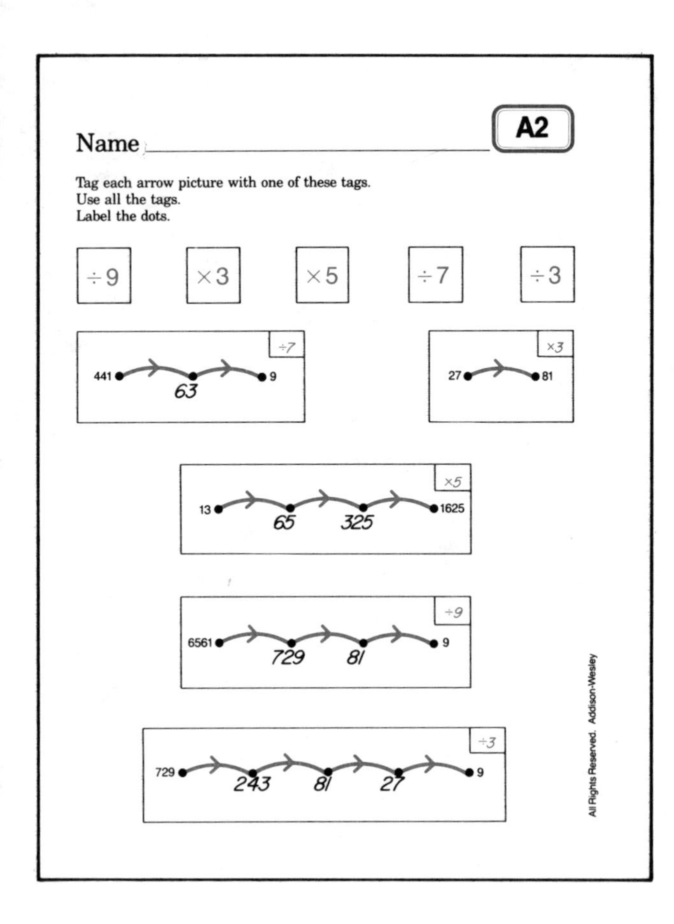

Name __________ **A2**

Tag each arrow picture with one of these tags.
Use all the tags.
Label the dots.

÷9 ×3 ×5 ÷7 ÷3

÷7: 441 → *63* → 9

×3: 27 → 81

×5: 13 → *65* → *325* → 1625

÷9: 6561 → *729* → *81* → 9

÷3: 729 → *243* → *81* → *27* → 9

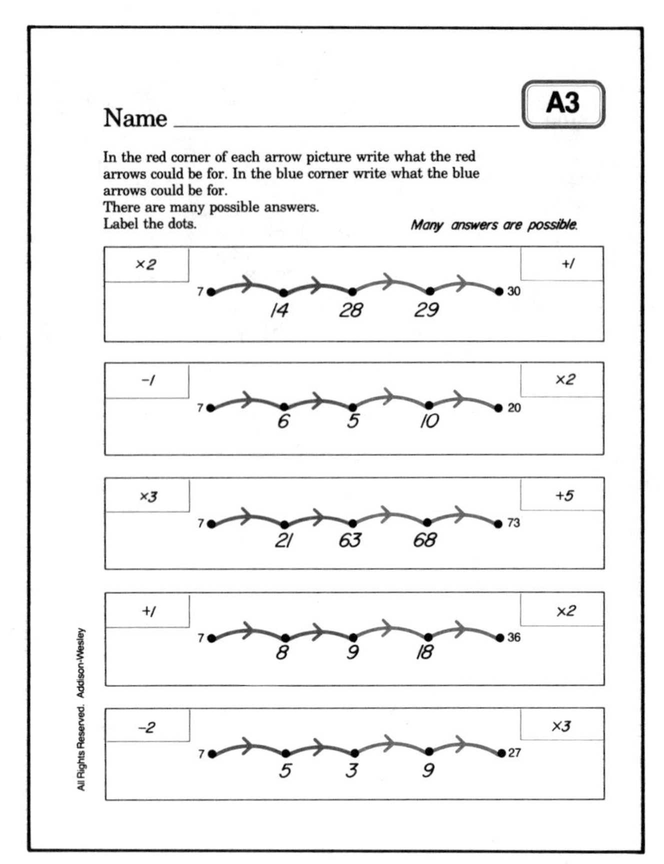

Name __________ **A3**

In the red corner of each arrow picture write what the red arrows could be for. In the blue corner write what the blue arrows could be for.
There are many possible answers.
Label the dots. *Many answers are possible.*

×2 / *+1*: 7 → *14* → *28* → *29* → 30

−1 / *×2*: 7 → *6* → *5* → *10* → 20

×3 / *+5*: 7 → *21* → *63* → *68* → 73

+1 / *×2*: 7 → *8* → *9* → *18* → 36

−2 / *×3*: 7 → *5* → *3* → *9* → 27

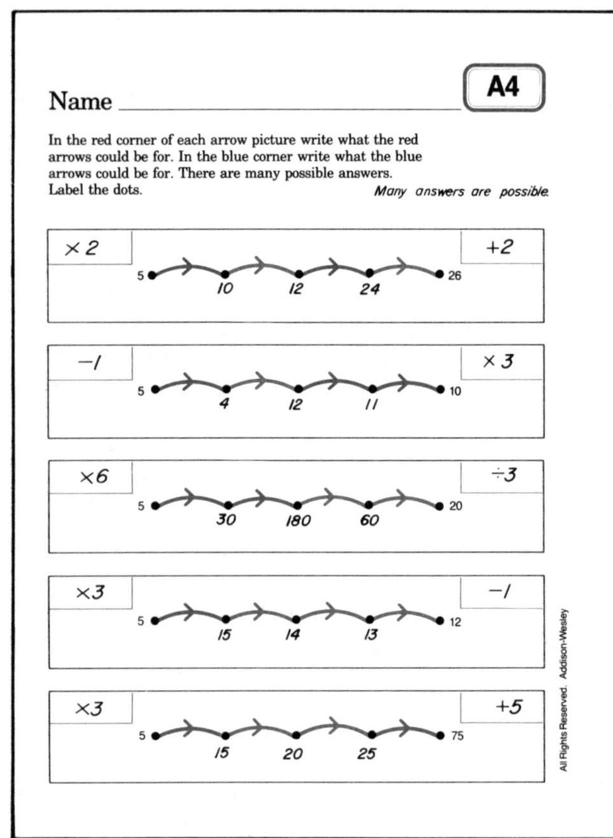

Name __________ **A4**

In the red corner of each arrow picture write what the red arrows could be for. In the blue corner write what the blue arrows could be for. There are many possible answers.
Label the dots. *Many answers are possible.*

×2 / *+2*: 5 → *10* → *12* → *24* → 26

−1 / *×3*: 5 → *4* → *12* → *11* → 10

×6 / *÷3*: 5 → *30* → *180* → *60* → 20

×3 / *−1*: 5 → *15* → *14* → *13* → 12

×3 / *+5*: 5 → *15* → *20* → *25* → 75

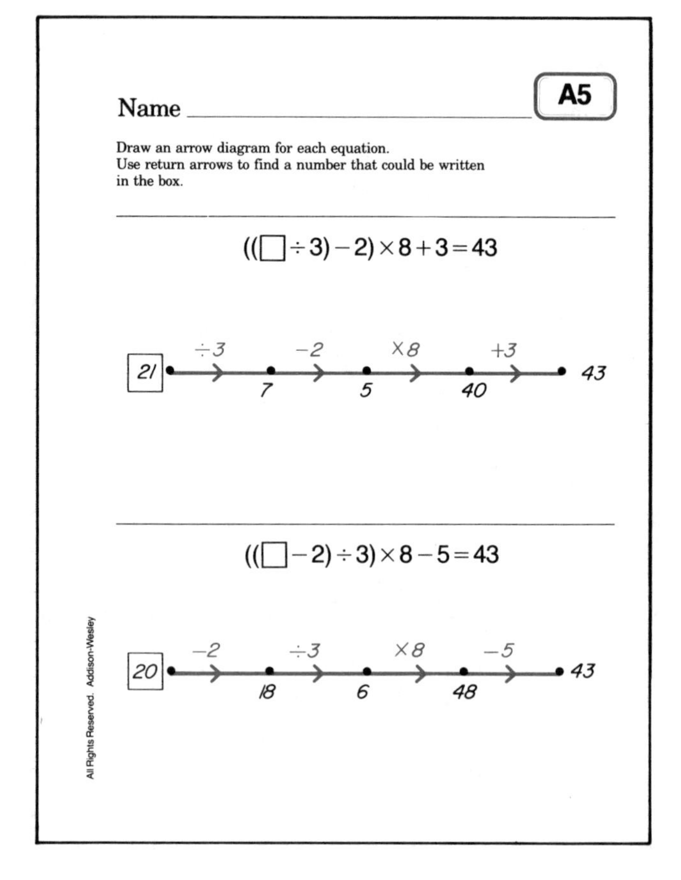

Name __________ **A5**

Draw an arrow diagram for each equation.
Use return arrows to find a number that could be written in the box.

$((\square \div 3) - 2) \times 8 + 3 = 43$

21 → (*÷3*) *7* → (*−2*) *5* → (*×8*) *40* → (*+3*) *43*

$((\square - 2) \div 3) \times 8 - 5 = 43$

20 → (*−2*) *18* → (*÷3*) *6* → (*×8*) *48* → (*−5*) *43*

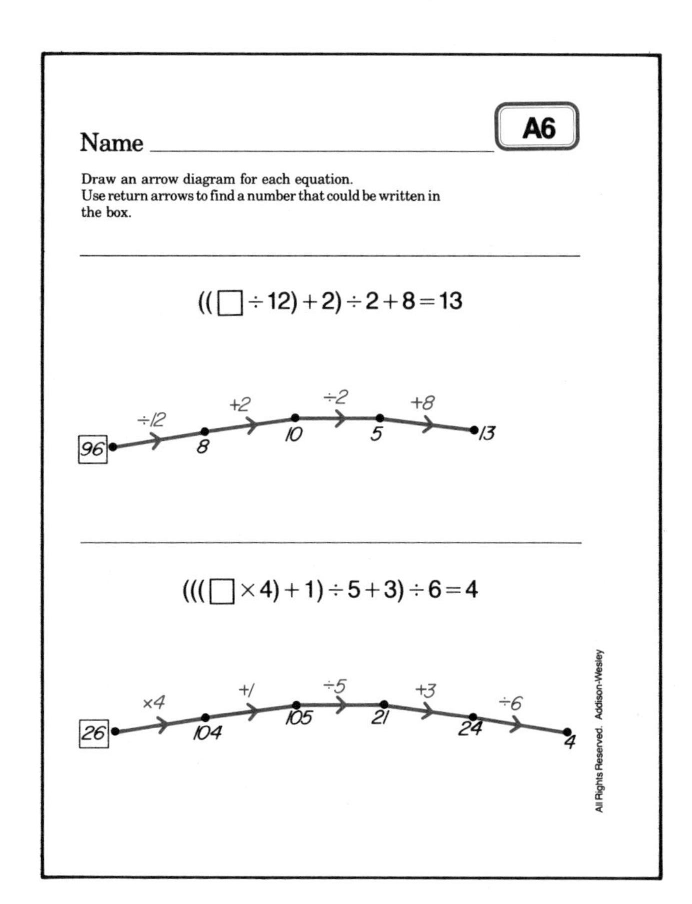
Name
A6
Draw an arrow diagram for each equation.
Use return arrows to find a number that could be written in the box.
((□ ÷ 12) + 2) ÷ 2 + 8 = 13
(((□ × 4) + 1) ÷ 5 + 3) ÷ 6 = 4
All Rights Reserved. Addison-Wesley

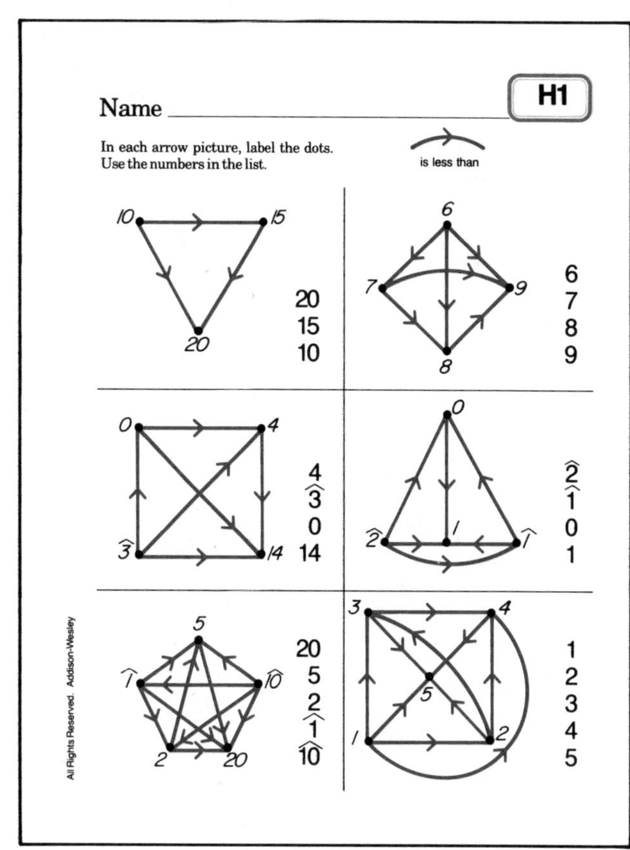
Name
H1
In each arrow picture, label the dots.
Use the numbers in the list.
is less than
20
15
10
6
7
8
9
4
3̂
0
14
2̂
1̂
0
1
20
5
2
1̂
1̂0̂
1
2
3
4
5
All Rights Reserved. Addison-Wesley

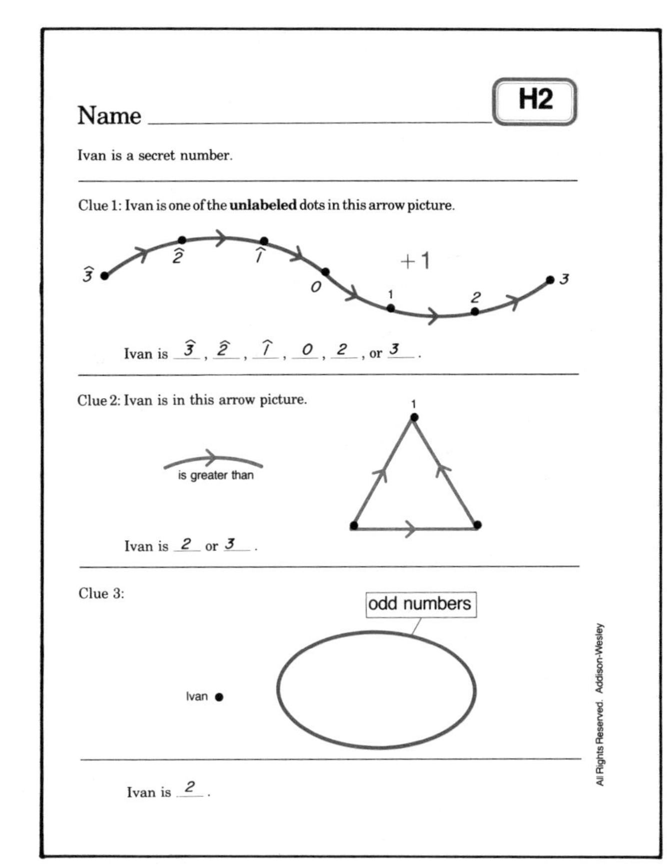
Name
H2
Ivan is a secret number.
Clue 1: Ivan is one of the **unlabeled** dots in this arrow picture.
+1
Ivan is ___, ___, ___, ___, ___, or ___.
Clue 2: Ivan is in this arrow picture.
is greater than
Ivan is ___ or ___.
Clue 3:
odd numbers
Ivan
Ivan is ___.
All Rights Reserved. Addison-Wesley

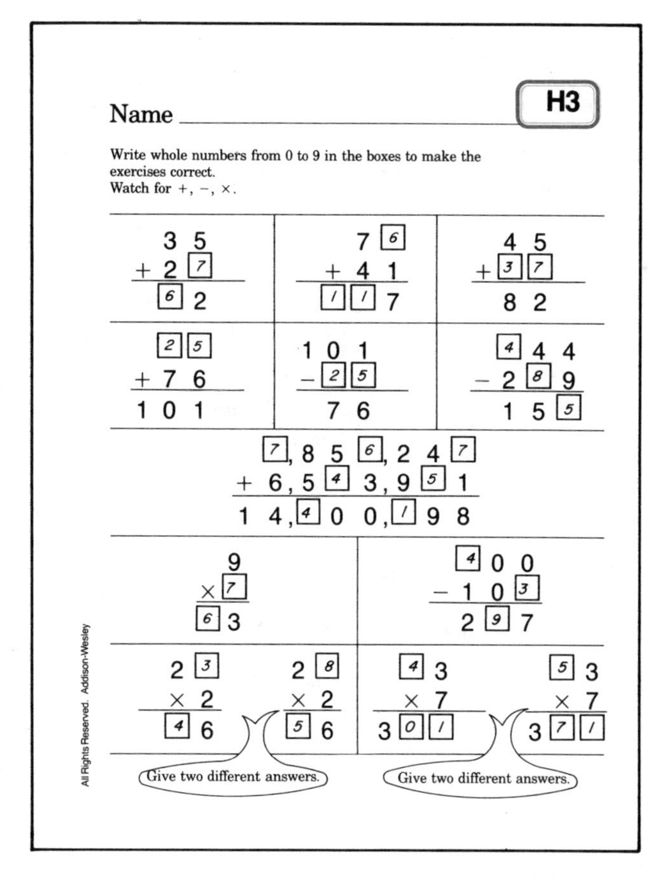
Name
H3
Write whole numbers from 0 to 9 in the boxes to make the exercises correct.
Watch for +, −, ×.
Give two different answers.
Give two different answers.
All Rights Reserved. Addison-Wesley

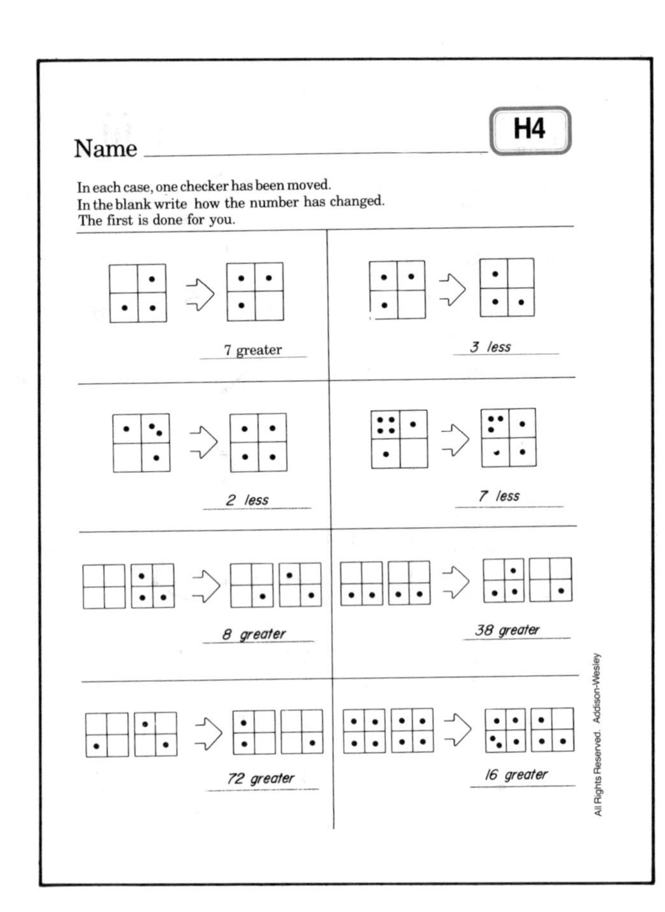
Name ____________ **H4**

In each case, one checker has been moved.
In the blank write how the number has changed.
The first is done for you.

7 greater

3 less

2 less

7 less

8 greater

38 greater

72 greater

16 greater

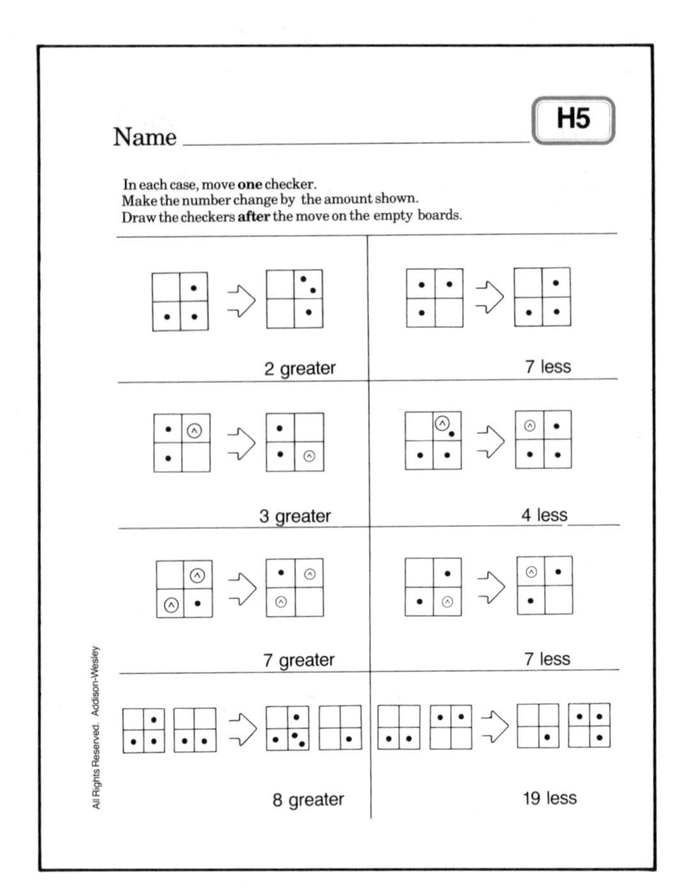
Name ____________ **H5**

In each case, move **one** checker.
Make the number change by the amount shown.
Draw the checkers **after** the move on the empty boards.

2 greater

7 less

3 greater

4 less

7 greater

7 less

8 greater

19 less

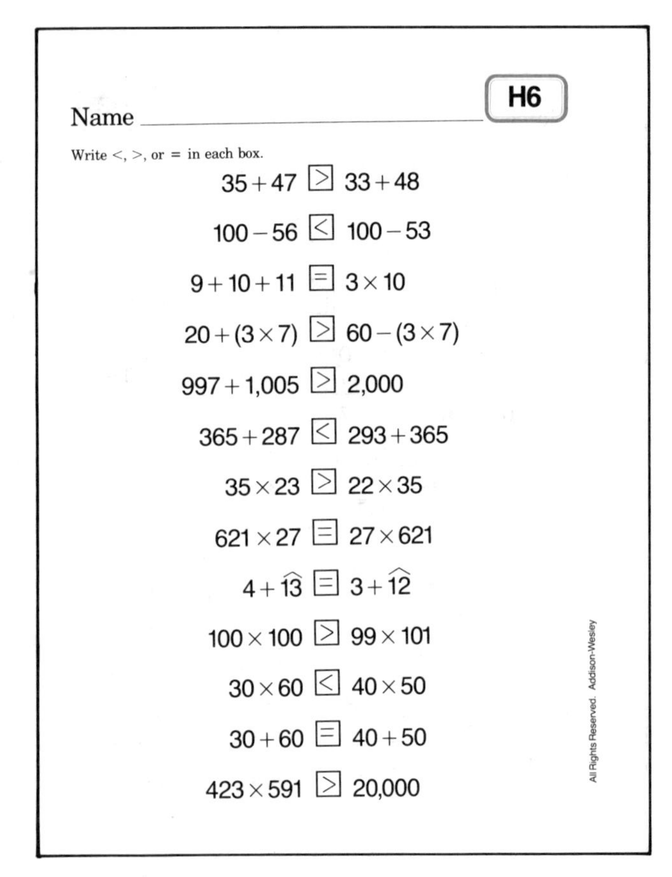
Name ____________ **H6**

Write <, >, or = in each box.

$35 + 47$ [>] $33 + 48$

$100 - 56$ [<] $100 - 53$

$9 + 10 + 11$ [=] 3×10

$20 + (3 \times 7)$ [>] $60 - (3 \times 7)$

$997 + 1{,}005$ [>] $2{,}000$

$365 + 287$ [<] $293 + 365$

35×23 [>] 22×35

621×27 [=] 27×621

$4 + \widehat{13}$ [=] $3 + \widehat{12}$

100×100 [>] 99×101

30×60 [<] 40×50

$30 + 60$ [=] $40 + 50$

423×591 [>] $20{,}000$

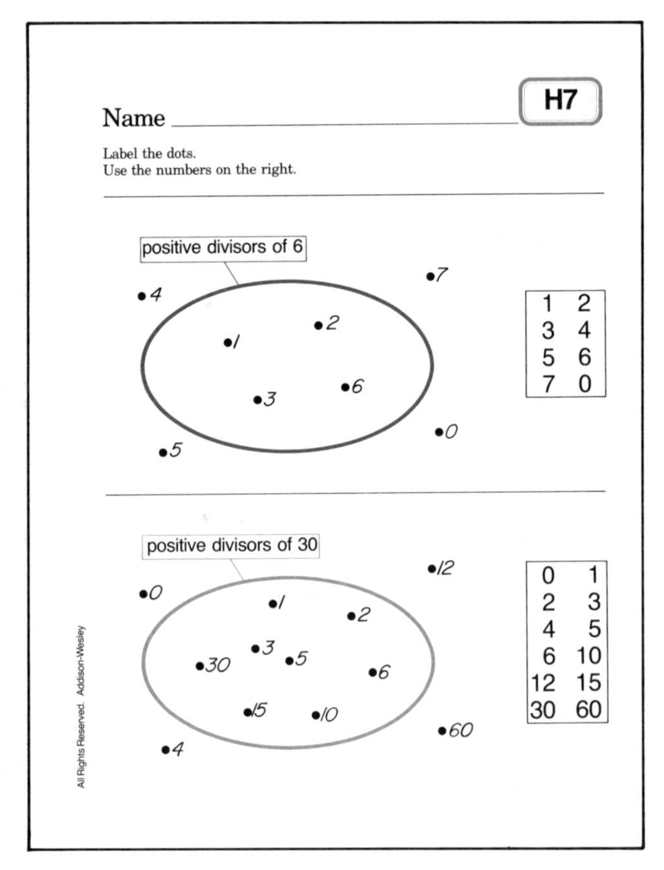
Name ____________ **H7**

Label the dots.
Use the numbers on the right.

1	2
3	4
5	6
7	0

0	1
2	3
4	5
6	10
12	15
30	60

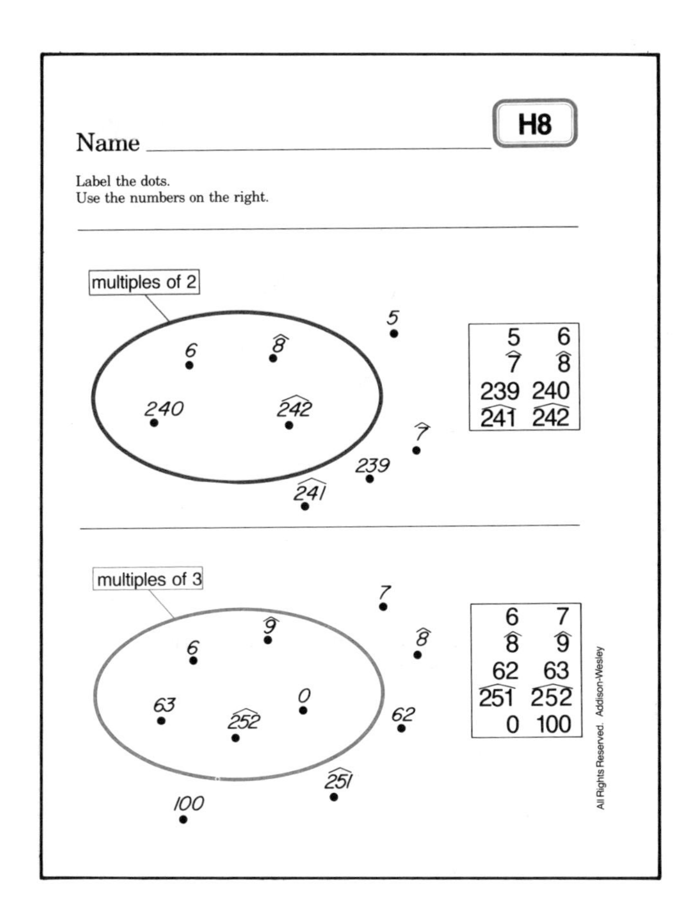
H8
Name
Label the dots.
Use the numbers on the right.
multiples of 2
multiples of 3
All Rights Reserved. Addison-Wesley

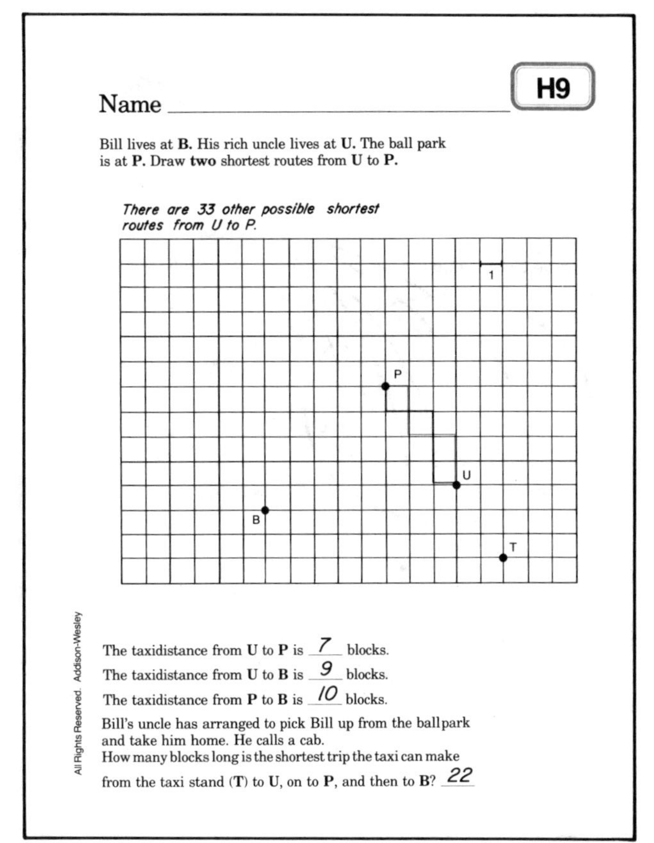
H9
Name
Bill lives at B. His rich uncle lives at U. The ball park is at P. Draw two shortest routes from U to P.
There are 33 other possible shortest routes from U to P.
The taxidistance from U to P is 7 blocks.
The taxidistance from U to B is 9 blocks.
The taxidistance from P to B is 10 blocks.
Bill's uncle has arranged to pick Bill up from the ballpark and take him home. He calls a cab.
How many blocks long is the shortest trip the taxi can make from the taxi stand (T) to U, on to P, and then to B? 22
All Rights Reserved. Addison-Wesley

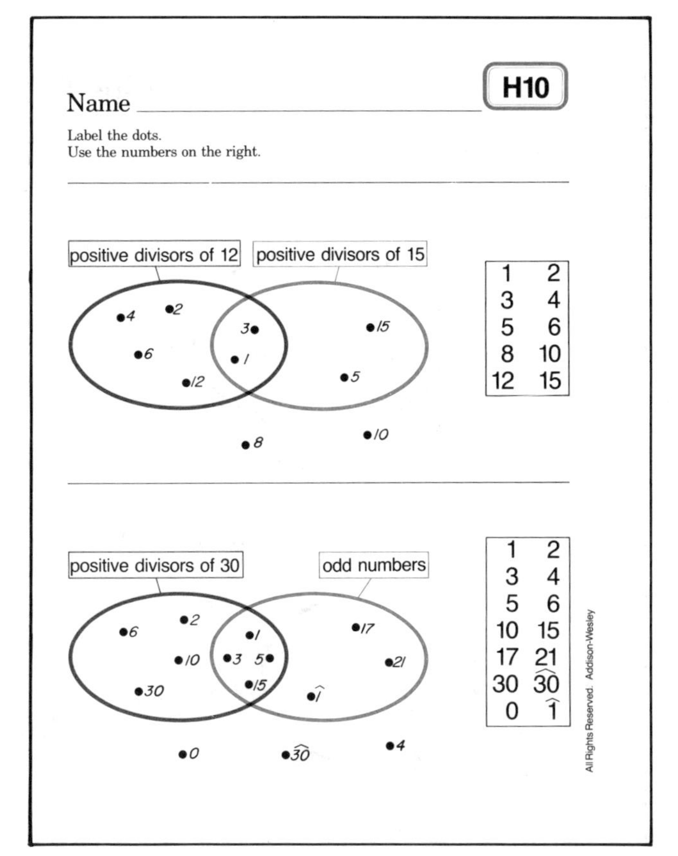
H10
Name
Label the dots.
Use the numbers on the right.
positive divisors of 12
positive divisors of 15
positive divisors of 30
odd numbers
All Rights Reserved. Addison-Wesley

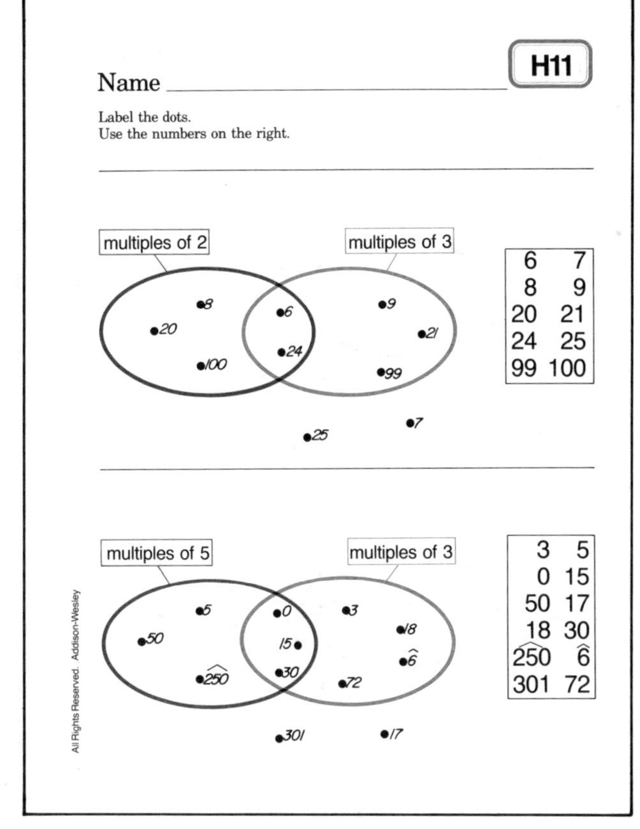
H11
Name
Label the dots.
Use the numbers on the right.
multiples of 2
multiples of 3
multiples of 5
multiples of 3
All Rights Reserved. Addison-Wesley

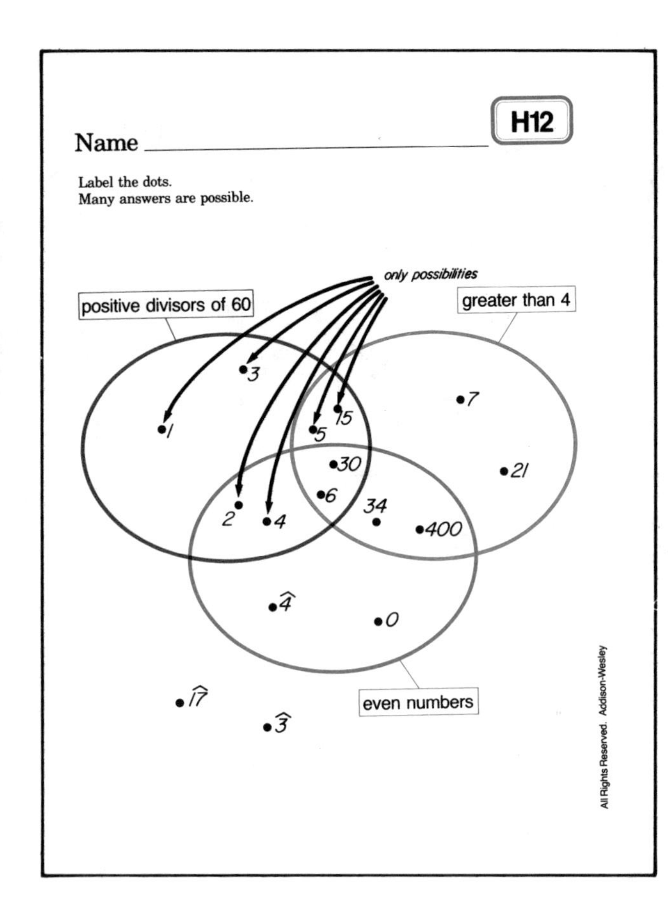
H12
Name
Label the dots.
Many answers are possible.
only possibilities
positive divisors of 60
greater than 4
even numbers
All Rights Reserved. Addison-Wesley

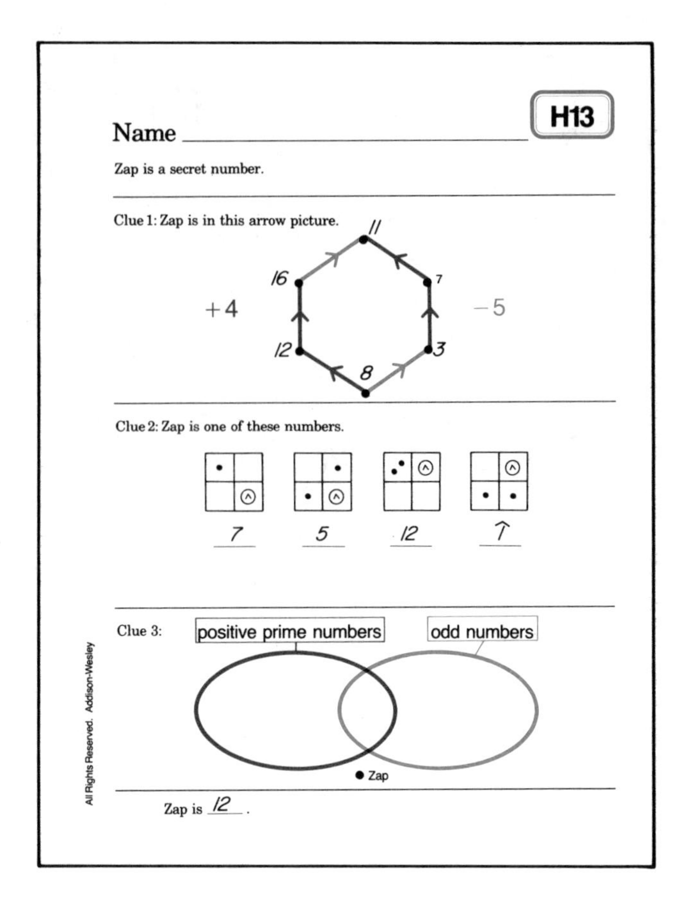
H13
Name
Zap is a secret number.
Clue 1: Zap is in this arrow picture.
+4
−5
Clue 2: Zap is one of these numbers.
Clue 3:
positive prime numbers
odd numbers
Zap
Zap is 12.
All Rights Reserved. Addison-Wesley

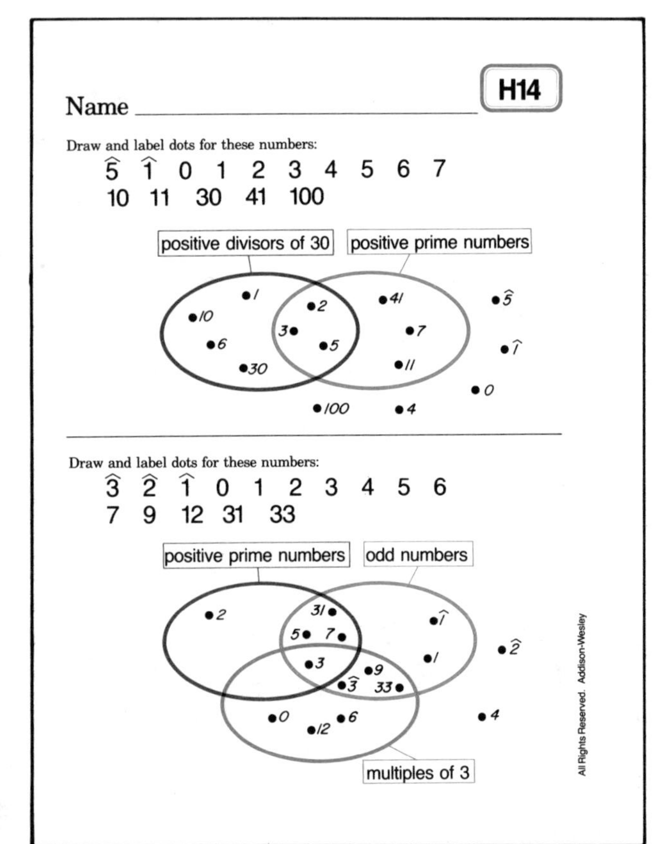
H14
Name
Draw and label dots for these numbers:
5̂ 1̂ 0 1 2 3 4 5 6 7
10 11 30 41 100
positive divisors of 30
positive prime numbers
Draw and label dots for these numbers:
3̂ 2̂ 1̂ 0 1 2 3 4 5 6
7 9 12 31 33
positive prime numbers
odd numbers
multiples of 3
All Rights Reserved. Addison-Wesley

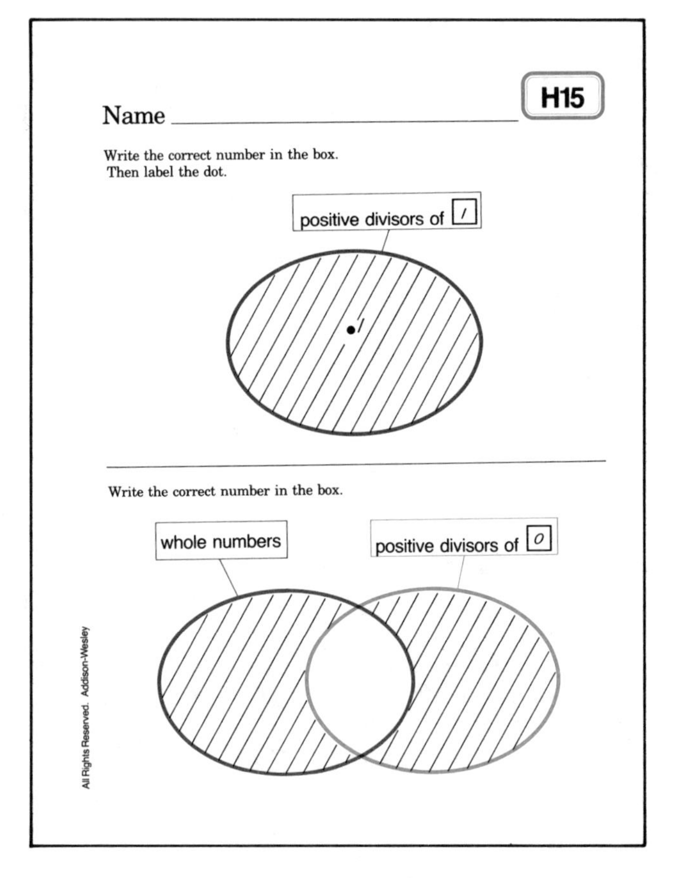
H15
Name
Write the correct number in the box.
Then label the dot.
positive divisors of
Write the correct number in the box.
whole numbers
positive divisors of
All Rights Reserved. Addison-Wesley

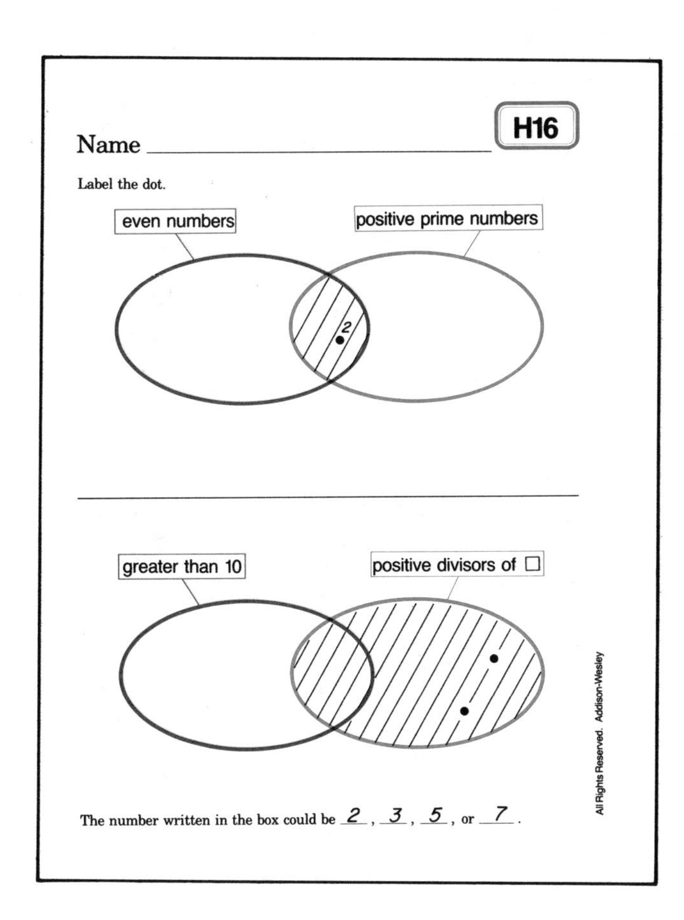

H16

Name ______________________

Label the dot.

The number written in the box could be 2, 3, 5, or 7.

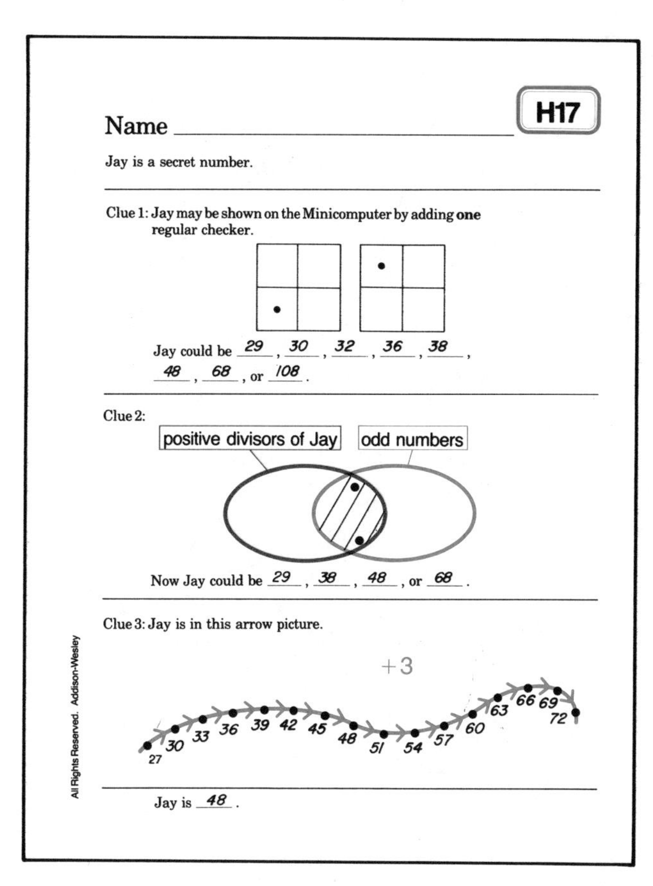

H17

Name ______________________

Jay is a secret number.

Clue 1: Jay may be shown on the Minicomputer by adding **one** regular checker.

Jay could be 29, 30, 32, 36, 38, 48, 68, or 108.

Clue 2:

Now Jay could be 29, 38, 48, or 68.

Clue 3: Jay is in this arrow picture.

Jay is 48.

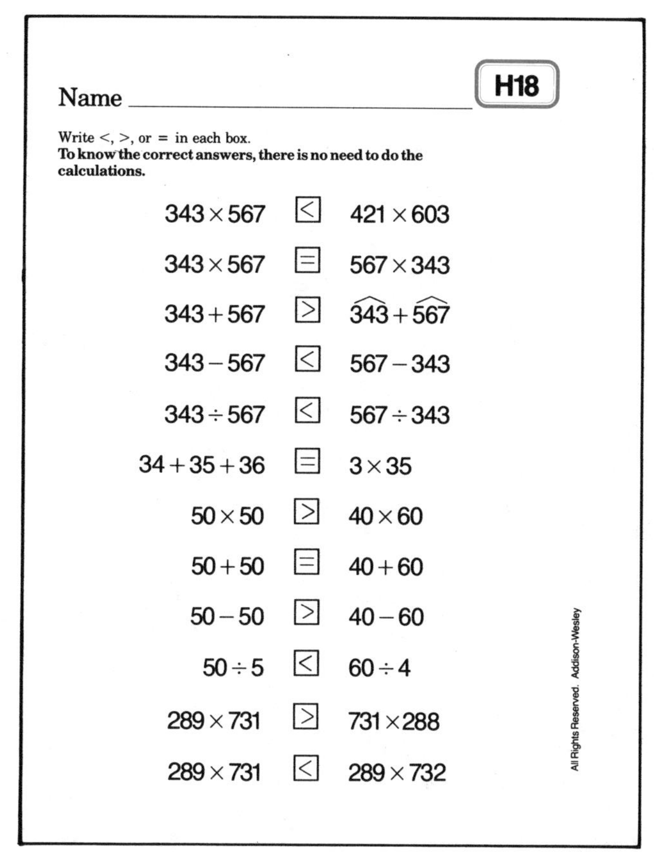

H18

Name ______________________

Write $<$, $>$, or $=$ in each box.
To know the correct answers, there is no need to do the calculations.

343×567	$<$	421×603
343×567	$=$	567×343
$343 + 567$	$>$	$\widehat{343} + \widehat{567}$
$343 - 567$	$<$	$567 - 343$
$343 \div 567$	$<$	$567 \div 343$
$34 + 35 + 36$	$=$	3×35
50×50	$>$	40×60
$50 + 50$	$=$	$40 + 60$
$50 - 50$	$>$	$40 - 60$
$50 \div 5$	$<$	$60 \div 4$
289×731	$>$	731×288
289×731	$<$	289×732

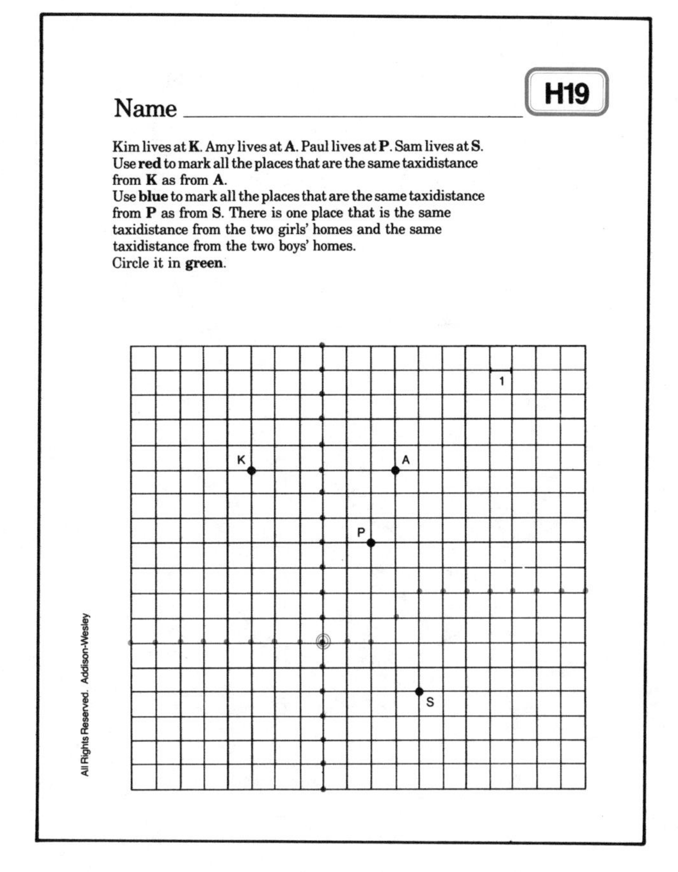

H19

Name ______________________

Kim lives at **K**. Amy lives at **A**. Paul lives at **P**. Sam lives at **S**.
Use **red** to mark all the places that are the same taxidistance from **K** as from **A**.
Use **blue** to mark all the places that are the same taxidistance from **P** as from **S**. There is one place that is the same taxidistance from the two girls' homes and the same taxidistance from the two boys' homes.
Circle it in **green**.

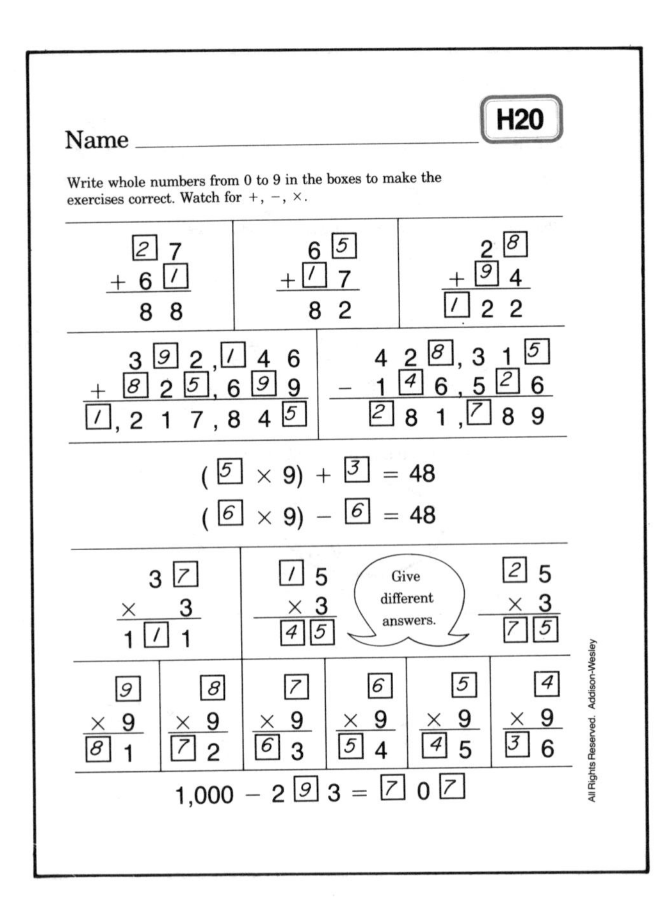

Name ____________ **H20**

Write whole numbers from 0 to 9 in the boxes to make the exercises correct. Watch for +, −, ×.

$2\boxed{7} + 6\boxed{1} = 88$ (boxes: 2, 1)

$6\boxed{5} + \boxed{1}7 = 82$

$2\boxed{8} + \boxed{9}4 = \boxed{1}22$

$3\boxed{9}2,\boxed{1}46 + \boxed{8}2\boxed{5},6\boxed{9}9 = \boxed{1},217,84\boxed{5}$

$42\boxed{8},31\boxed{5} - 1\boxed{4}6,5\boxed{2}6 = \boxed{2}81,\boxed{7}89$

$(\boxed{5} \times 9) + \boxed{3} = 48$

$(\boxed{6} \times 9) - \boxed{6} = 48$

$3\boxed{7} \times 3 = 1\boxed{1}1$

$\boxed{1}5 \times 3 = \boxed{4}\boxed{5}$ — Give different answers. — $\boxed{2}5 \times 3 = \boxed{7}\boxed{5}$

$\boxed{9} \times 9 = \boxed{8}1$; $\boxed{8} \times 9 = \boxed{7}2$; $\boxed{7} \times 9 = \boxed{6}3$; $\boxed{6} \times 9 = \boxed{5}4$; $\boxed{5} \times 9 = \boxed{4}5$; $\boxed{4} \times 9 = \boxed{3}6$

$1,000 - 2\boxed{9}3 = \boxed{7}0\boxed{7}$

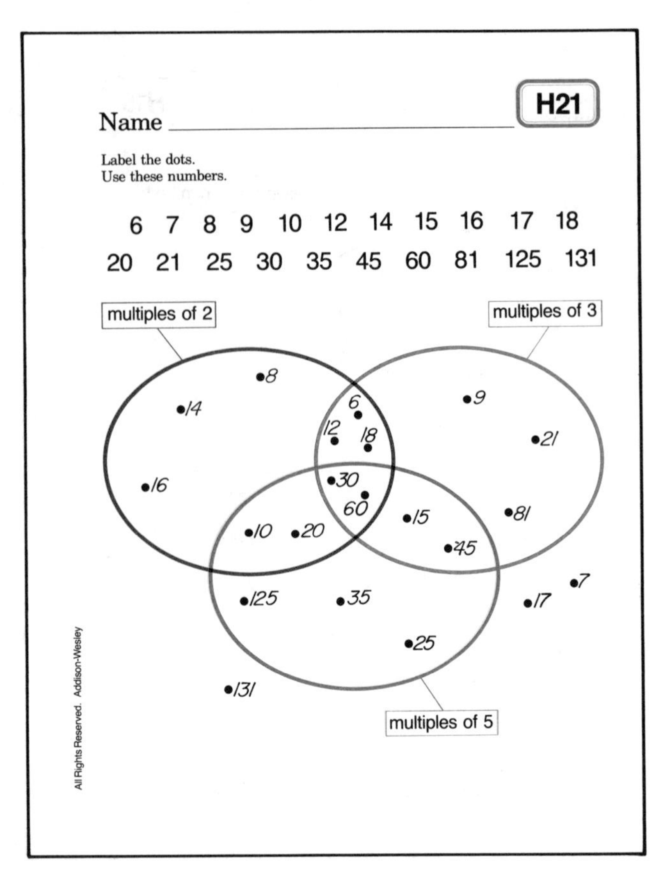

Name ____________ **H21**

Label the dots.
Use these numbers.

6 7 8 9 10 12 14 15 16 17 18
20 21 25 30 35 45 60 81 125 131

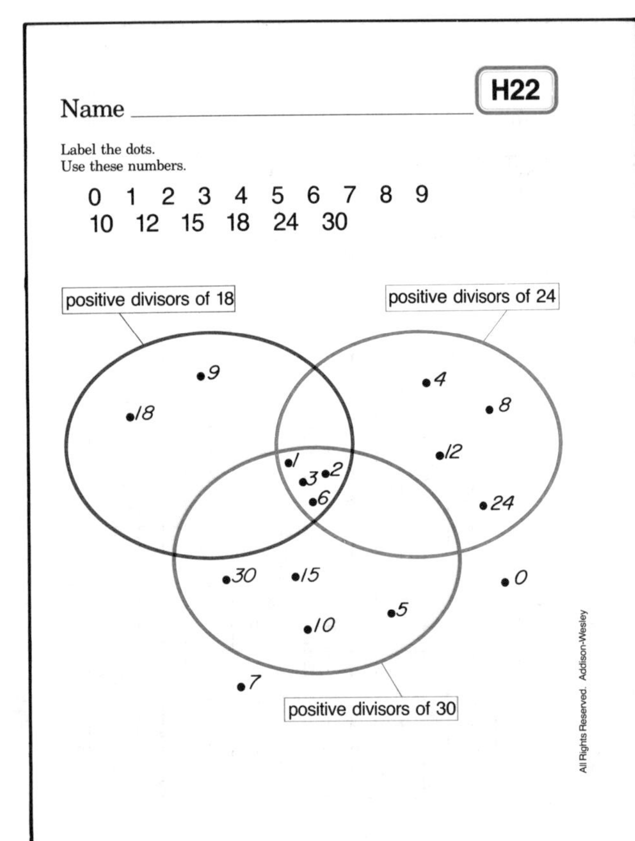

Name ____________ **H22**

Label the dots.
Use these numbers.

0 1 2 3 4 5 6 7 8 9
10 12 15 18 24 30

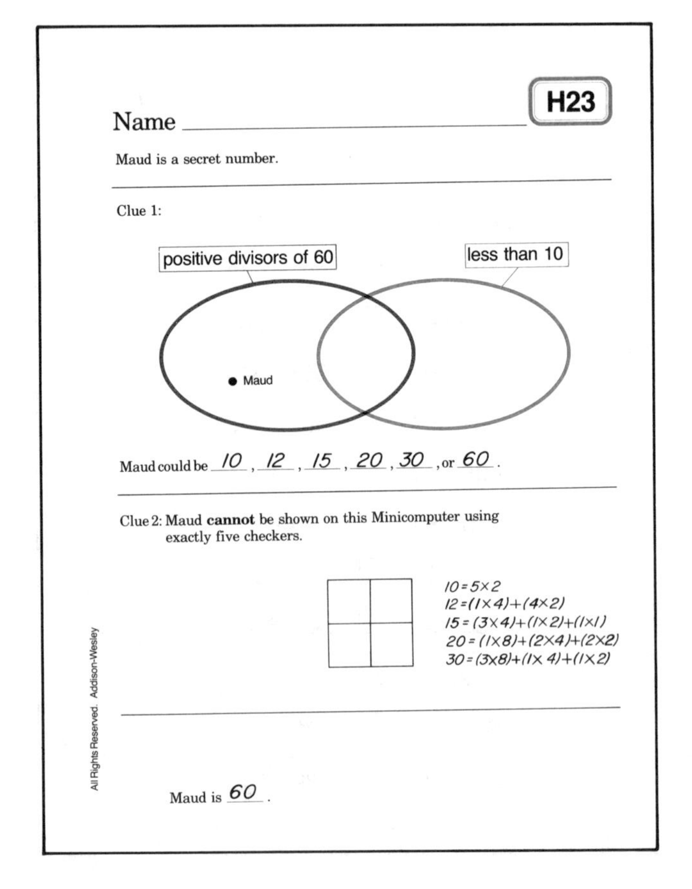

Name ____________ **H23**

Maud is a secret number.

Clue 1:

Maud could be 10, 12, 15, 20, 30, or 60.

Clue 2: Maud **cannot** be shown on this Minicomputer using exactly five checkers.

Maud is 60.

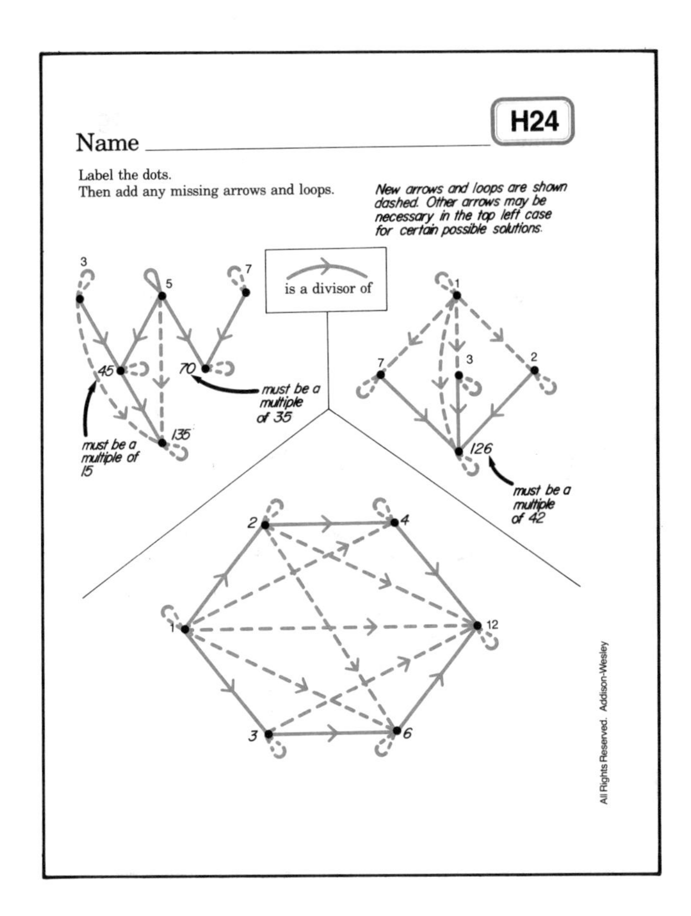

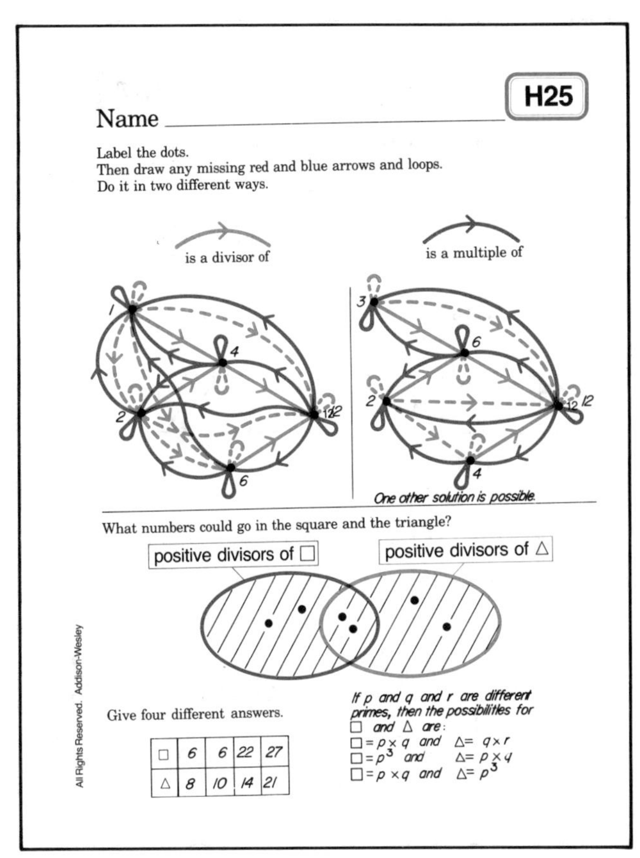

□	6	6	22	27
△	8	10	14	21

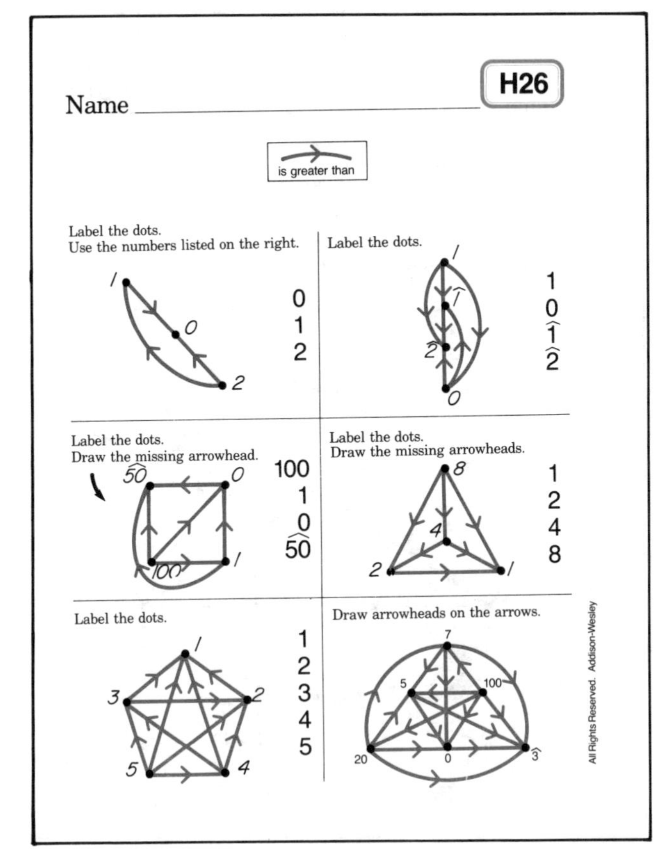

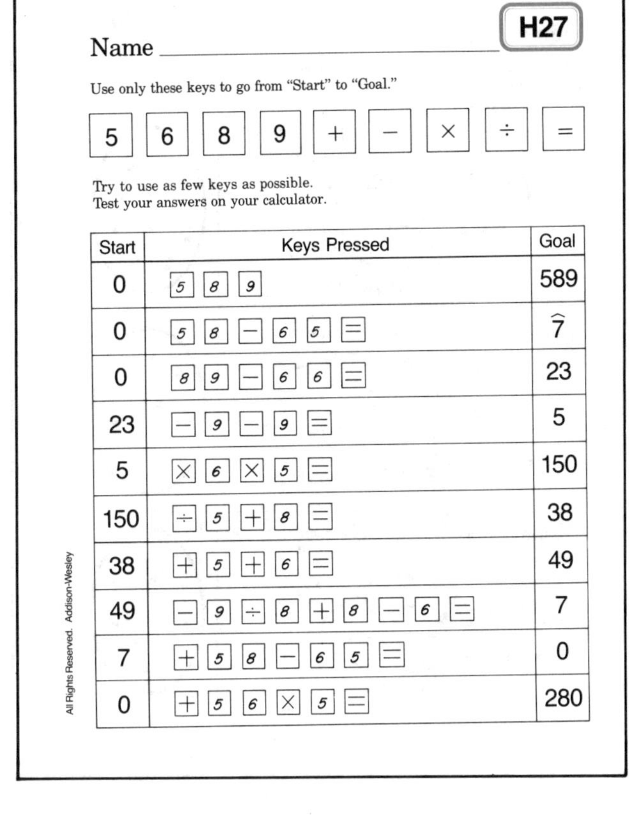

Start	Keys Pressed	Goal
0	5 8 9	589
0	5 8 − 6 5 =	$\hat{7}$
0	8 9 − 6 6 =	23
23	− 9 − 9 =	5
5	× 6 × 5 =	150
150	÷ 5 + 8 =	38
38	+ 5 + 6 =	49
49	− 9 ÷ 8 + 8 − 6 =	7
7	+ 5 8 − 6 5 =	0
0	+ 5 6 × 5 =	280

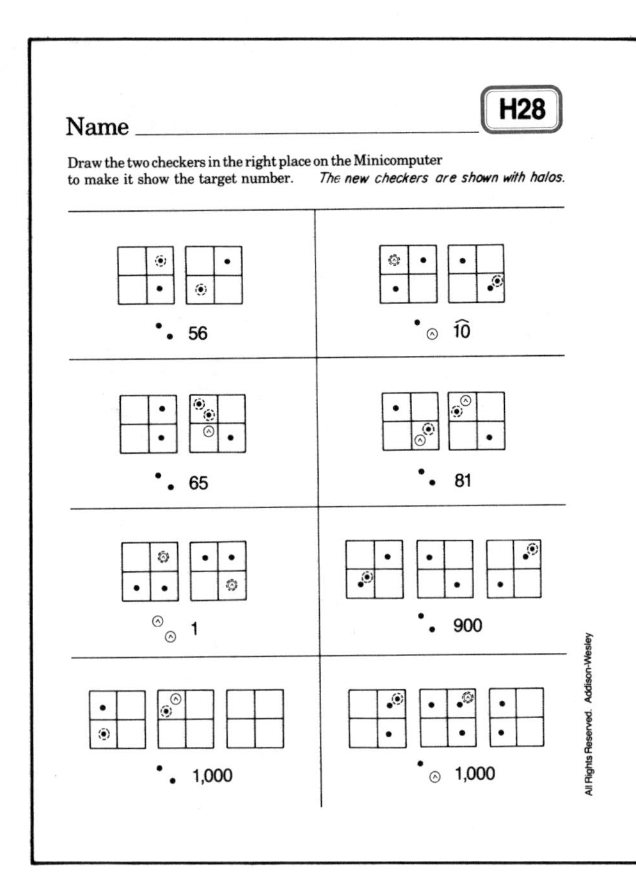
Name
H28
Draw the two checkers in the right place on the Minicomputer to make it show the target number. The new checkers are shown with halos.
56
10
65
81
1
900
1,000
1,000
All Rights Reserved. Addison-Wesley

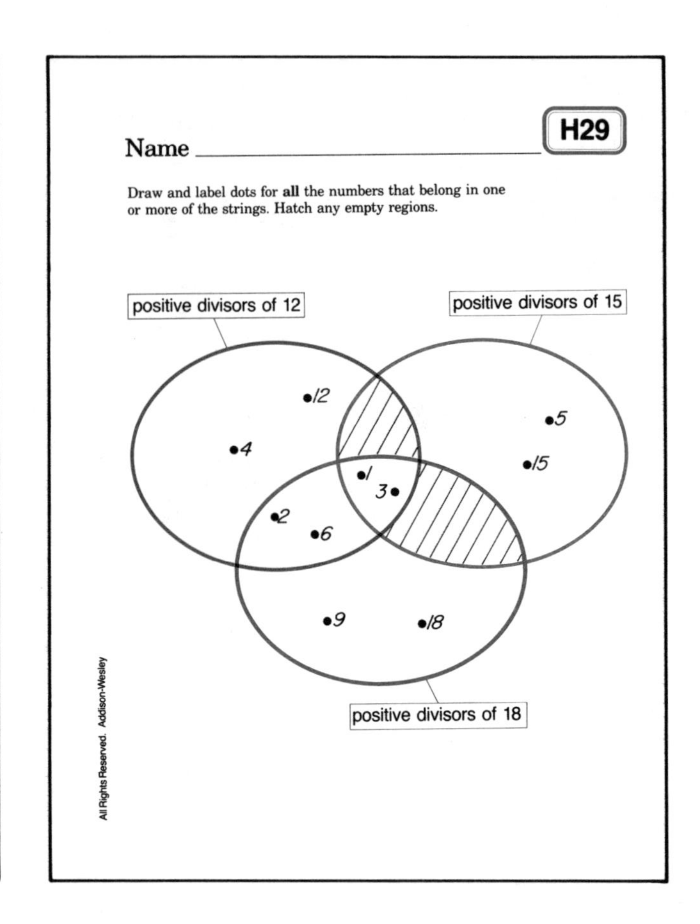
Name
H29
Draw and label dots for all the numbers that belong in one or more of the strings. Hatch any empty regions.
positive divisors of 12
positive divisors of 15
positive divisors of 18
12
4
5
15
1
3
2
6
9
18
All Rights Reserved. Addison-Wesley

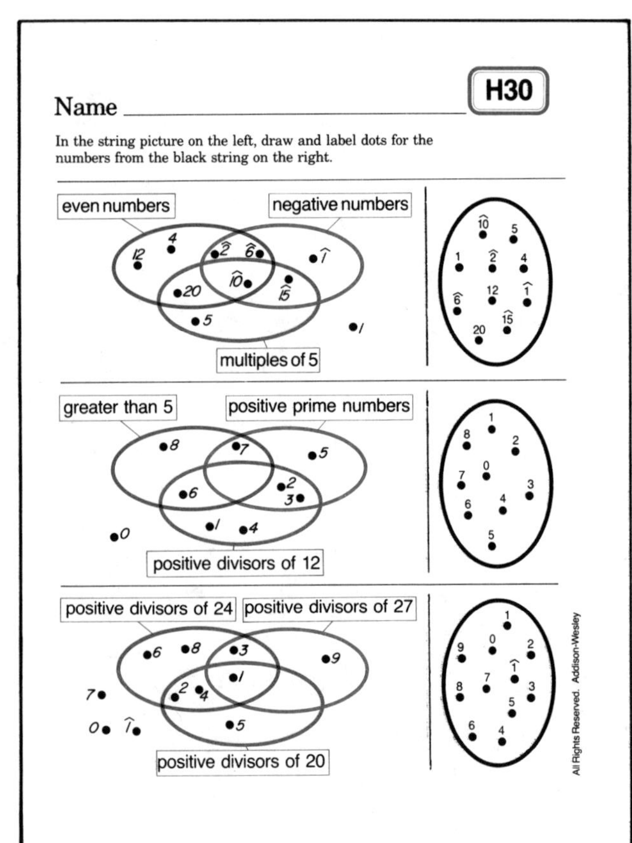
Name
H30
In the string picture on the left, draw and label dots for the numbers from the black string on the right.
even numbers
negative numbers
multiples of 5
greater than 5
positive prime numbers
positive divisors of 12
positive divisors of 24
positive divisors of 27
positive divisors of 20
All Rights Reserved. Addison-Wesley

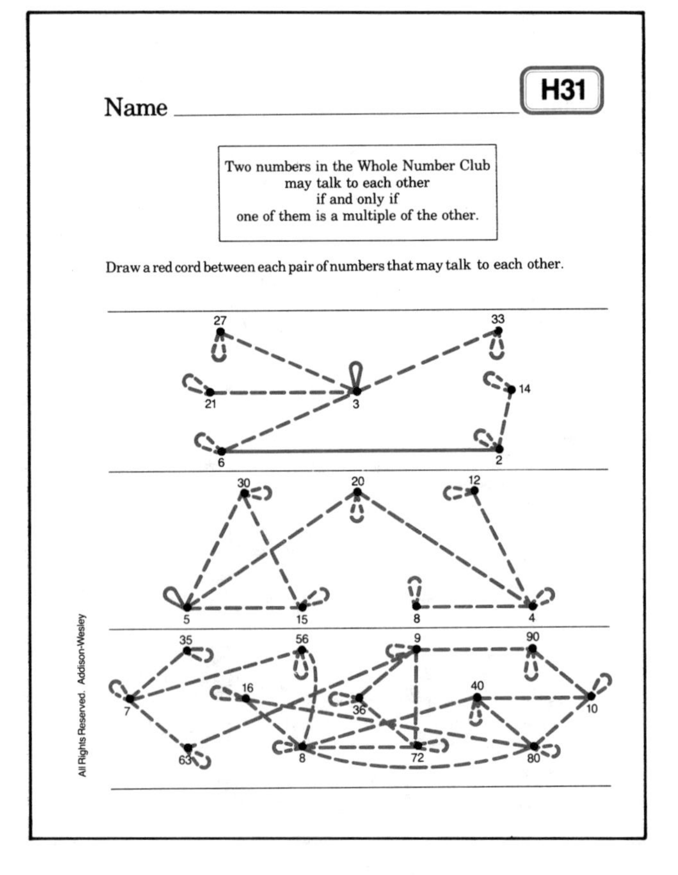
Name
H31
Two numbers in the Whole Number Club
may talk to each other
if and only if
one of them is a multiple of the other.
Draw a red cord between each pair of numbers that may talk to each other.
27
33
21
3
14
6
2
30
20
12
5
15
8
4
35
56
9
90
16
40
7
36
10
63
8
72
80
All Rights Reserved. Addison-Wesley

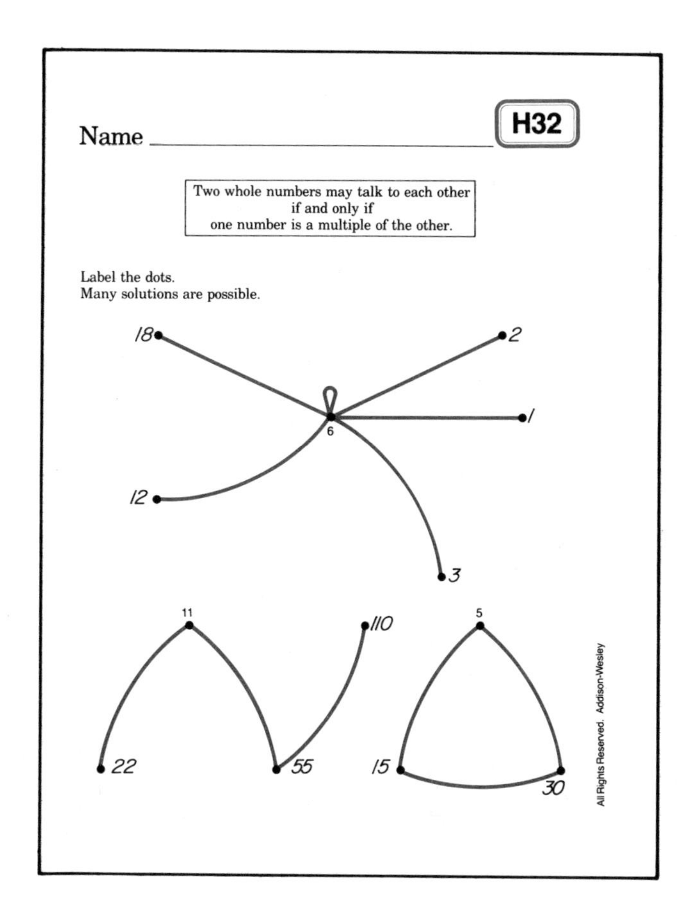

H32

Name ______________________

Two whole numbers may talk to each other
if and only if
one number is a multiple of the other.

Label the dots.
Many solutions are possible.

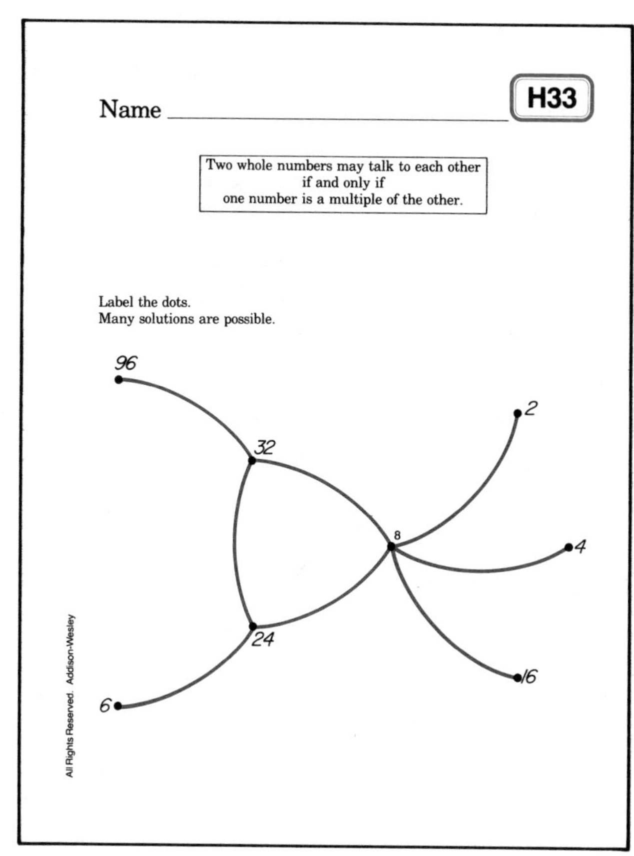

H33

Name ______________________

Two whole numbers may talk to each other
if and only if
one number is a multiple of the other.

Label the dots.
Many solutions are possible.

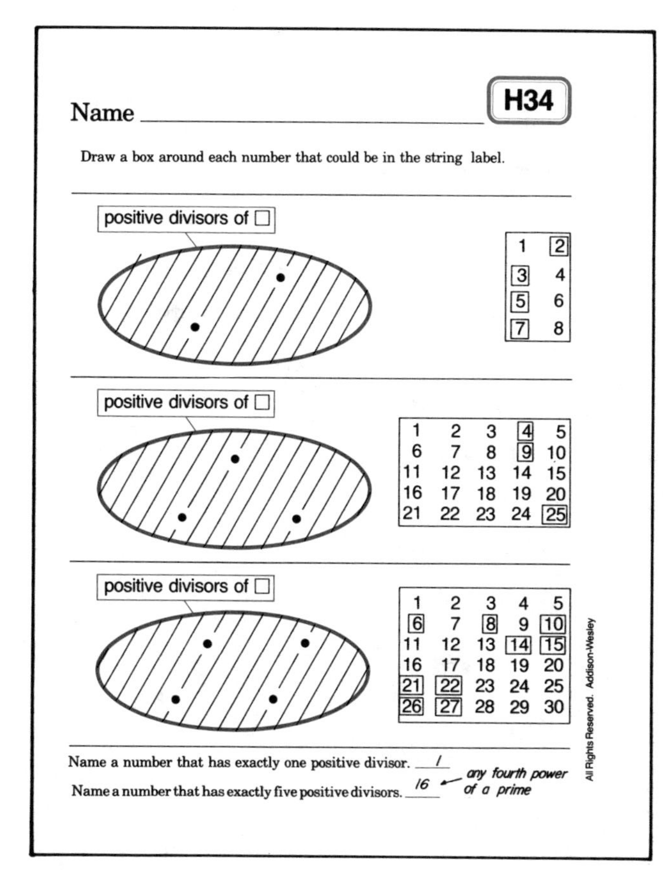

H34

Name ______________________

Draw a box around each number that could be in the string label.

1	[2]
[3]	4
[5]	6
[7]	8

1	2	3	[4]	5
6	7	8	[9]	10
11	12	13	14	15
16	17	18	19	20
21	22	23	24	[25]

1	2	3	4	5
[6]	7	[8]	9	[10]
11	12	13	[14]	[15]
16	17	18	19	20
[21]	[22]	23	24	25
[26]	[27]	28	29	30

Name a number that has exactly one positive divisor. 1

Name a number that has exactly five positive divisors. 16 ← any fourth power of a prime

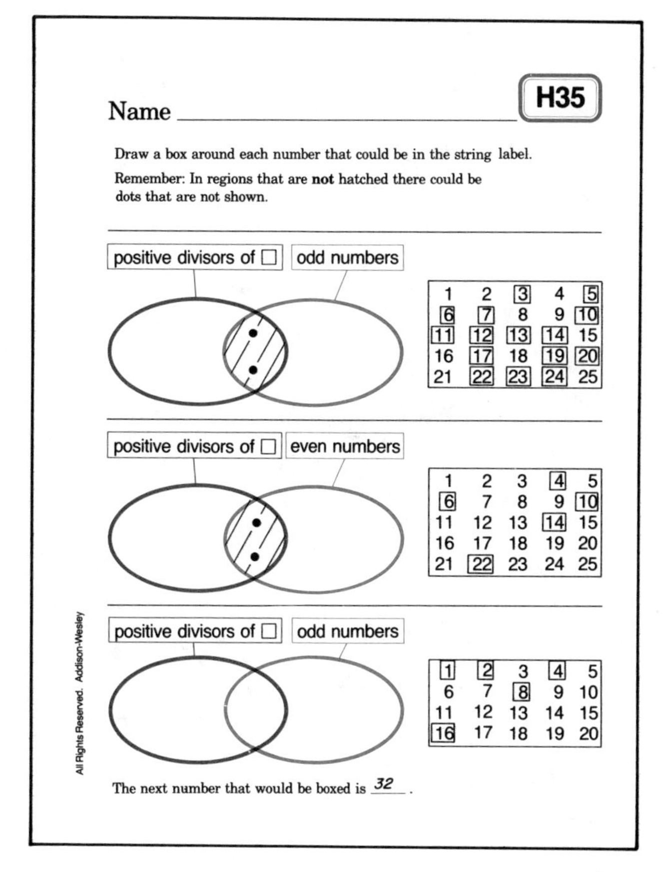

H35

Name ______________________

Draw a box around each number that could be in the string label.

Remember: In regions that are **not** hatched there could be dots that are not shown.

1	2	[3]	4	[5]
[6]	[7]	8	9	[10]
[11]	[12]	[13]	[14]	15
16	[17]	18	[19]	[20]
21	[22]	[23]	[24]	25

1	2	3	[4]	5
[6]	7	8	9	[10]
11	12	13	[14]	15
16	17	18	19	20
21	[22]	23	24	25

[1]	[2]	3	[4]	5
6	7	[8]	9	10
11	12	13	14	15
[16]	17	18	19	20

The next number that would be boxed is 32.

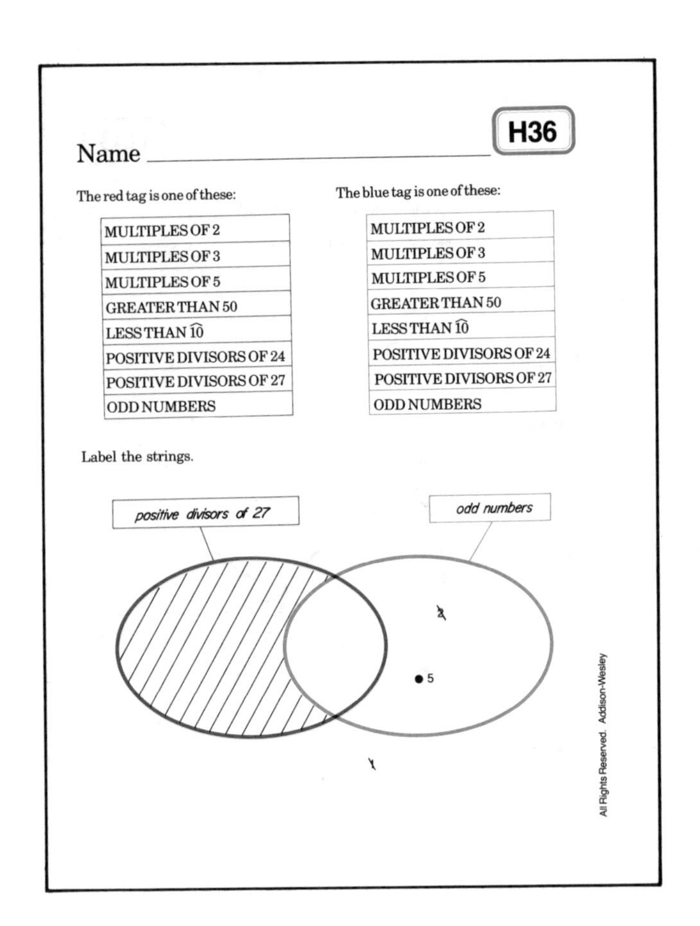
H36

Name ____________

The red tag is one of these:

MULTIPLES OF 2
MULTIPLES OF 3
MULTIPLES OF 5
GREATER THAN 50
LESS THAN $\hat{10}$
POSITIVE DIVISORS OF 24
POSITIVE DIVISORS OF 27
ODD NUMBERS

The blue tag is one of these:

MULTIPLES OF 2
MULTIPLES OF 3
MULTIPLES OF 5
GREATER THAN 50
LESS THAN $\hat{10}$
POSITIVE DIVISORS OF 24
POSITIVE DIVISORS OF 27
ODD NUMBERS

Label the strings.

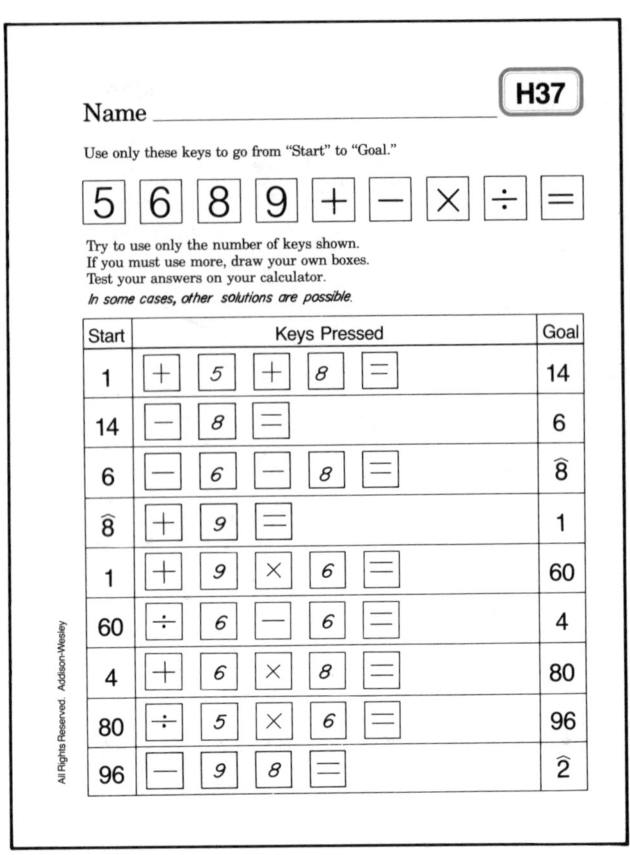
H37

Name ____________

Use only these keys to go from "Start" to "Goal."

5 6 8 9 + − × ÷ =

Try to use only the number of keys shown.
If you must use more, draw your own boxes.
Test your answers on your calculator.
In some cases, other solutions are possible.

Start	Keys Pressed	Goal
1	+ 5 + 8 =	14
14	− 8 =	6
6	− 6 − 8 =	$\hat{8}$
$\hat{8}$	+ 9 =	1
1	+ 9 × 6 =	60
60	÷ 6 − 6 =	4
4	+ 6 × 8 =	80
80	÷ 5 × 6 =	96
96	− 9 8 =	$\hat{2}$

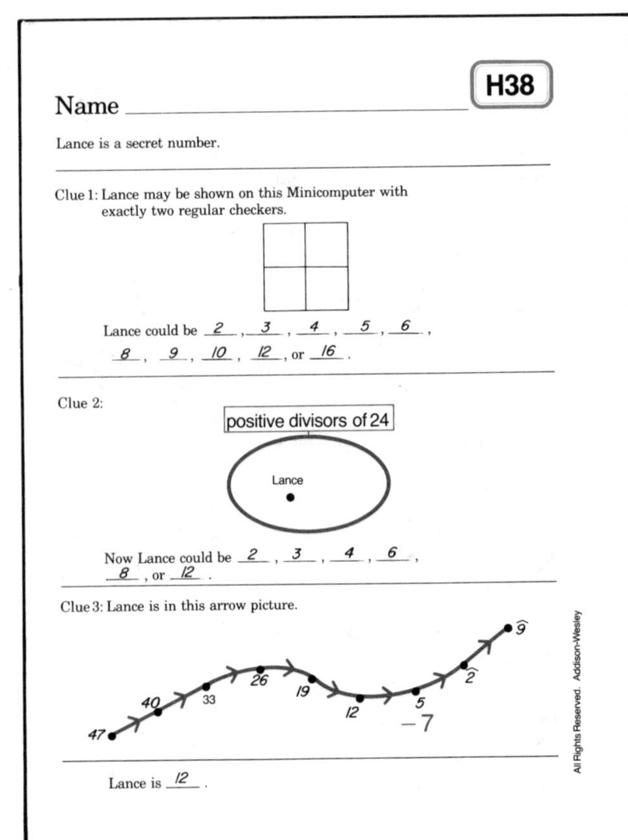
H38

Name ____________

Lance is a secret number.

Clue 1: Lance may be shown on this Minicomputer with exactly two regular checkers.

Lance could be 2, 3, 4, 5, 6, 8, 9, 10, 12, or 16.

Clue 2:

Now Lance could be 2, 3, 4, 6, 8, or 12.

Clue 3: Lance is in this arrow picture.

Lance is 12.

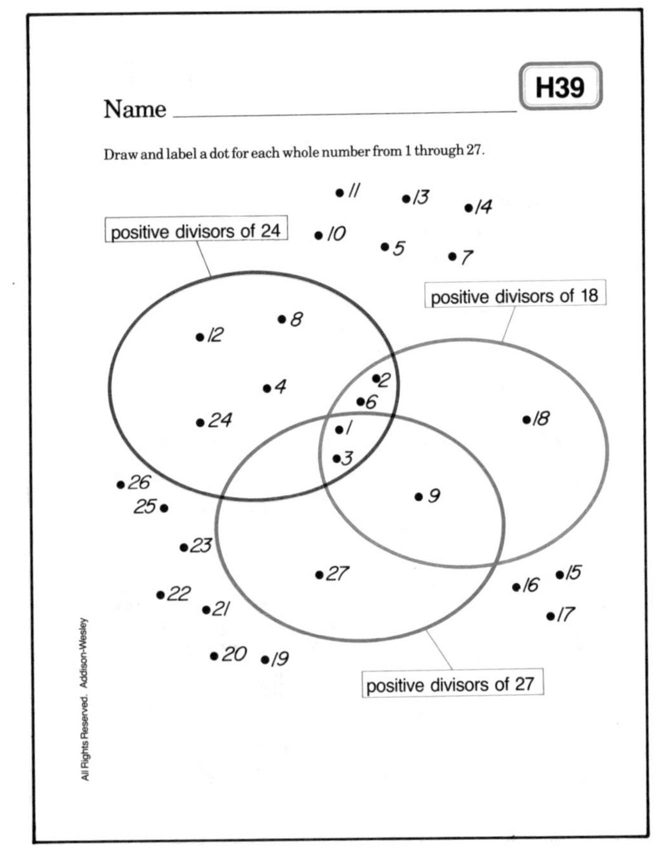
H39

Name ____________

Draw and label a dot for each whole number from 1 through 27.

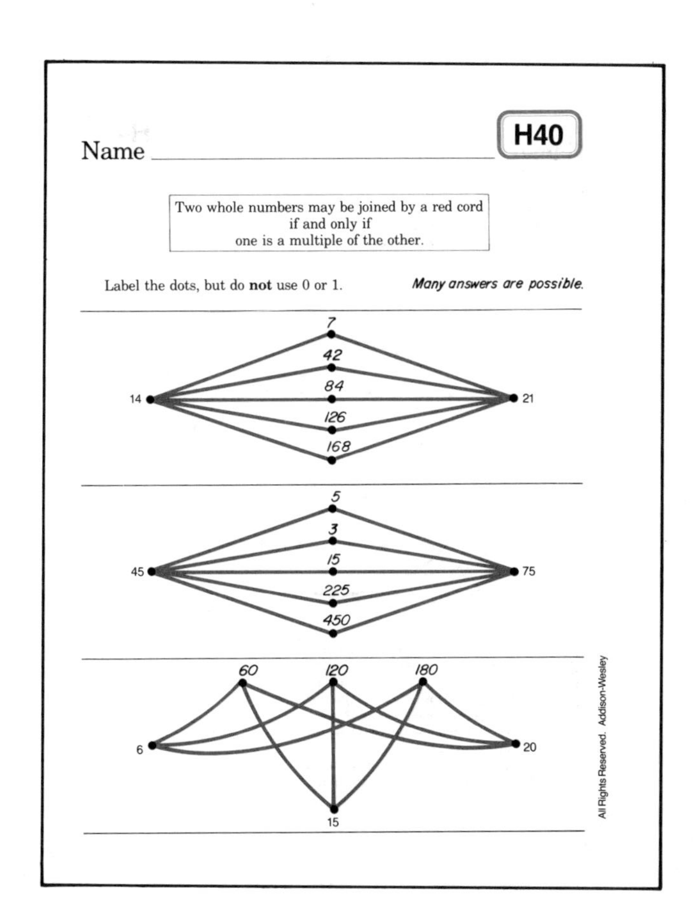

Name ____________ **H40**

Two whole numbers may be joined by a red cord if and only if one is a multiple of the other.

Label the dots, but do **not** use 0 or 1. *Many answers are possible.*

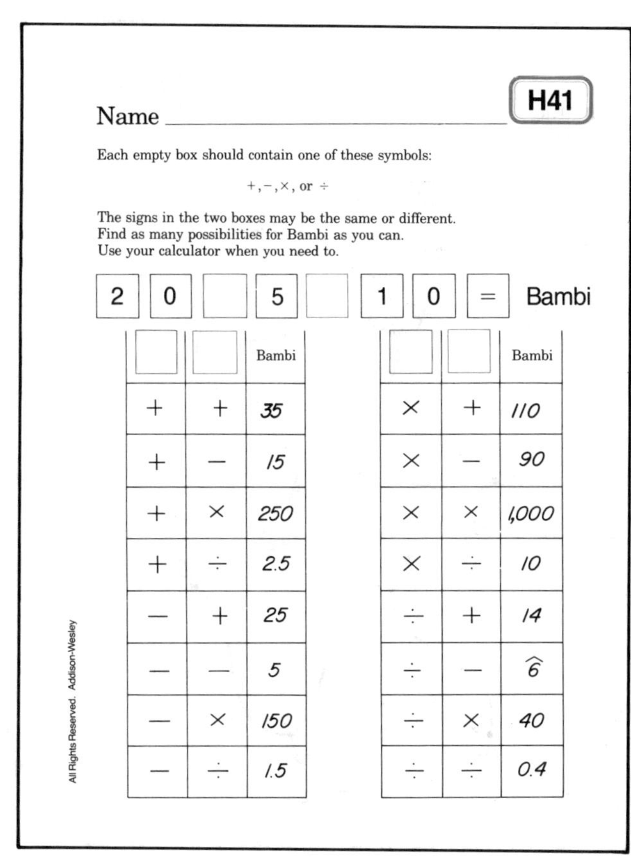

Name ____________ **H41**

Each empty box should contain one of these symbols:

+, −, ×, or ÷

The signs in the two boxes may be the same or different.
Find as many possibilities for Bambi as you can.
Use your calculator when you need to.

2 0 ☐ 5 ☐ 1 0 = Bambi

☐	☐	Bambi
+	+	35
+	−	15
+	×	250
+	÷	2.5
−	+	25
−	−	5
−	×	150
−	÷	1.5

☐	☐	Bambi
×	+	110
×	−	90
×	×	1,000
×	÷	10
÷	+	14
÷	−	$\hat{6}$
÷	×	40
÷	÷	0.4

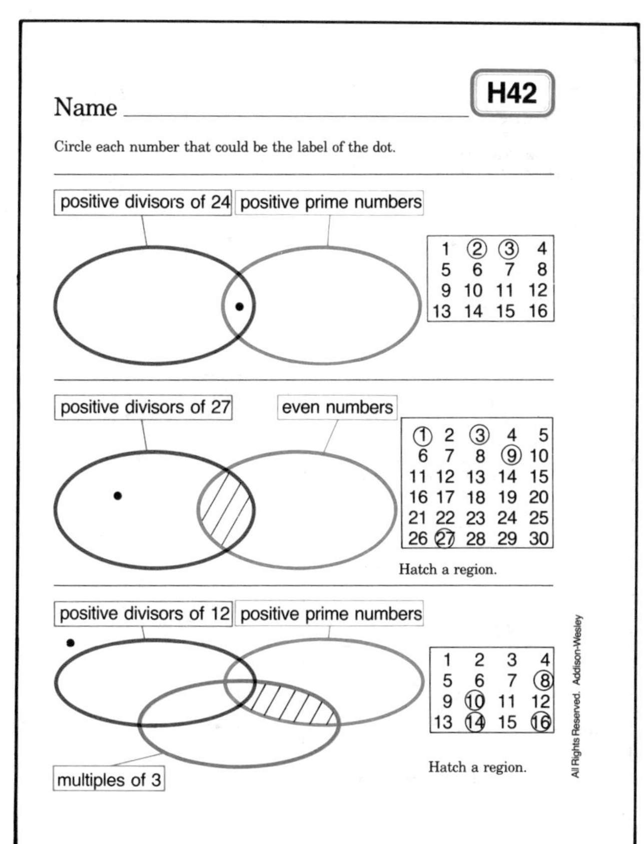

Name ____________ **H42**

Circle each number that could be the label of the dot.

1	②	③	4
5	6	7	8
9	10	11	12
13	14	15	16

①	2	③	4	5
6	7	8	⑨	10
11	12	13	14	15
16	17	18	19	20
21	22	23	24	25
26	㉗	28	29	30

Hatch a region.

1	2	3	4
5	6	7	⑧
9	⑩	11	12
13	⑭	15	⑯

Hatch a region.

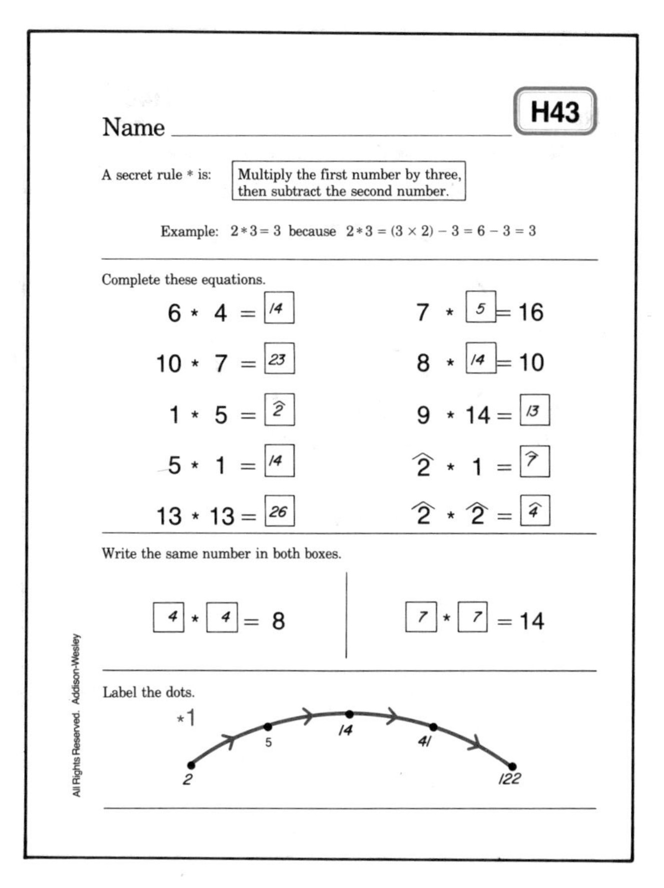

Name ____________ **H43**

A secret rule * is: Multiply the first number by three, then subtract the second number.

Example: 2*3 = 3 because 2*3 = (3 × 2) − 3 = 6 − 3 = 3

Complete these equations.

6 * 4 = [14]
7 * [5] = 16
10 * 7 = [23]
8 * [14] = 10
1 * 5 = [$\hat{2}$]
9 * 14 = [13]
5 * 1 = [14]
$\hat{2}$ * 1 = [$\hat{7}$]
13 * 13 = [26]
$\hat{2}$ * $\hat{2}$ = [$\hat{4}$]

Write the same number in both boxes.

[4] * [4] = 8

[7] * [7] = 14

Label the dots.

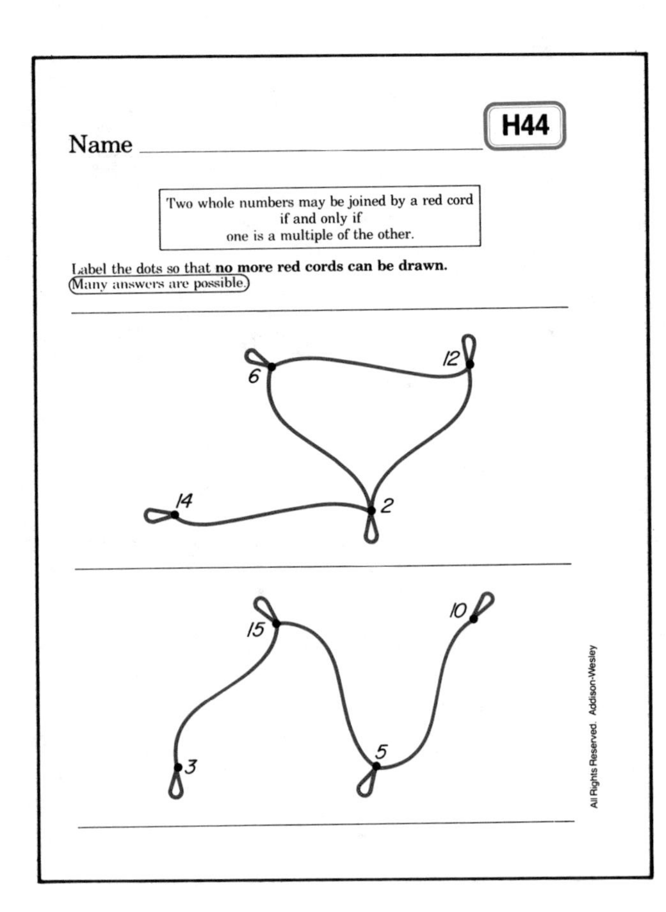
H44
Name
Two whole numbers may be joined by a red cord
if and only if
one is a multiple of the other.
Label the dots so that no more red cords can be drawn.
Many answers are possible.
6
12
14
2
15
10
3
5
All Rights Reserved. Addison-Wesley

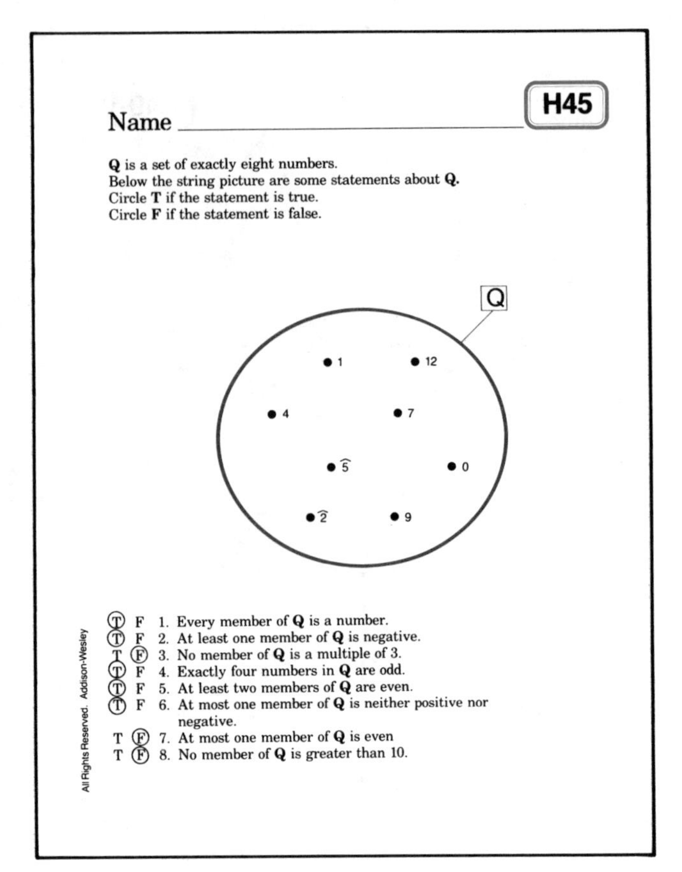
H45
Name
Q is a set of exactly eight numbers.
Below the string picture are some statements about Q.
Circle T if the statement is true.
Circle F if the statement is false.
Q
1
12
4
7
5
0
2
9
T F 1. Every member of Q is a number.
T F 2. At least one member of Q is negative.
T F 3. No member of Q is a multiple of 3.
T F 4. Exactly four numbers in Q are odd.
T F 5. At least two members of Q are even.
T F 6. At most one member of Q is neither positive nor negative.
T F 7. At most one member of Q is even
T F 8. No member of Q is greater than 10.
All Rights Reserved. Addison-Wesley

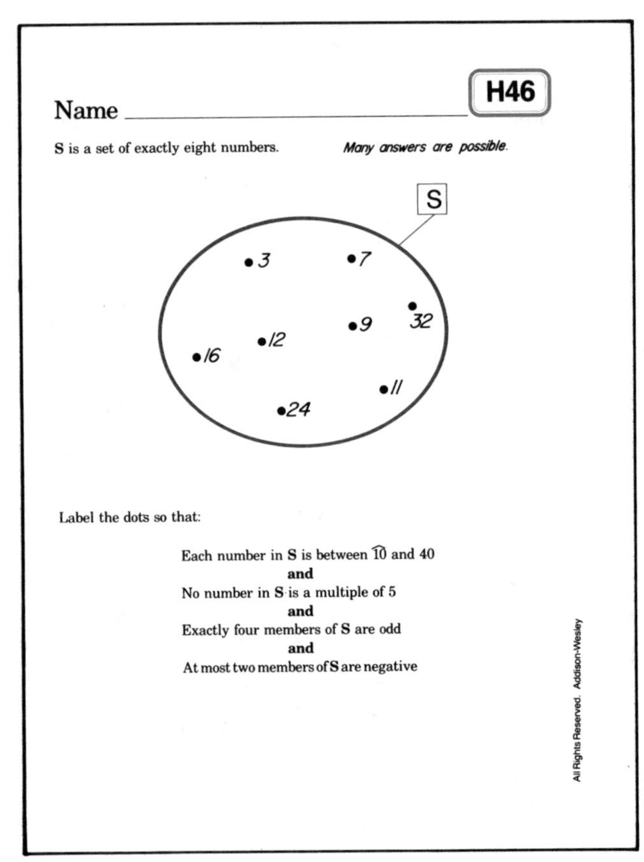
H46
Name
S is a set of exactly eight numbers.
Many answers are possible.
S
3
7
32
9
12
16
11
24
Label the dots so that:
Each number in S is between 10 and 40
and
No number in S is a multiple of 5
and
Exactly four members of S are odd
and
At most two members of S are negative
All Rights Reserved. Addison-Wesley

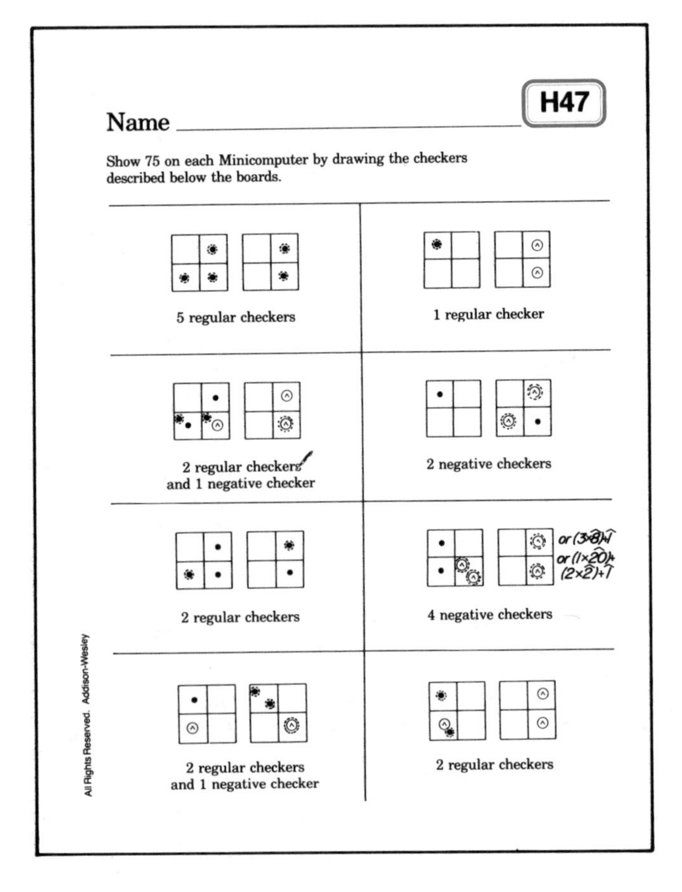
H47
Name
Show 75 on each Minicomputer by drawing the checkers
described below the boards.
5 regular checkers
1 regular checker
2 regular checkers
and 1 negative checker
2 negative checkers
2 regular checkers
4 negative checkers
2 regular checkers
and 1 negative checker
2 regular checkers
All Rights Reserved. Addison-Wesley

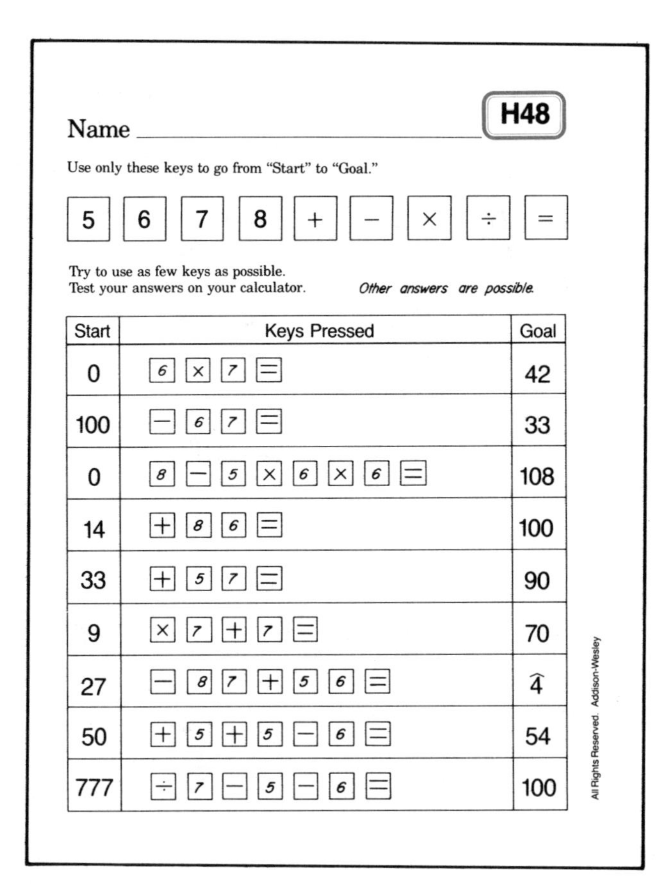

Name ______________________ **H48**

Use only these keys to go from "Start" to "Goal."

5 | 6 | 7 | 8 | + | − | × | ÷ | =

Try to use as few keys as possible.
Test your answers on your calculator. *Other answers are possible.*

Start	Keys Pressed	Goal
0	6 × 7 =	42
100	− 6 7 =	33
0	8 − 5 × 6 × 6 =	108
14	+ 8 6 =	100
33	+ 5 7 =	90
9	× 7 + 7 =	70
27	− 8 7 + 5 6 =	$\hat{4}$
50	+ 5 + 5 − 6 =	54
777	÷ 7 − 5 − 6 =	100

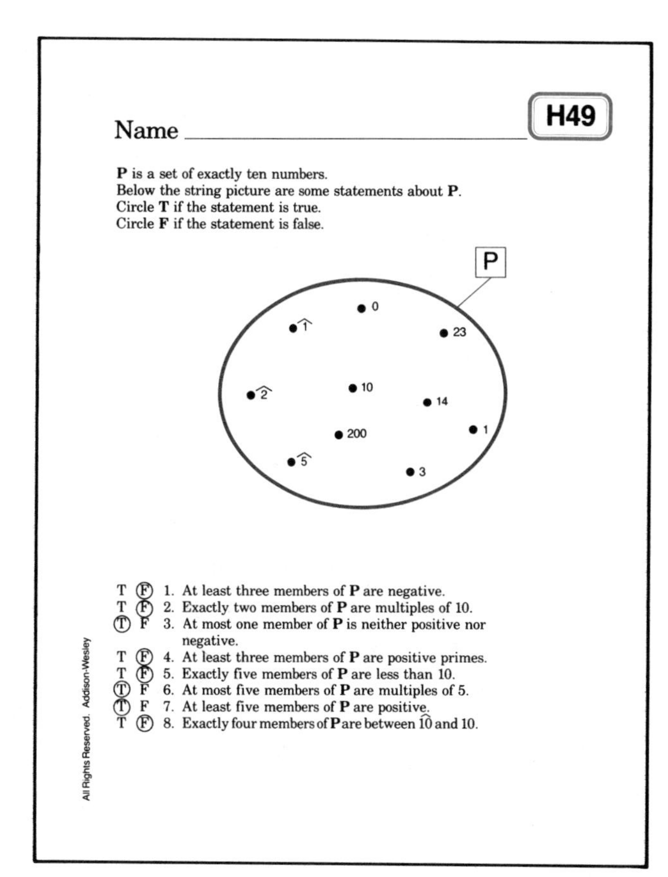

Name ______________________ **H49**

P is a set of exactly ten numbers.
Below the string picture are some statements about **P**.
Circle **T** if the statement is true.
Circle **F** if the statement is false.

T (F) 1. At least three members of **P** are negative.
T (F) 2. Exactly two members of **P** are multiples of 10.
(T) F 3. At most one member of **P** is neither positive nor negative.
T (F) 4. At least three members of **P** are positive primes.
T (F) 5. Exactly five members of **P** are less than 10.
(T) F 6. At most five members of **P** are multiples of 5.
(T) F 7. At least five members of **P** are positive.
T (F) 8. Exactly four members of **P** are between $\hat{10}$ and 10.

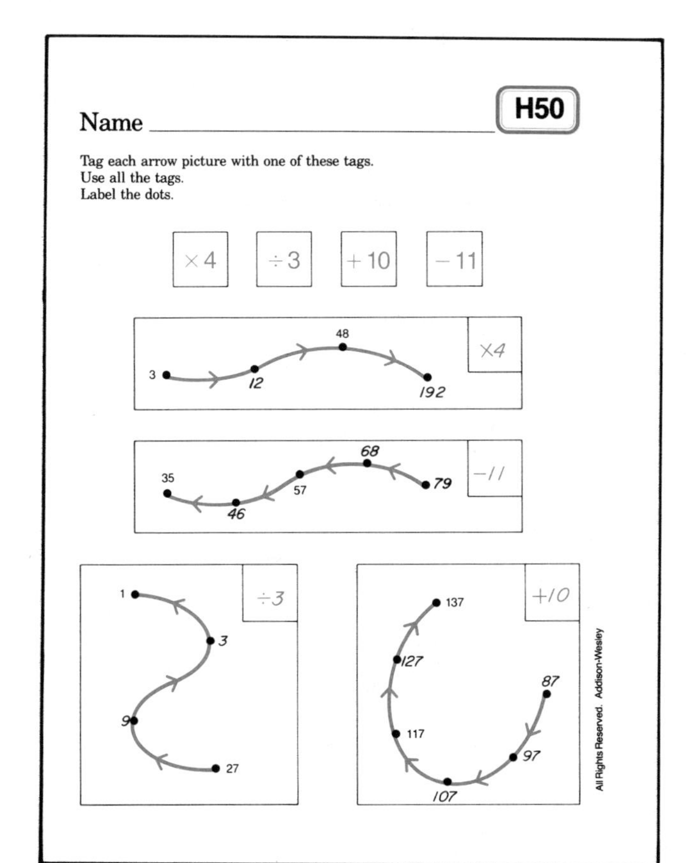

Name ______________________ **H50**

Tag each arrow picture with one of these tags.
Use all the tags.
Label the dots.

×4 | ÷3 | +10 | −11

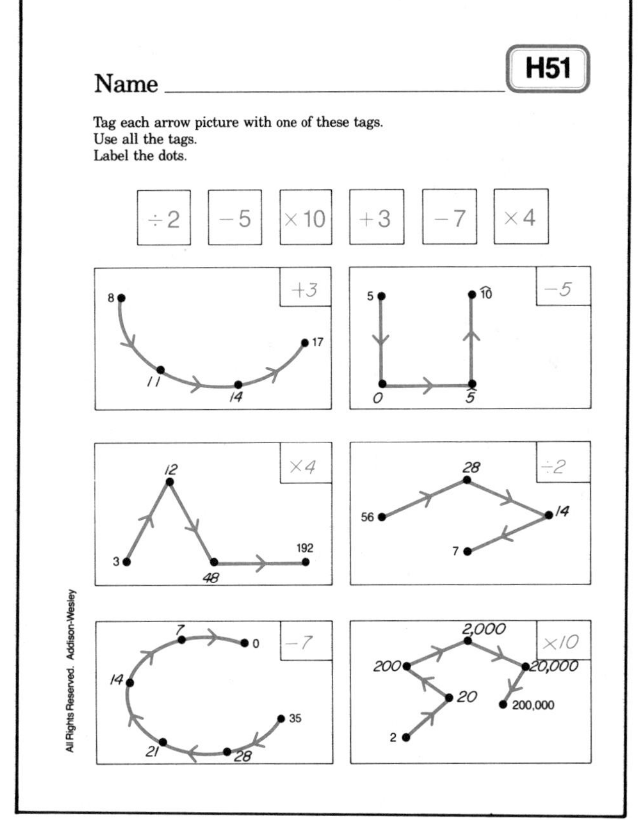

Name ______________________ **H51**

Tag each arrow picture with one of these tags.
Use all the tags.
Label the dots.

÷2 | −5 | ×10 | +3 | −7 | ×4

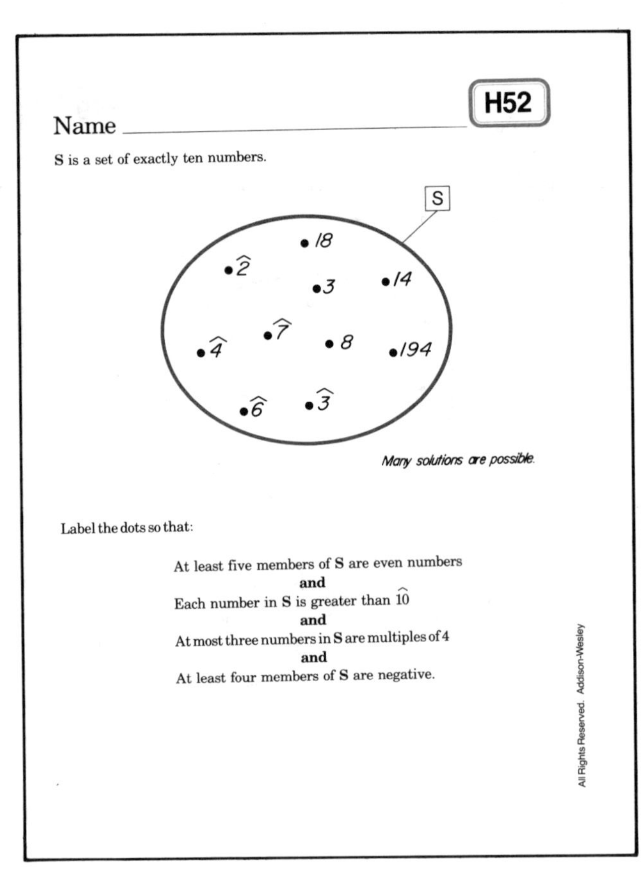

Name ______________________ **H52**

S is a set of exactly ten numbers.

Label the dots so that:

At least five members of **S** are even numbers
and
Each number in **S** is greater than $\hat{10}$
and
At most three numbers in **S** are multiples of 4
and
At least four members of **S** are negative.

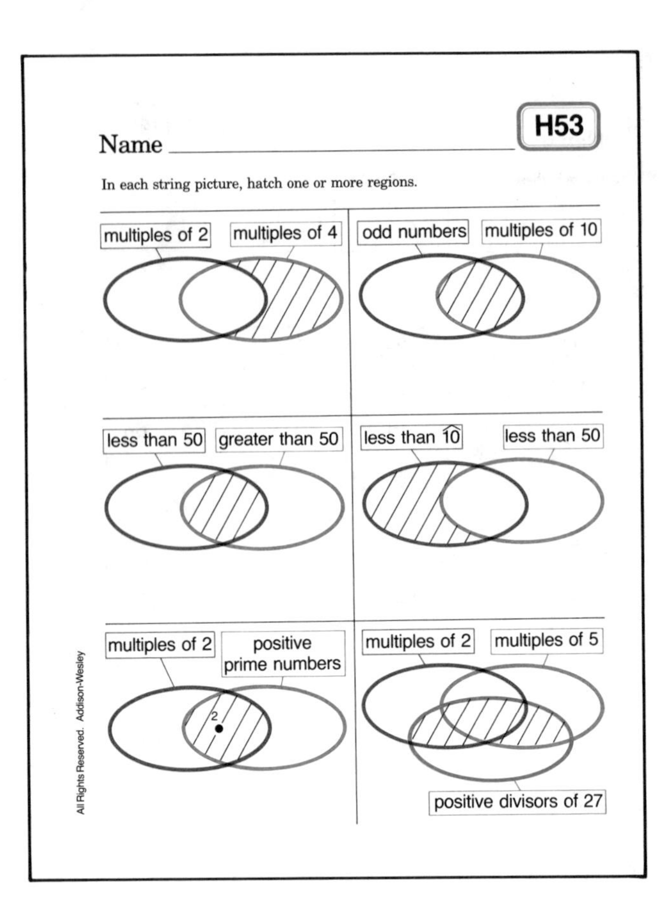

Name ______________________ **H53**

In each string picture, hatch one or more regions.

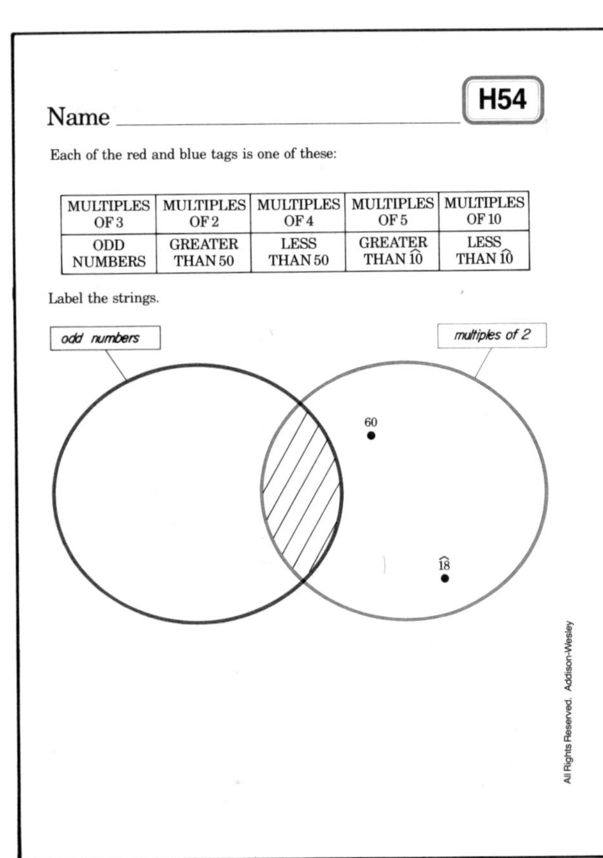

Name ______________________ **H54**

Each of the red and blue tags is one of these:

MULTIPLES OF 3	MULTIPLES OF 2	MULTIPLES OF 4	MULTIPLES OF 5	MULTIPLES OF 10
ODD NUMBERS	GREATER THAN 50	LESS THAN 50	GREATER THAN $\hat{10}$	LESS THAN $\hat{10}$

Label the strings.

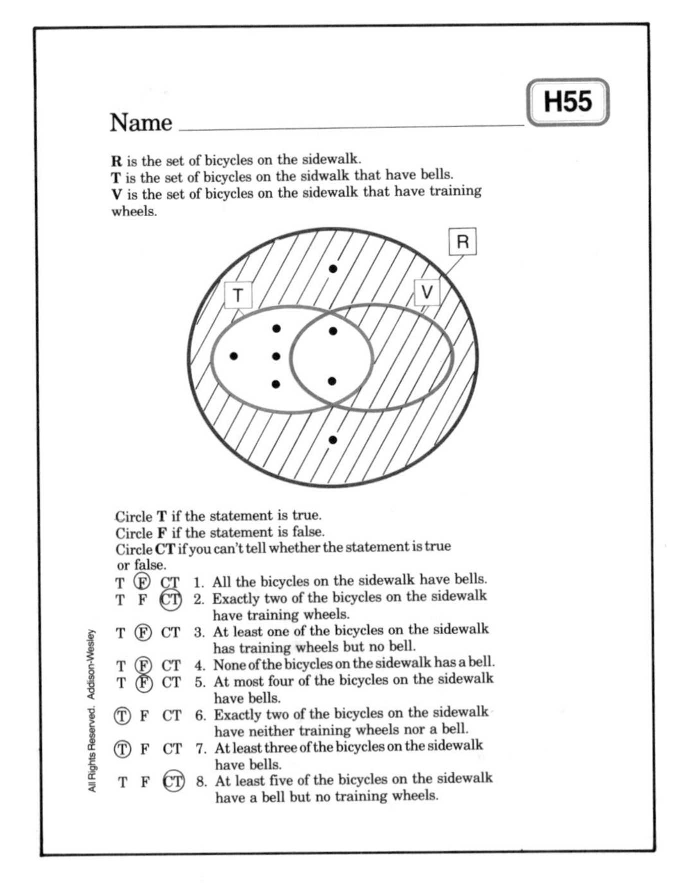

Name ______________________ **H55**

R is the set of bicycles on the sidewalk.
T is the set of bicycles on the sidwalk that have bells.
V is the set of bicycles on the sidewalk that have training wheels.

Circle **T** if the statement is true.
Circle **F** if the statement is false.
Circle **CT** if you can't tell whether the statement is true or false.

T (F) CT 1. All the bicycles on the sidewalk have bells.
T F (CT) 2. Exactly two of the bicycles on the sidewalk have training wheels.
T (F) CT 3. At least one of the bicycles on the sidewalk has training wheels but no bell.
T (F) CT 4. None of the bicycles on the sidewalk has a bell.
T (F) CT 5. At most four of the bicycles on the sidewalk have bells.
(T) F CT 6. Exactly two of the bicycles on the sidewalk have neither training wheels nor a bell.
(T) F CT 7. At least three of the bicycles on the sidewalk have bells.
T F (CT) 8. At least five of the bicycles on the sidewalk have a bell but no training wheels.

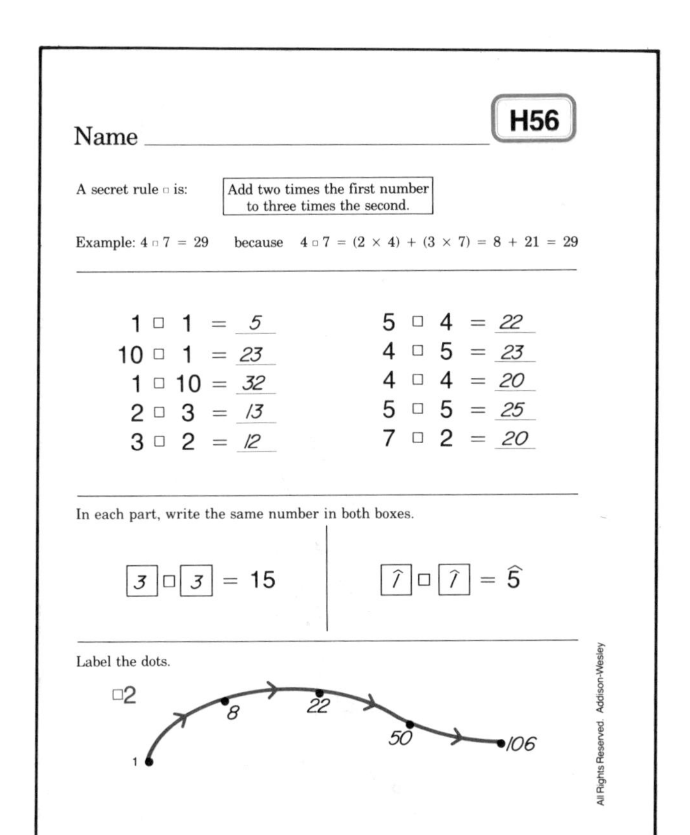

Name ______________________ **H56**

A secret rule □ is: Add two times the first number to three times the second.

Example: 4 □ 7 = 29 because 4 □ 7 = (2 × 4) + (3 × 7) = 8 + 21 = 29

1 □ 1 = *5*		5 □ 4 = *22*
10 □ 1 = *23*		4 □ 5 = *23*
1 □ 10 = *32*		4 □ 4 = *20*
2 □ 3 = *13*		5 □ 5 = *25*
3 □ 2 = *12*		7 □ 2 = *20*

In each part, write the same number in both boxes.

[*3*] □ [*3*] = 15 | [*1*] □ [*1*] = 5

Label the dots.

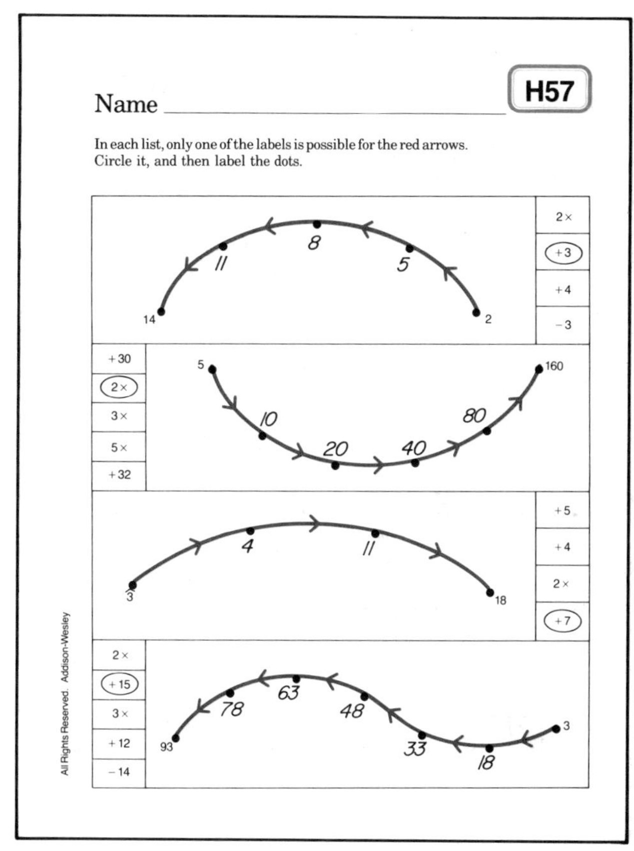

Name ______________________ **H57**

In each list, only one of the labels is possible for the red arrows.
Circle it, and then label the dots.

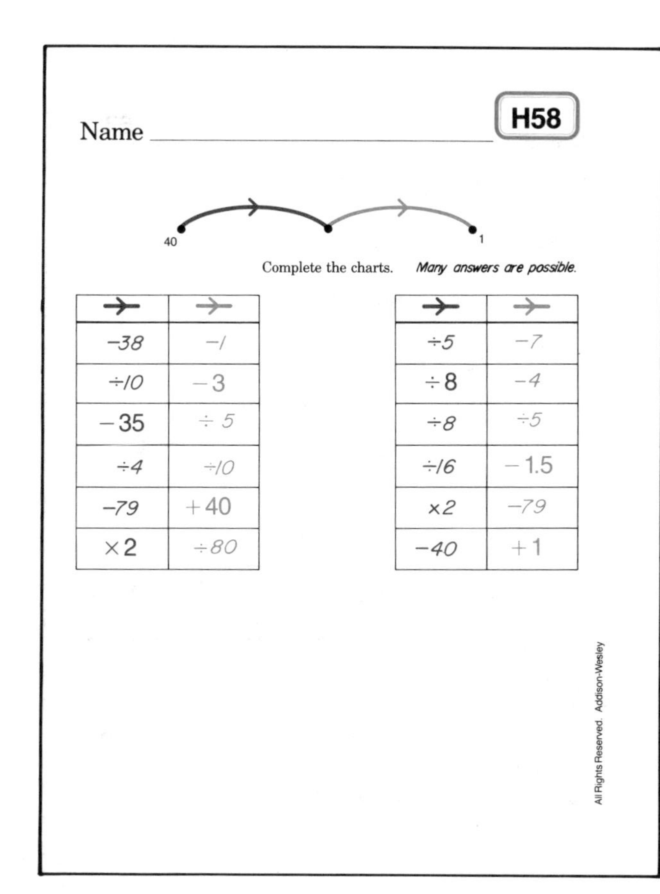

Name ______________________ **H58**

Complete the charts. *Many answers are possible.*

→	→
−38	*−1*
÷10	−3
−35	*÷5*
÷4	*÷10*
−79	+40
×2	*÷80*

→	→
÷5	*−7*
÷8	*−4*
÷8	*÷5*
÷16	−1.5
×2	*−79*
−40	+1

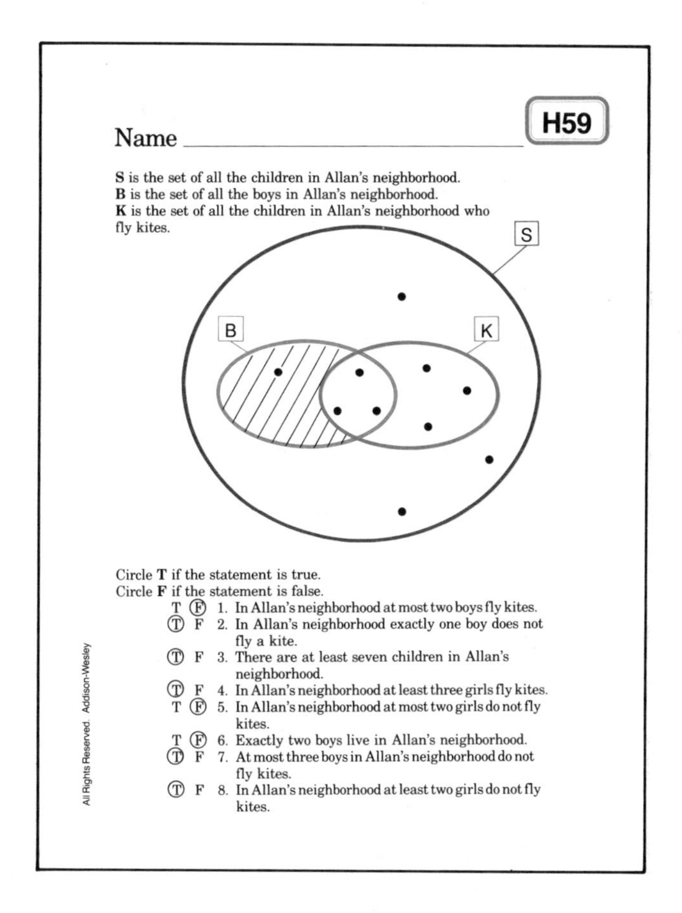

Name ______________________ **H59**

S is the set of all the children in Allan's neighborhood.
B is the set of all the boys in Allan's neighborhood.
K is the set of all the children in Allan's neighborhood who fly kites.

Circle **T** if the statement is true.
Circle **F** if the statement is false.

T (F) 1. In Allan's neighborhood at most two boys fly kites.
(T) F 2. In Allan's neighborhood exactly one boy does not fly a kite.
(T) F 3. There are at least seven children in Allan's neighborhood.
(T) F 4. In Allan's neighborhood at least three girls fly kites.
T (F) 5. In Allan's neighborhood at most two girls do not fly kites.
T (F) 6. Exactly two boys live in Allan's neighborhood.
(T) F 7. At most three boys in Allan's neighborhood do not fly kites.
(T) F 8. In Allan's neighborhood at least two girls do not fly kites.

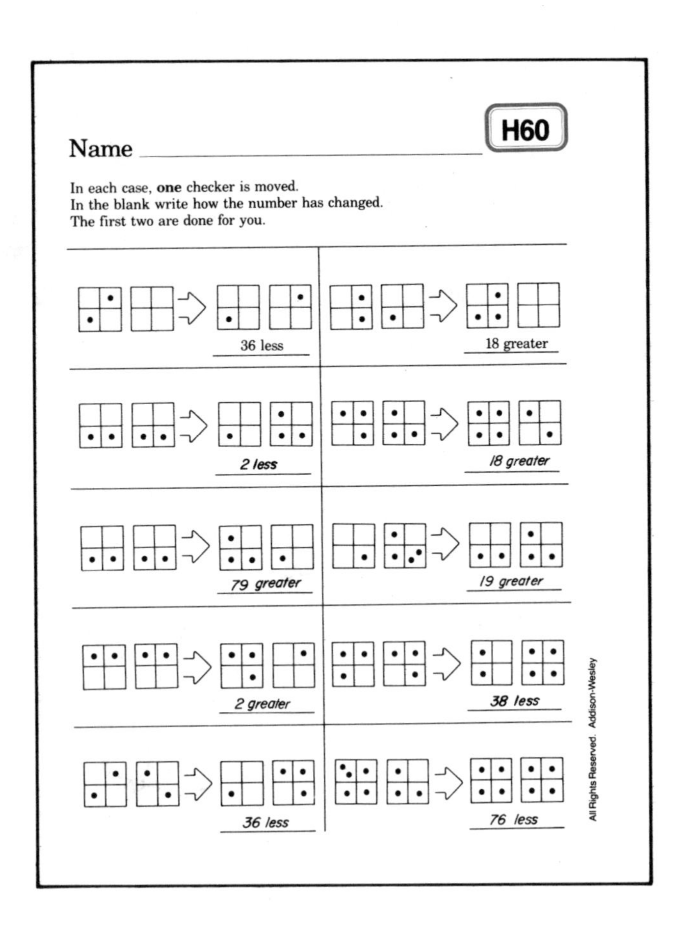
H60

Name ____________

In each case, **one** checker is moved.
In the blank write how the number has changed.
The first two are done for you.

36 less

18 greater

2 less

18 greater

79 greater

19 greater

2 greater

38 less

36 less

76 less

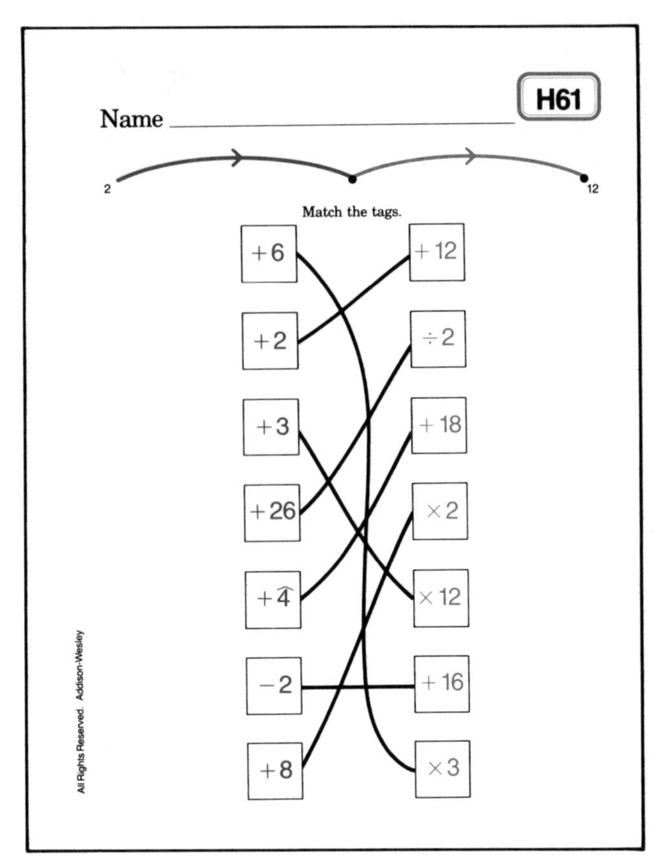
H61

Name ____________

Match the tags.

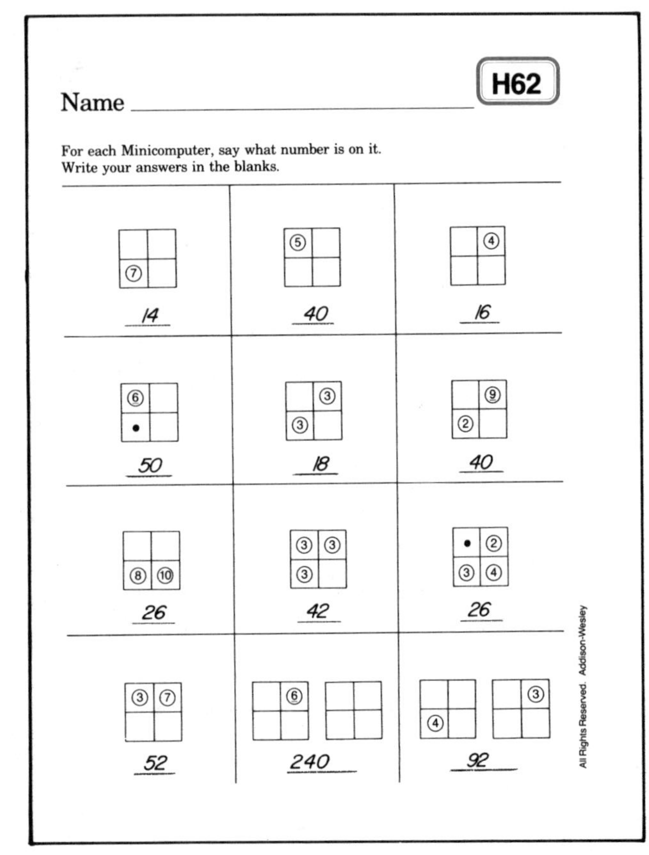
H62

Name ____________

For each Minicomputer, say what number is on it.
Write your answers in the blanks.

14

40

16

50

18

40

26

42

26

52

240

92

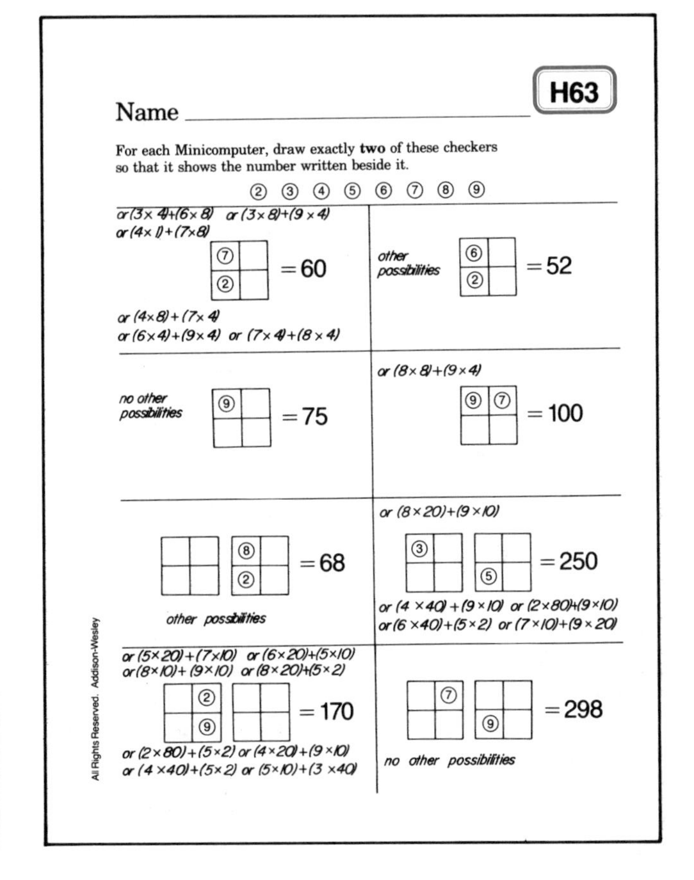
H63

Name ____________

For each Minicomputer, draw exactly **two** of these checkers
so that it shows the number written beside it.

② ③ ④ ⑤ ⑥ ⑦ ⑧ ⑨

or (3 × 4)+(6 × 8) or (3 × 8)+(9 × 4)
or (4 × 1)+(7 × 8)

= 60

or (4 × 8) + (7 × 4)
or (6 × 4)+(9 × 4) or (7 × 4)+(8 × 4)

other possibilities

= 52

no other possibilities

= 75

or (8 × 8)+(9 × 4)

= 100

= 68

other possibilities

or (8 × 20)+(9 × 10)

= 250

or (4 × 40) + (9 × 10) or (2 × 80)+(9 × 10)
or (6 × 40)+(5 × 2) or (7 × 10)+(9 × 20)

or (5 × 20)+(7 × 10) or (6 × 20)+(5 × 10)
or (8 × 10)+ (9 × 10) or (8 × 20)+(5 × 2)

= 170

or (2 × 80)+(5 × 2) or (4 × 20)+(9 × 10)
or (4 × 40)+(5 × 2) or (5 × 10)+(3 × 40)

= 298

no other possibilities

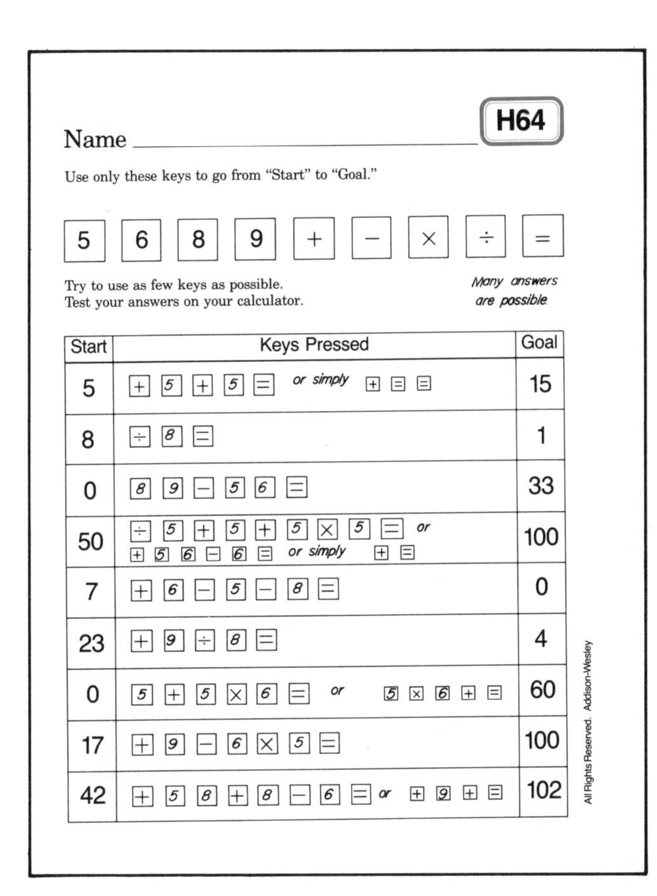

Name ______________________ **H64**

Use only these keys to go from "Start" to "Goal."

5 6 8 9 + − × ÷ =

Try to use as few keys as possible.
Test your answers on your calculator.

Many answers are possible

Start	Keys Pressed	Goal
5	+ 5 + 5 = *or simply* + = =	15
8	÷ 8 =	1
0	8 9 − 5 6 =	33
50	÷ 5 + 5 + 5 × 5 = *or* + 5 6 − 6 = *or simply* + =	100
7	+ 6 − 5 − 8 =	0
23	+ 9 ÷ 8 =	4
0	5 + 5 × 6 = *or* 5 × 6 + =	60
17	+ 9 − 6 × 5 =	100
42	+ 5 8 + 8 − 6 = *or* + 9 + =	102

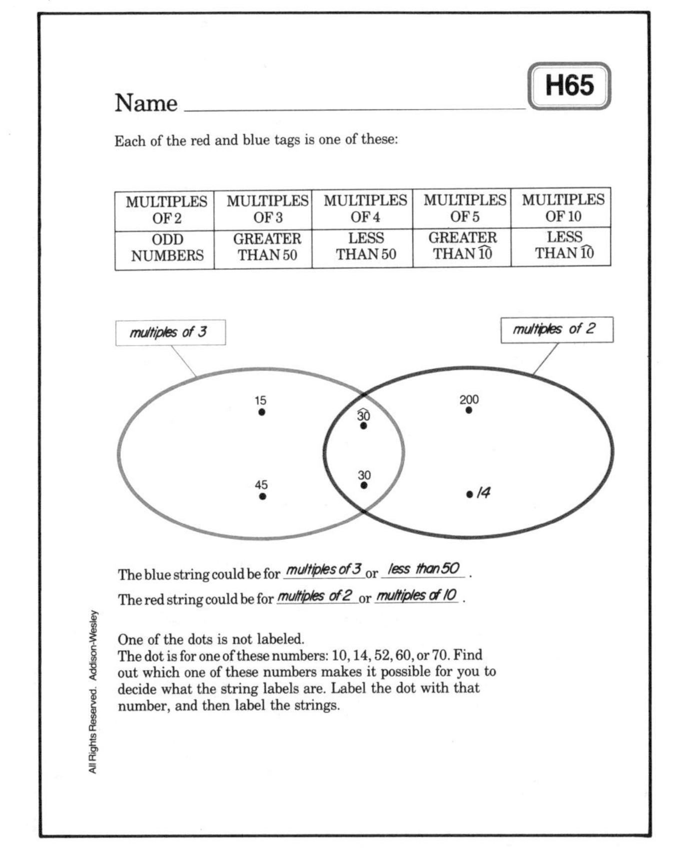

Name ______________________ **H65**

Each of the red and blue tags is one of these:

MULTIPLES OF 2	MULTIPLES OF 3	MULTIPLES OF 4	MULTIPLES OF 5	MULTIPLES OF 10
ODD NUMBERS	GREATER THAN 50	LESS THAN 50	GREATER THAN 10	LESS THAN 10

The blue string could be for *multiples of 3* or *less than 50*.

The red string could be for *multiples of 2* or *multiples of 10*.

One of the dots is not labeled.
The dot is for one of these numbers: 10, 14, 52, 60, or 70. Find out which one of these numbers makes it possible for you to decide what the string labels are. Label the dot with that number, and then label the strings.

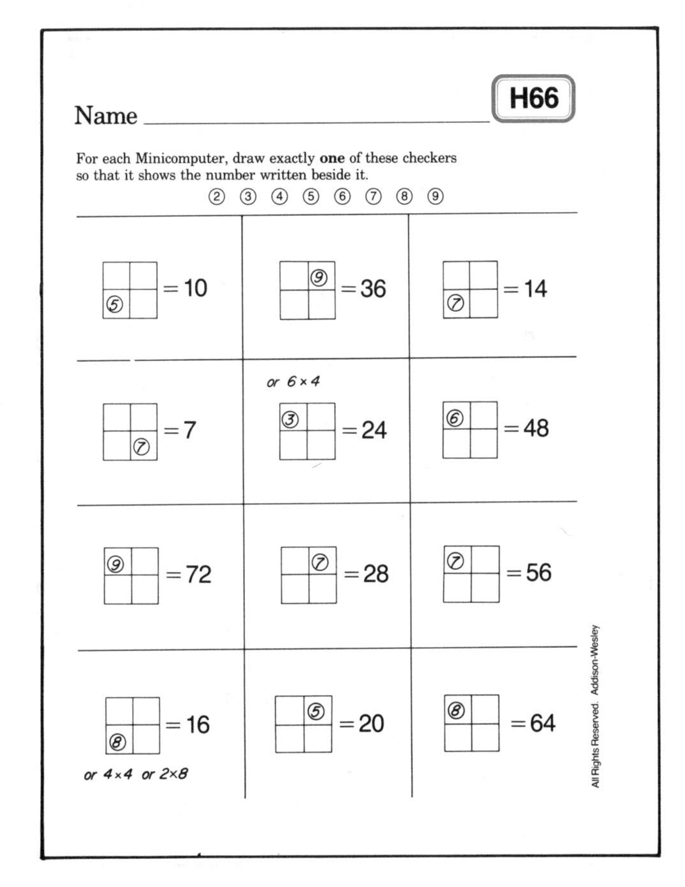

Name ______________________ **H66**

For each Minicomputer, draw exactly **one** of these checkers so that it shows the number written beside it.

② ③ ④ ⑤ ⑥ ⑦ ⑧ ⑨

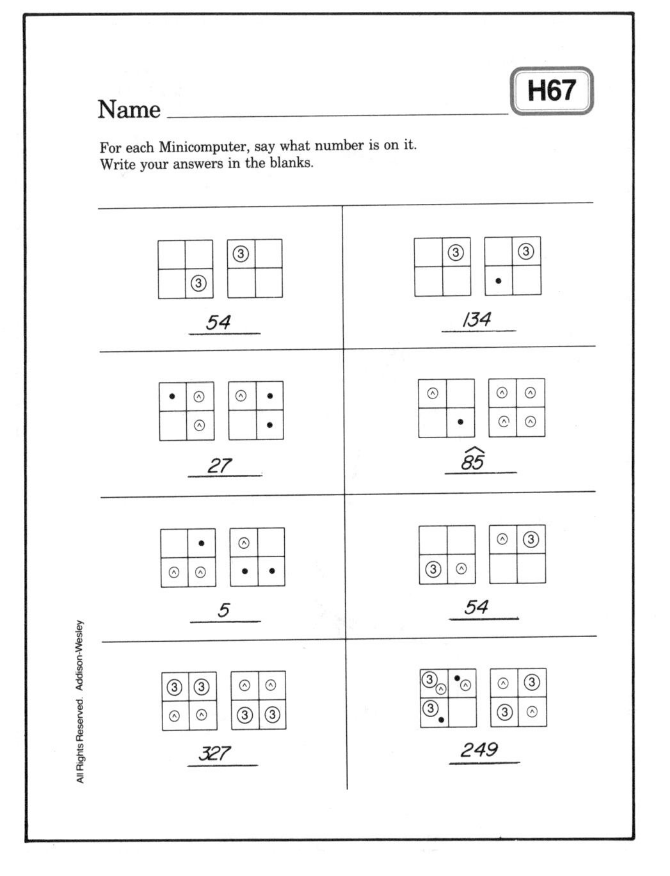

Name ______________________ **H67**

For each Minicomputer, say what number is on it.
Write your answers in the blanks.

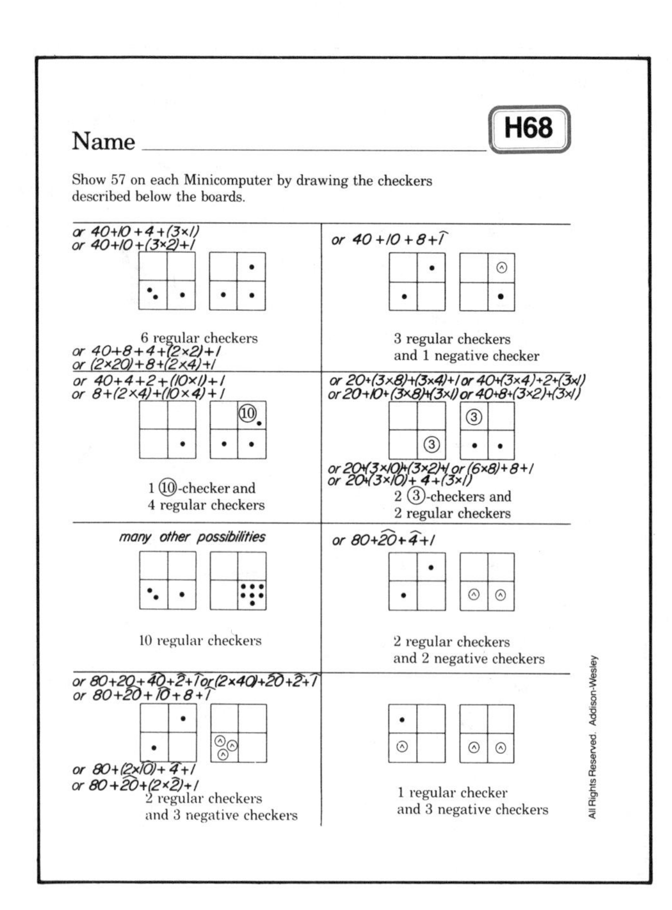
Name
H68
Show 57 on each Minicomputer by drawing the checkers described below the boards.
or 40+10+4+(3×1)
or 40+10+(3×2)+1
6 regular checkers
or 40+8+4+(2×2)+1
or (2×20)+8+(2×4)+1
or 40+10+8+1̂
3 regular checkers
and 1 negative checker
or 40+4+2+(10×1)+1
or 8+(2×4)+(10×4)+1
1 ⑩-checker and
4 regular checkers
2 ③-checkers and
2 regular checkers
many other possibilities
10 regular checkers
or 80+2̂0+4̂+1
2 regular checkers
and 2 negative checkers
2 regular checkers
and 3 negative checkers
1 regular checker
and 3 negative checkers
All Rights Reserved. Addison-Wesley
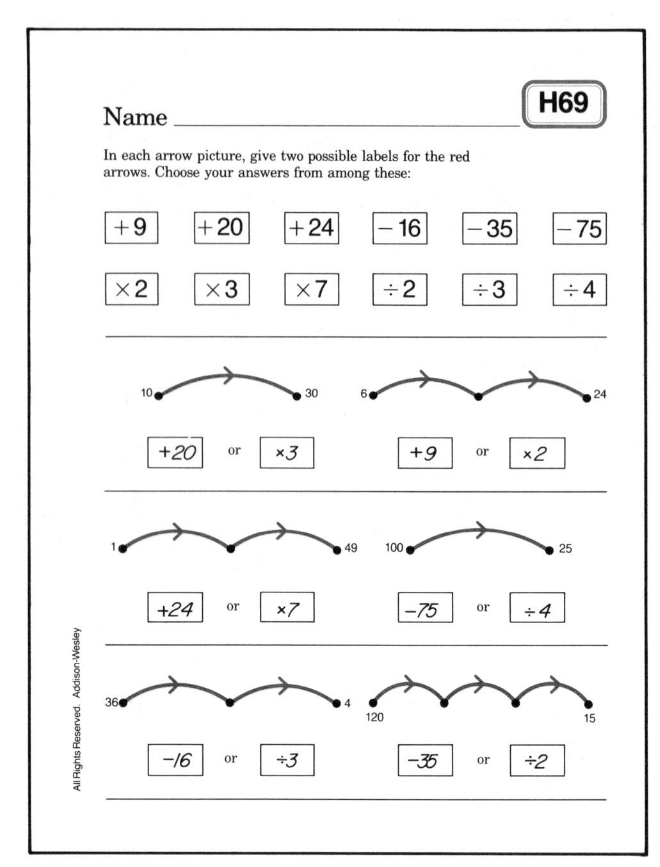
Name
H69
In each arrow picture, give two possible labels for the red arrows. Choose your answers from among these:
+9
+20
+24
−16
−35
−75
×2
×3
×7
÷2
÷3
÷4
+20 or ×3
+9 or ×2
+24 or ×7
−75 or ÷4
−16 or ÷3
−35 or ÷2
All Rights Reserved. Addison-Wesley
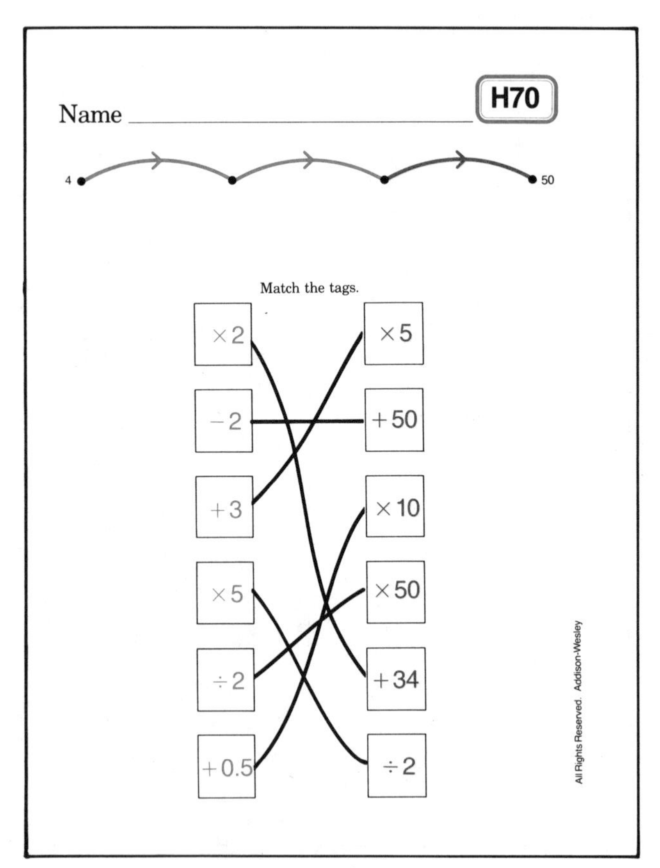
Name
H70
Match the tags.
×2
−2
+3
×5
÷2
+0.5
×5
+50
×10
×50
+34
÷2
All Rights Reserved. Addison-Wesley
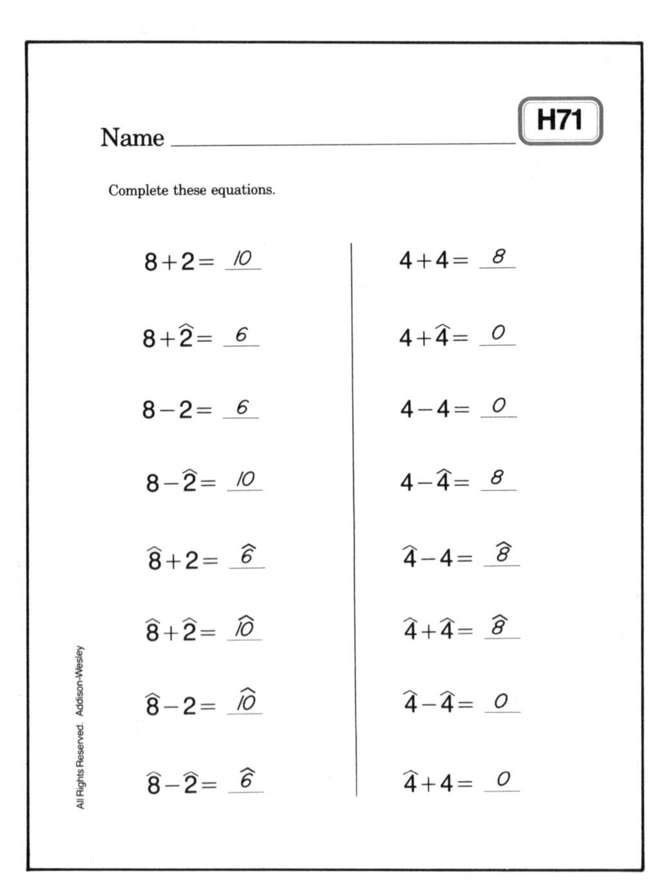
Name
H71
Complete these equations.
8+2= 10
8+2̂= 6
8−2= 6
8−2̂= 10
8̂+2= 6̂
8̂+2̂= 1̂0
8̂−2= 1̂0
8̂−2̂= 6̂
4+4= 8
4+4̂= 0
4−4= 0
4−4̂= 8
4̂−4= 8̂
4̂+4̂= 8̂
4̂−4̂= 0
4̂+4= 0
All Rights Reserved. Addison-Wesley

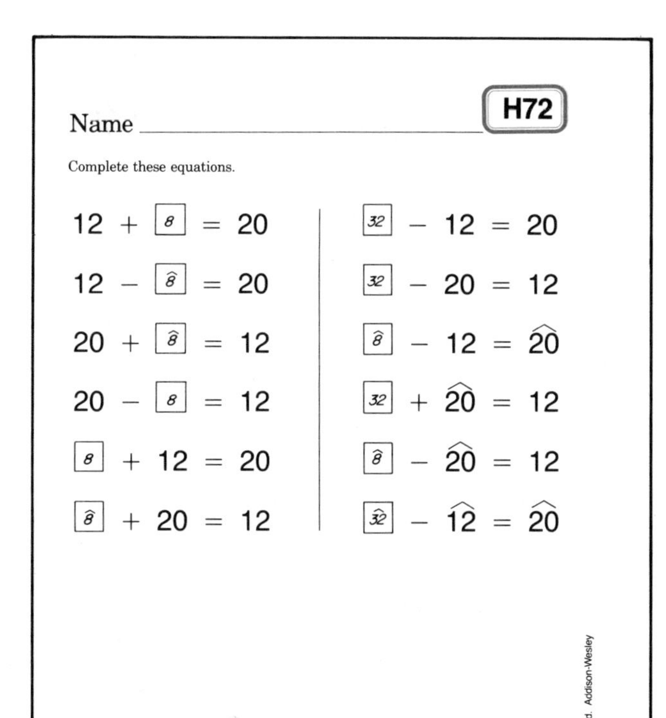
H72

Name ______________________

Complete these equations.

$12 + \boxed{8} = 20$

$12 - \boxed{\hat{8}} = 20$

$20 + \boxed{\hat{8}} = 12$

$20 - \boxed{8} = 12$

$\boxed{8} + 12 = 20$

$\boxed{\hat{8}} + 20 = 12$

$\boxed{32} - 12 = 20$

$\boxed{32} - 20 = 12$

$\boxed{\hat{8}} - 12 = \hat{20}$

$\boxed{32} + \hat{20} = 12$

$\boxed{\hat{8}} - \hat{20} = 12$

$\boxed{\hat{32}} - \hat{12} = \hat{20}$

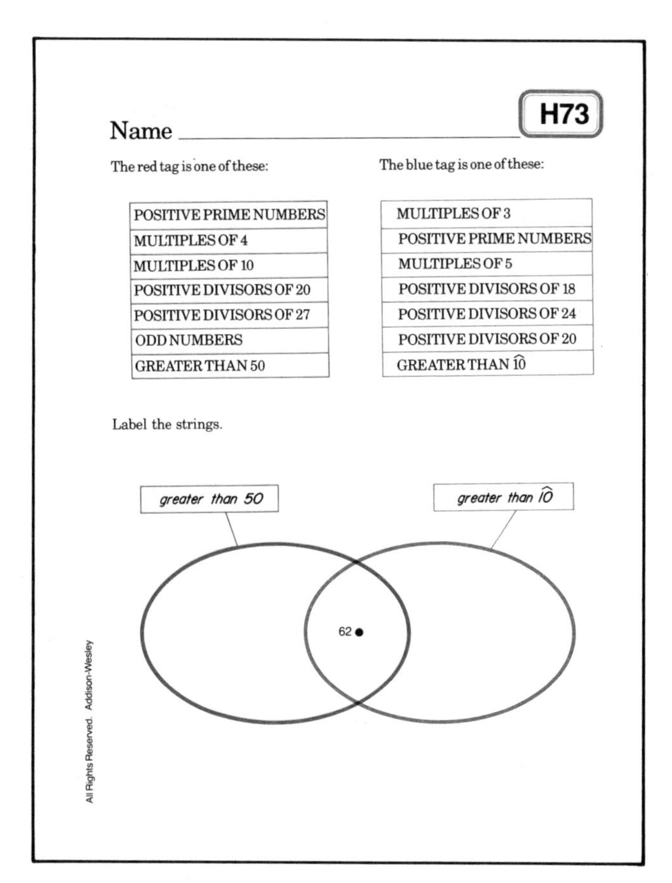
H73

Name ______________________

The red tag is one of these:

POSITIVE PRIME NUMBERS
MULTIPLES OF 4
MULTIPLES OF 10
POSITIVE DIVISORS OF 20
POSITIVE DIVISORS OF 27
ODD NUMBERS
GREATER THAN 50

The blue tag is one of these:

MULTIPLES OF 3
POSITIVE PRIME NUMBERS
MULTIPLES OF 5
POSITIVE DIVISORS OF 18
POSITIVE DIVISORS OF 24
POSITIVE DIVISORS OF 20
GREATER THAN $\hat{10}$

Label the strings.

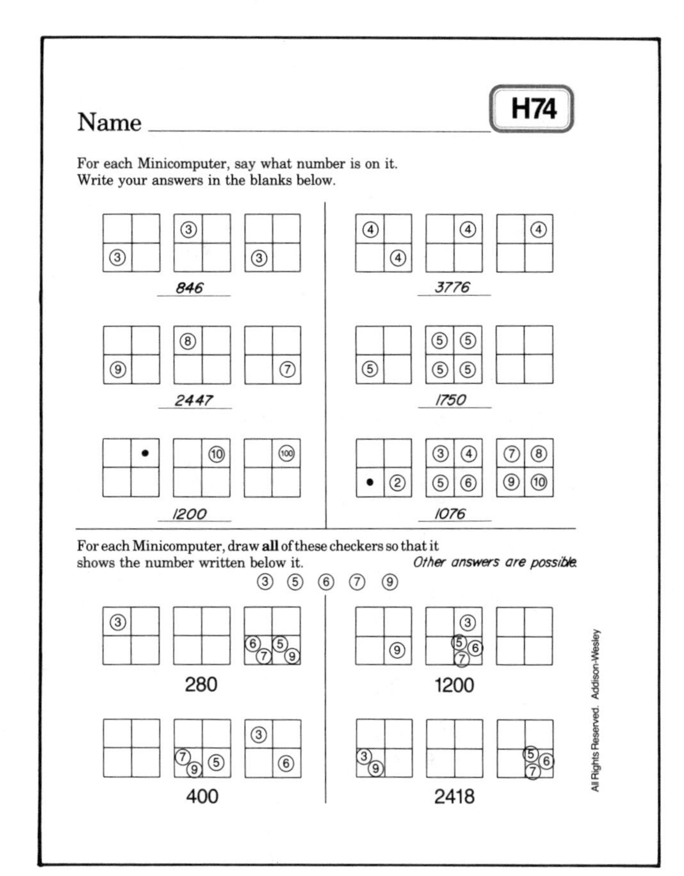
H74

Name ______________________

For each Minicomputer, say what number is on it.
Write your answers in the blanks below.

For each Minicomputer, draw **all** of these checkers so that it shows the number written below it. *Other answers are possible.*

③ ⑤ ⑥ ⑦ ⑨

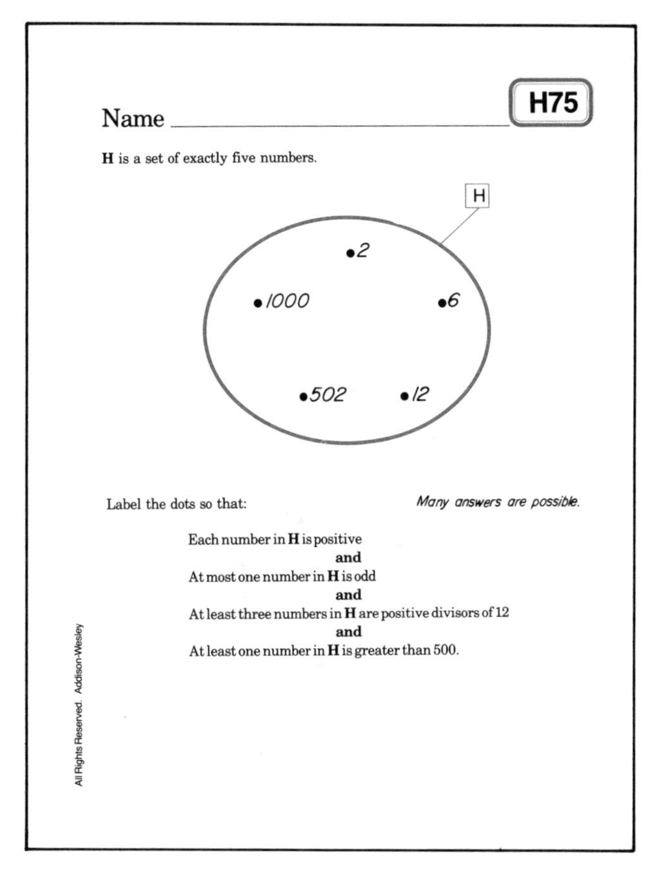
H75

Name ______________________

H is a set of exactly five numbers.

Label the dots so that: *Many answers are possible.*

Each number in **H** is positive
and
At most one number in **H** is odd
and
At least three numbers in **H** are positive divisors of 12
and
At least one number in **H** is greater than 500.

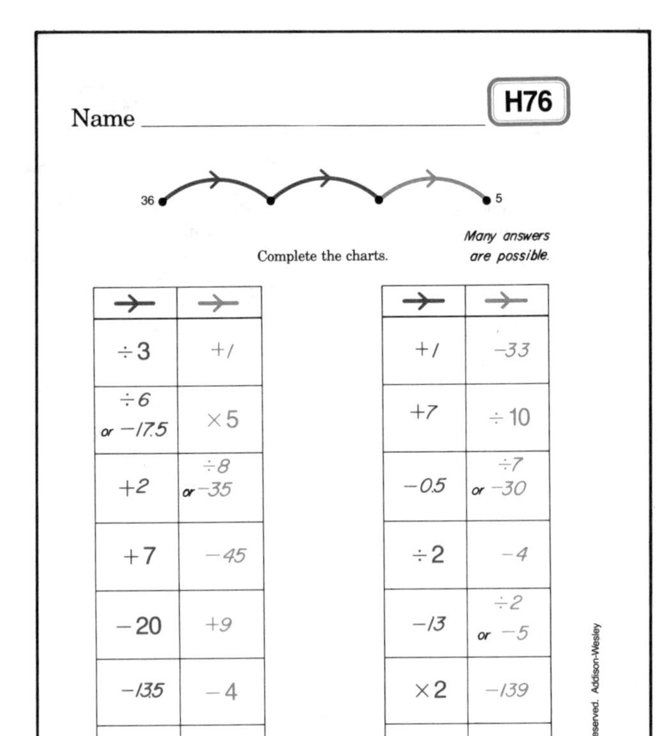

Name ______________________ **H76**

36 → → → 5

Complete the charts.

Many answers are possible.

→	→
÷3	+1
÷6 or −17.5	×5
+2	÷8 or −35
+7	−45
−20	+9
−135	−4
−15	−1

→	→
+1	−33
+7	÷10
−0.5	÷7 or −30
÷2	−4
−13	÷2 or −5
×2	−139
−16	+1

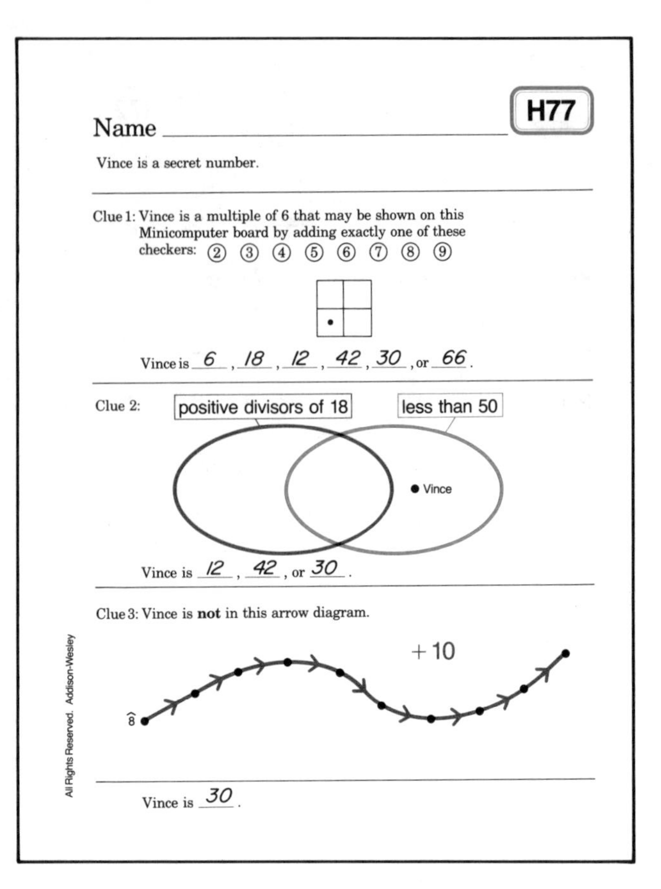

Name ______________________ **H77**

Vince is a secret number.

Clue 1: Vince is a multiple of 6 that may be shown on this Minicomputer board by adding exactly one of these checkers: ② ③ ④ ⑤ ⑥ ⑦ ⑧ ⑨

Vince is 6, 18, 12, 42, 30, or 66.

Clue 2: positive divisors of 18 | less than 50

Vince is 12, 42, or 30.

Clue 3: Vince is **not** in this arrow diagram.

Vince is 30.

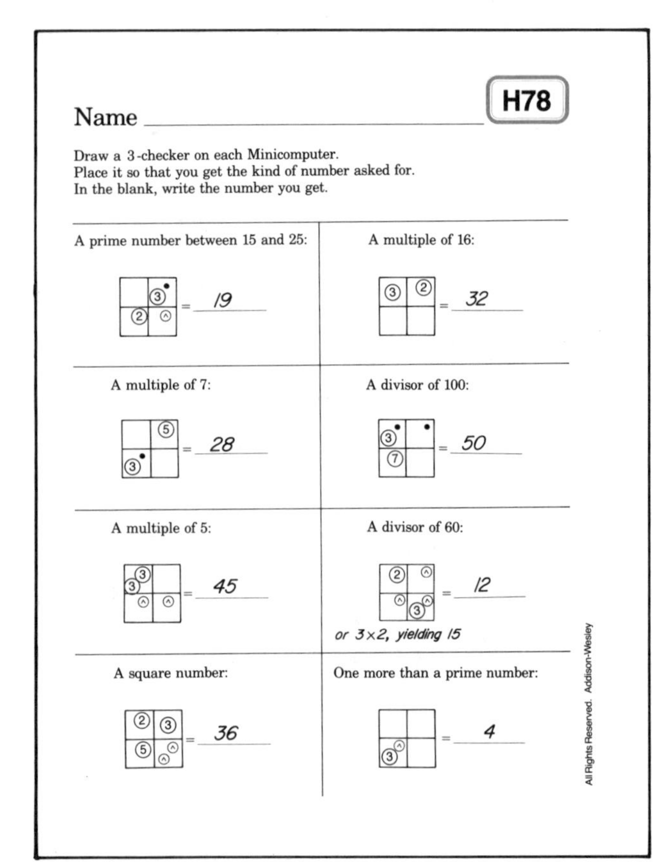

Name ______________________ **H78**

Draw a 3-checker on each Minicomputer.
Place it so that you get the kind of number asked for.
In the blank, write the number you get.

A prime number between 15 and 25: = 19

A multiple of 16: = 32

A multiple of 7: = 28

A divisor of 100: = 50

A multiple of 5: = 45

A divisor of 60: = 12

or 3×2, yielding 15

A square number: = 36

One more than a prime number: = 4

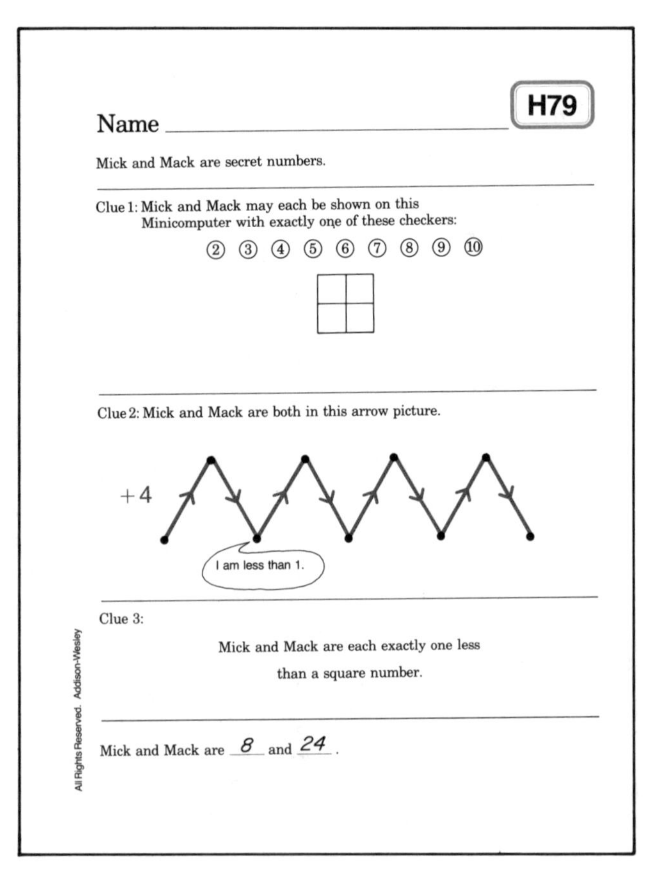

Name ______________________ **H79**

Mick and Mack are secret numbers.

Clue 1: Mick and Mack may each be shown on this Minicomputer with exactly one of these checkers:

② ③ ④ ⑤ ⑥ ⑦ ⑧ ⑨ ⑩

Clue 2: Mick and Mack are both in this arrow picture.

Clue 3:

Mick and Mack are each exactly one less than a square number.

Mick and Mack are 8 and 24.

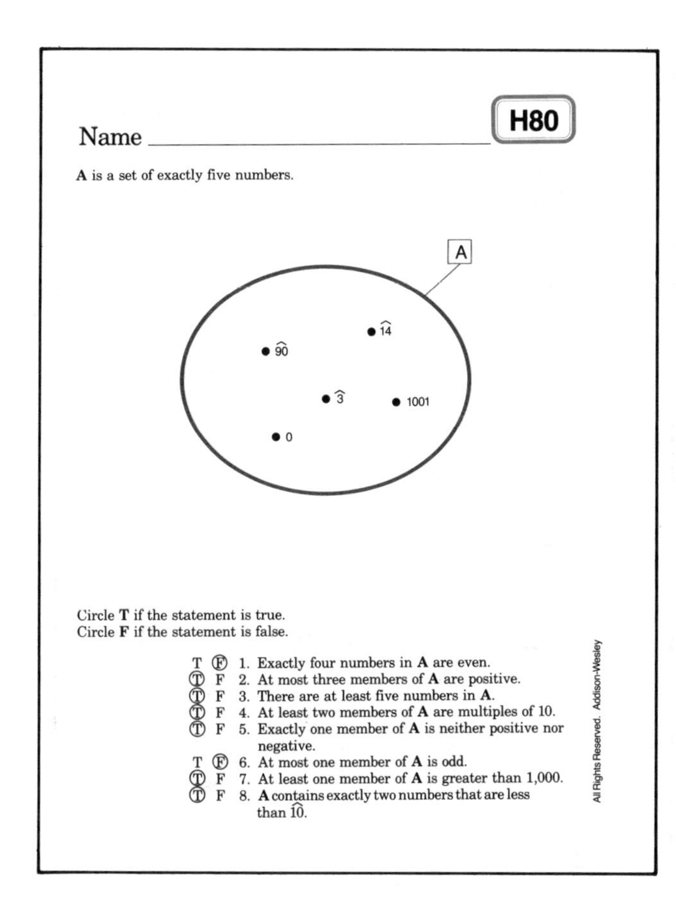
Name ______________ **H80**

A is a set of exactly five numbers.

Circle **T** if the statement is true.
Circle **F** if the statement is false.

T (F) 1. Exactly four numbers in **A** are even.
(T) F 2. At most three members of **A** are positive.
(T) F 3. There are at least five numbers in **A**.
(T) F 4. At least two members of **A** are multiples of 10.
(T) F 5. Exactly one member of **A** is neither positive nor negative.
T (F) 6. At most one member of **A** is odd.
(T) F 7. At least one member of **A** is greater than 1,000.
(T) F 8. **A** contains exactly two numbers that are less than $\hat{10}$.

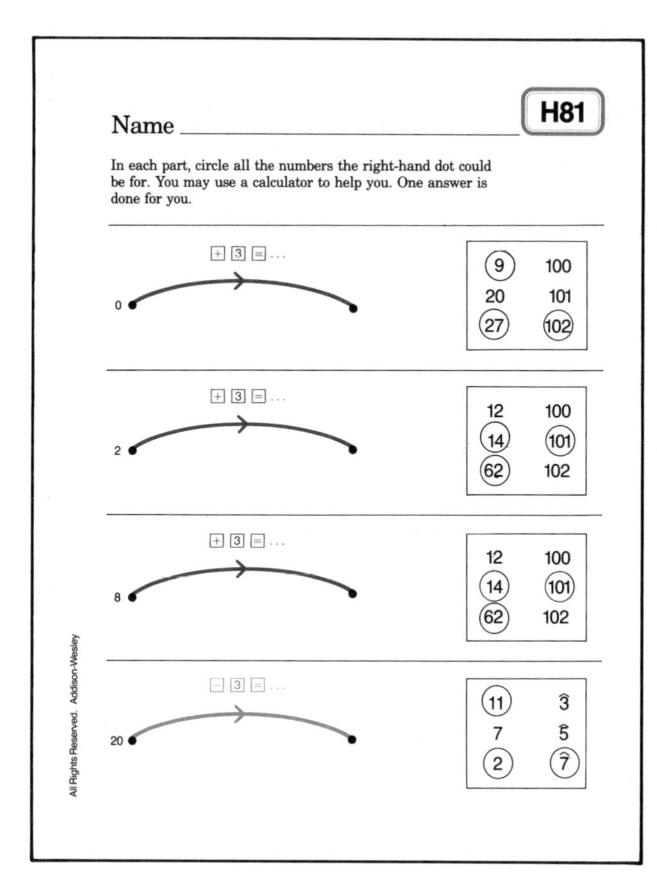
Name ______________ **H81**

In each part, circle all the numbers the right-hand dot could be for. You may use a calculator to help you. One answer is done for you.

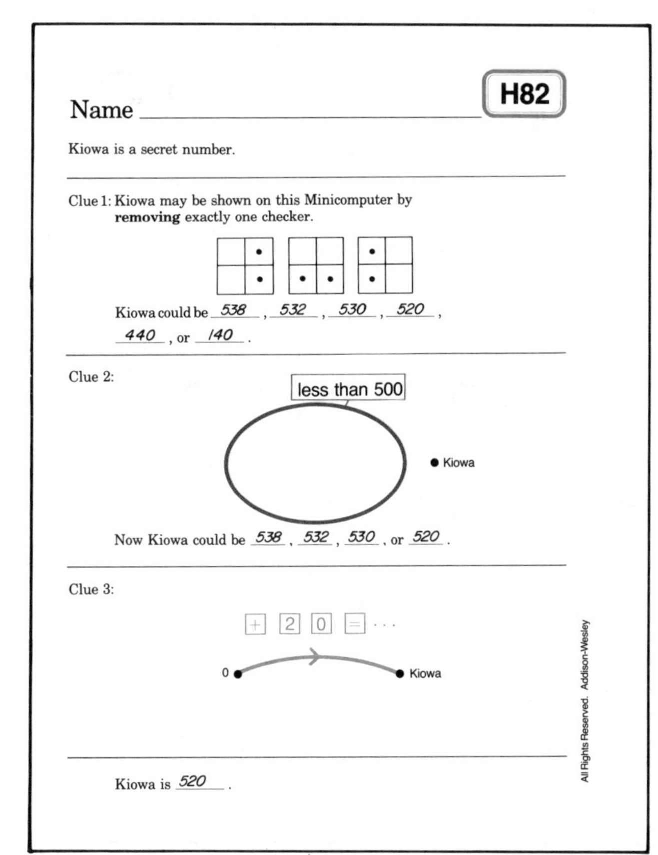
Name ______________ **H82**

Kiowa is a secret number.

Clue 1: Kiowa may be shown on this Minicomputer by **removing** exactly one checker.

Kiowa could be 538, 532, 530, 520, 440, or 140.

Clue 2:

Now Kiowa could be 538, 532, 530, or 520.

Clue 3:

Kiowa is 520.

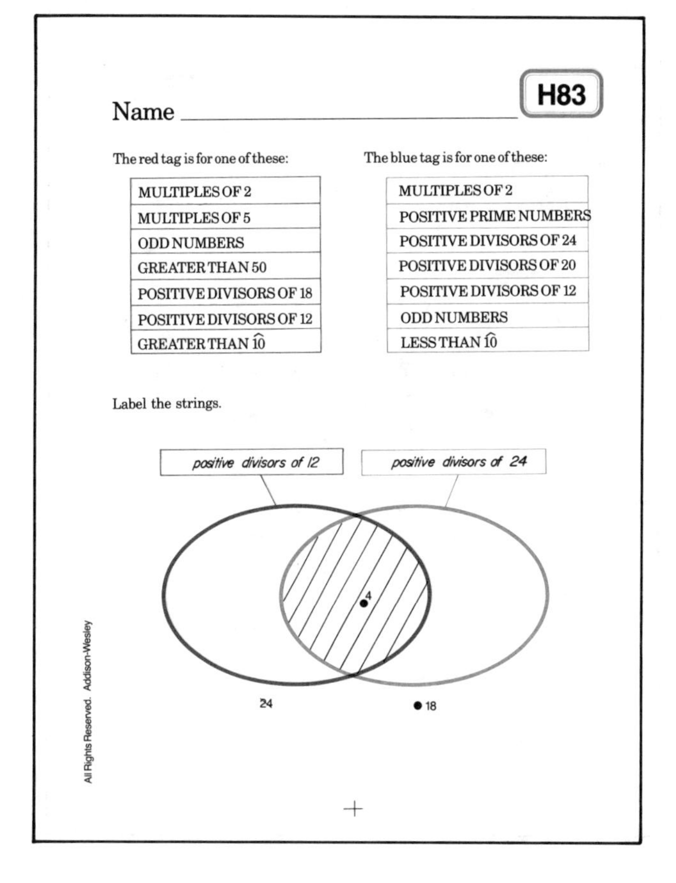
Name ______________ **H83**

The red tag is for one of these:

MULTIPLES OF 2
MULTIPLES OF 5
ODD NUMBERS
GREATER THAN 50
POSITIVE DIVISORS OF 18
POSITIVE DIVISORS OF 12
GREATER THAN $\hat{10}$

The blue tag is for one of these:

MULTIPLES OF 2
POSITIVE PRIME NUMBERS
POSITIVE DIVISORS OF 24
POSITIVE DIVISORS OF 20
POSITIVE DIVISORS OF 12
ODD NUMBERS
LESS THAN $\hat{10}$

Label the strings.

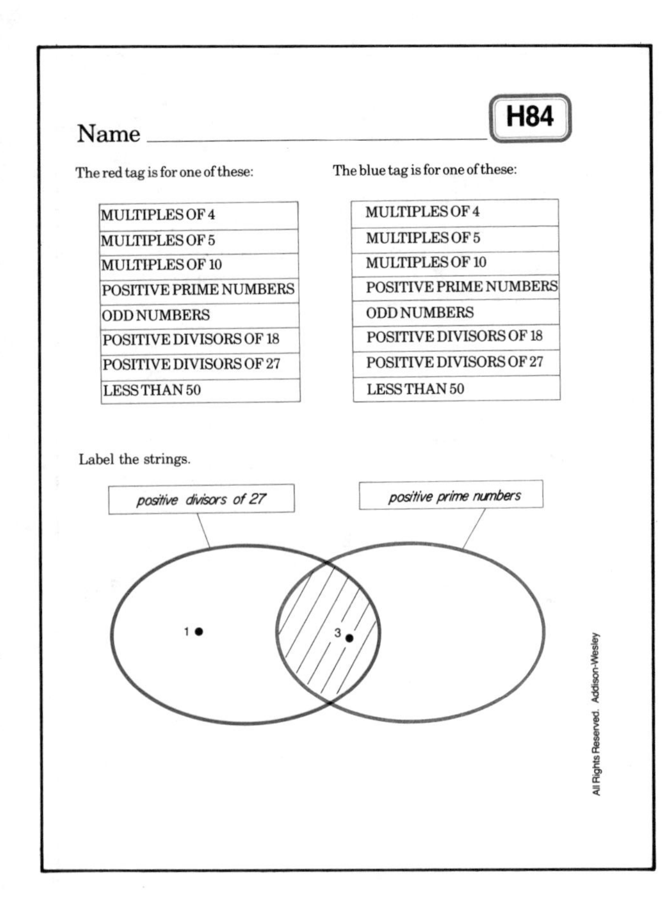

Name ______ **H84**

The red tag is for one of these:

MULTIPLES OF 4
MULTIPLES OF 5
MULTIPLES OF 10
POSITIVE PRIME NUMBERS
ODD NUMBERS
POSITIVE DIVISORS OF 18
POSITIVE DIVISORS OF 27
LESS THAN 50

The blue tag is for one of these:

MULTIPLES OF 4
MULTIPLES OF 5
MULTIPLES OF 10
POSITIVE PRIME NUMBERS
ODD NUMBERS
POSITIVE DIVISORS OF 18
POSITIVE DIVISORS OF 27
LESS THAN 50

Label the strings.

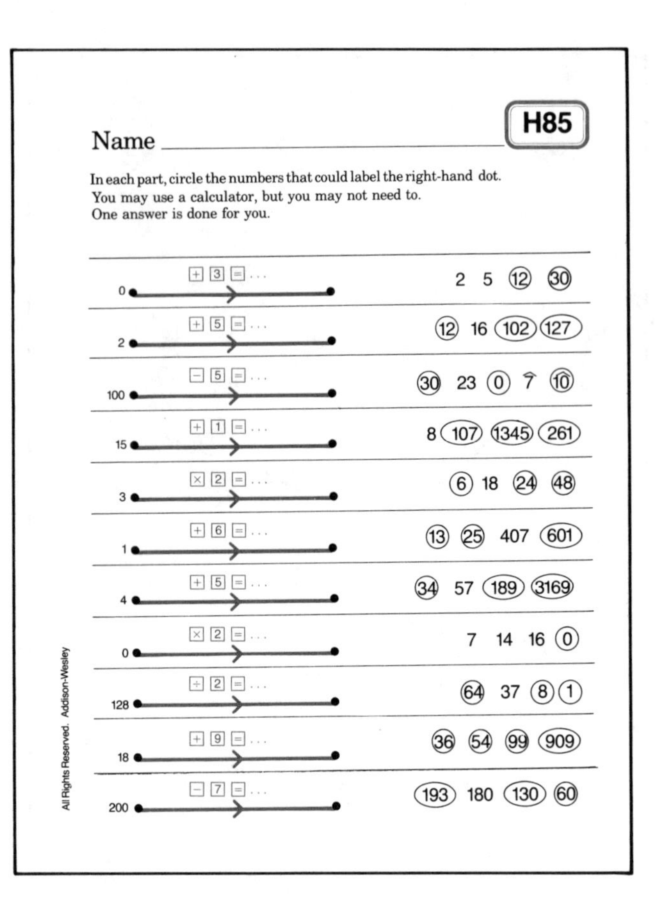

Name ______ **H85**

In each part, circle the numbers that could label the right-hand dot.
You may use a calculator, but you may not need to.
One answer is done for you.

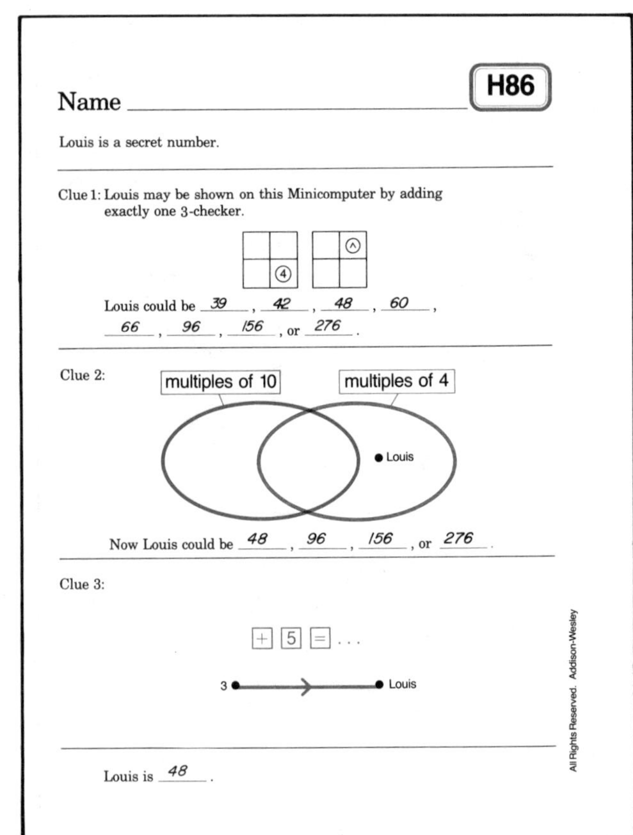

Name ______ **H86**

Louis is a secret number.

Clue 1: Louis may be shown on this Minicomputer by adding exactly one 3-checker.

Louis could be 39, 42, 48, 60, 66, 96, 156, or 276.

Clue 2:

Now Louis could be 48, 96, 156, or 276.

Clue 3:

Louis is 48.

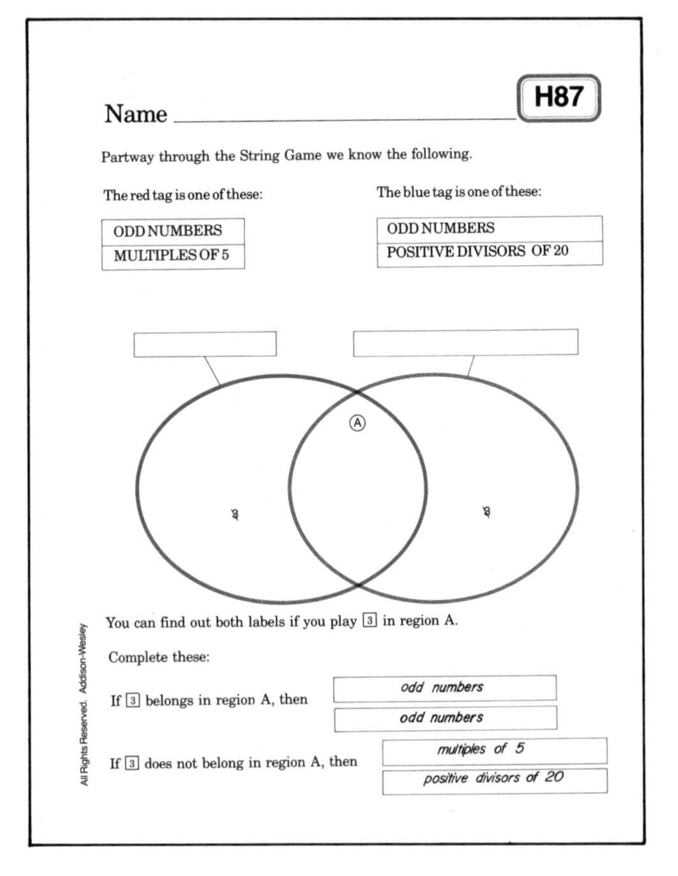

Name ______ **H87**

Partway through the String Game we know the following.

The red tag is one of these:

ODD NUMBERS
MULTIPLES OF 5

The blue tag is one of these:

ODD NUMBERS
POSITIVE DIVISORS OF 20

You can find out both labels if you play 3 in region A.

Complete these:

If 3 belongs in region A, then *odd numbers* / *odd numbers*

If 3 does not belong in region A, then *multiples of 5* / *positive divisors of 20*

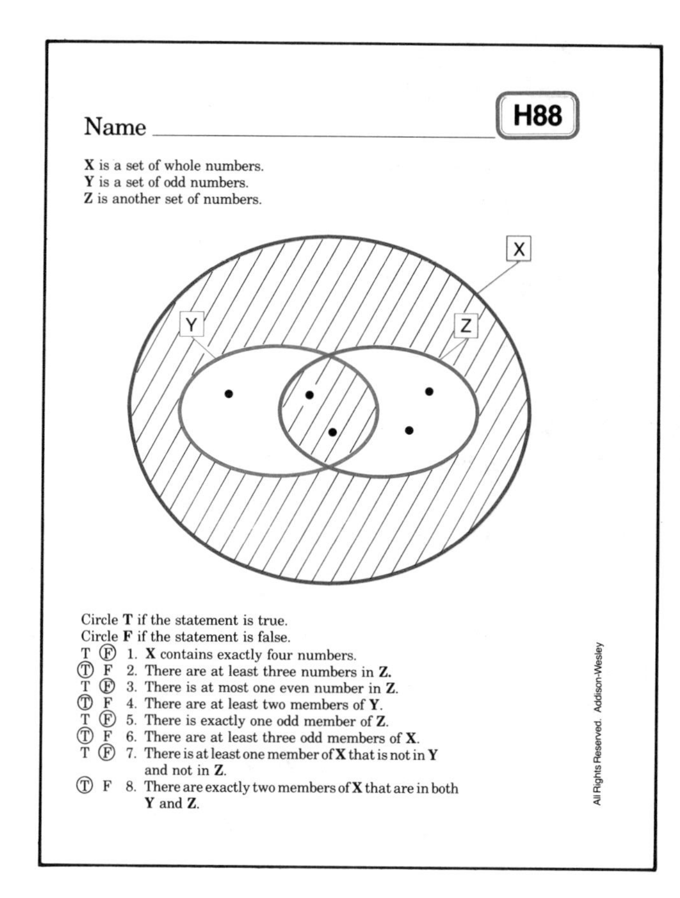

Name ____________ **H88**

X is a set of whole numbers.
Y is a set of odd numbers.
Z is another set of numbers.

Circle **T** if the statement is true.
Circle **F** if the statement is false.

T (F) 1. **X** contains exactly four numbers.
(T) F 2. There are at least three numbers in **Z**.
T (F) 3. There is at most one even number in **Z**.
(T) F 4. There are at least two members of **Y**.
T (F) 5. There is exactly one odd member of **Z**.
(T) F 6. There are at least three odd members of **X**.
T (F) 7. There is at least one member of **X** that is not in **Y** and not in **Z**.
(T) F 8. There are exactly two members of **X** that are in both **Y** and **Z**.

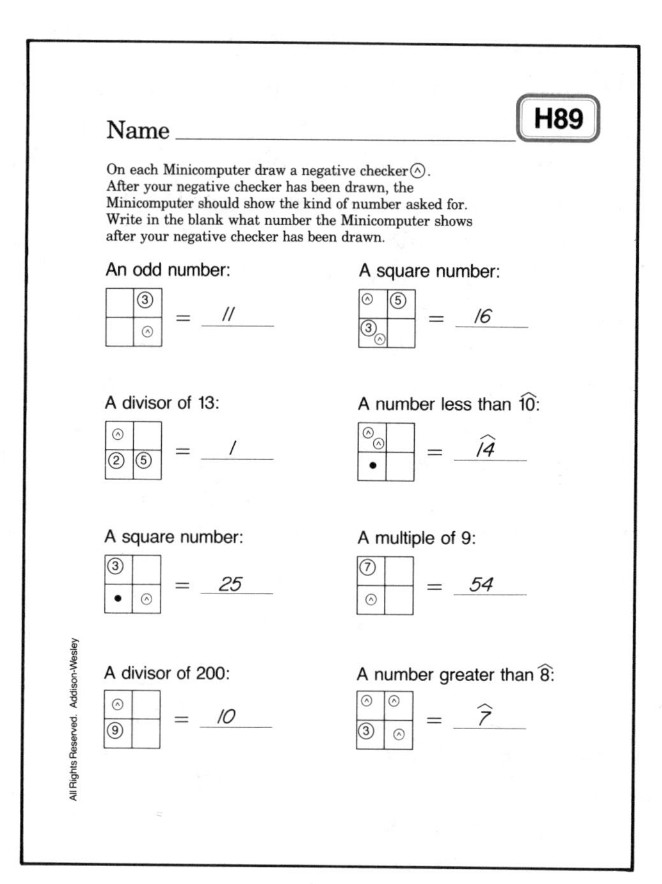

Name ____________ **H89**

On each Minicomputer draw a negative checker ⓐ. After your negative checker has been drawn, the Minicomputer should show the kind of number asked for. Write in the blank what number the Minicomputer shows after your negative checker has been drawn.

An odd number: = 11

A square number: = 16

A divisor of 13: = 1

A number less than $\hat{10}$: = $\hat{14}$

A square number: = 25

A multiple of 9: = 54

A divisor of 200: = 10

A number greater than $\hat{8}$: = $\hat{7}$

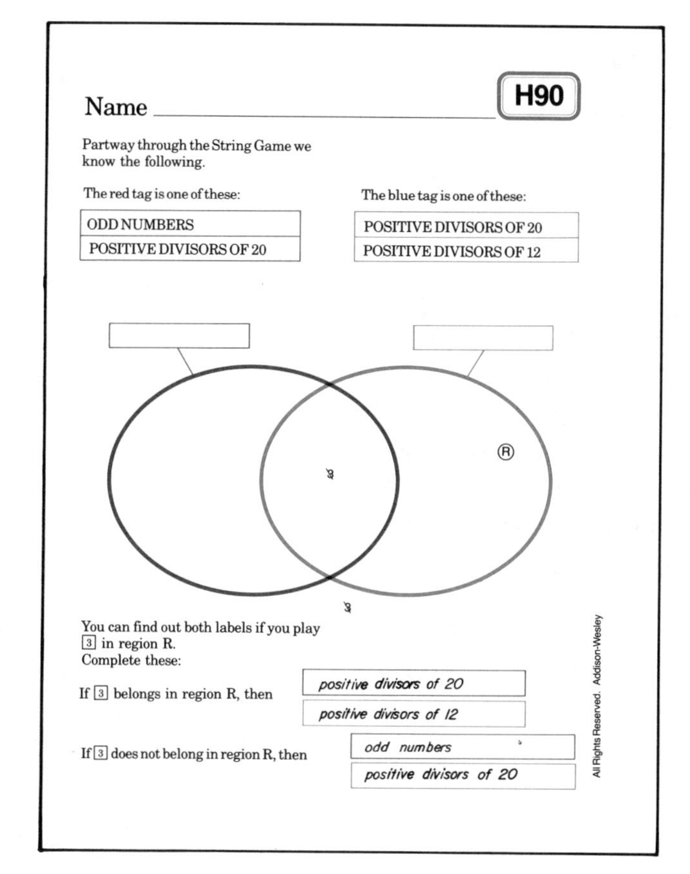

Name ____________ **H90**

Partway through the String Game we know the following.

The red tag is one of these:

ODD NUMBERS
POSITIVE DIVISORS OF 20

The blue tag is one of these:

POSITIVE DIVISORS OF 20
POSITIVE DIVISORS OF 12

You can find out both labels if you play [3] in region R.
Complete these:

If [3] belongs in region R, then *positive divisors of 20* / *positive divisors of 12*

If [3] does not belong in region R, then *odd numbers* / *positive divisors of 20*

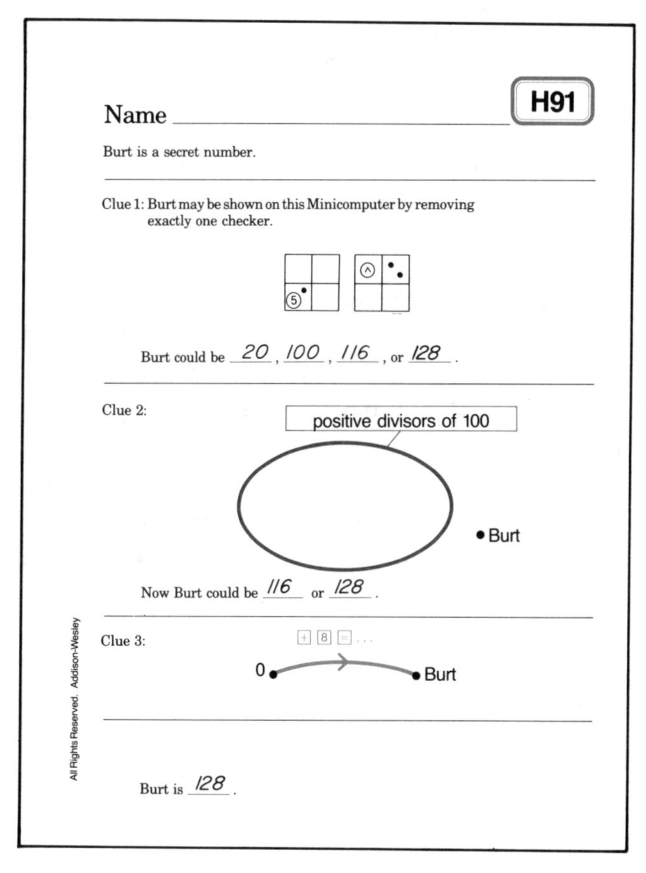

Name ____________ **H91**

Burt is a secret number.

Clue 1: Burt may be shown on this Minicomputer by removing exactly one checker.

Burt could be *20*, *100*, *116*, or *128*.

Clue 2:

Now Burt could be *116* or *128*.

Clue 3:

Burt is *128*.

Preparation for Teachers New to the Program

The best preparation for teaching Volume 2 of this series is, of course, teaching Volume 1. Observing Volume 1 instruction would also help. You may find yourself teaching Volume 2 to students who studied Volume 1 with other teachers. If you take your task seriously and prepare adequately for this instruction, you should have little difficulty. You will find that the lesson dialogs will provide strong support for your teaching until you become more secure with the materials and can become less tied to the specifics of the dialogs.

There are certain tasks you should undertake before you present the first lesson to your class. Familiarize yourself with the basic pedagogical tools of the program by carefully studying selected introductory activities from Volume 1. The following are the topics together with activities in Volume 1 that will give you necessary background.

Topic	Activity Number in Volume 1
Minicomputer	1, 2, 6, 9, 10, 14, 43, 44, 46, 49
Negative numbers	11, 12, 13
Arrow diagrams	47, 48
Multiples and divisors	19, 20
Detective stories	5
String diagrams	4, 7
Minicomputer Golf	64
Minicomputer Tug-of-War	24

You may wish to explore the given series of activities immediately before you teach a lesson on that topic.

The above review we have suggested will give you a *general* understanding of teaching devices you will be using. You will find that your students will know still more than you at the outset. We urge you to be open with them about this. A statement like the following will help you gain the support of you students: "You all know that M . . . is not available to continue teaching this program. The content is new to me. Although I have studied it carefully, I will need to rely on each of you to share with me and your classmates your understanding of what you have studied."